Camping and Caravan Sites

Your comprehensive guide to dog friendly Camping and Caravan Sites

First published in Great Britain in 2008
by Dog Friendly

The Dog Friendly team telephone every venue at least once a year to ensure that our data base is accurate as it can be – but things do change.
So please always check before you visit.

A CIP Catalogue of this book is available from
the British Library

ISBN 978-0-9560459-3-5

Printed and bound in
Great Britain by
Print Direction
www.printdirection.co.uk

In Memory of Blossom, our retired greyhound who changed our lives for the better and inspired us to start Dog Friendly

Blossom
1993 to 2006

England

Cambridgeshire

Appleacre Park

Address: London Road, Fowlmere, Cambridgeshire SG8 7RU
Telephone: 01763 208354
Website: www.appleacrepark.co.uk
Extra charge for dogs? No
Any breed restrictions? No
Dog bins?
Area for walking dogs? No
Static caravans? Private
Cost of static?
Mobile caravans? Yes
Cost of mobile? £5.00 per pitch + £3.00 per person
Tents? Yes
Cost of tent pitch? £5.00 - £10.00
Electricity at the pitch? Yes
Showers? Yes
Onsite Entertainment? No
Opening times? All Year

Burleigh Hill Camping Site

Address: Burleigh Hill Farm, Somersham Road, St. Ives, Cambridgeshire PE27 3LY
Telephone: 01480 462173
Website:
Extra charge for dogs? No
Any breed restrictions? No
Dog bins?
Area for walking dogs? Dog Walks
Static caravans? Yes
Cost of static? £6.50 per night
Mobile caravans? Yes
Cost of mobile? 6.50
Tents? Yes
Cost of tent pitch? 2.50
Electricity at the pitch? Yes
Showers? No
Onsite Entertainment? No
Opening times? All Year
Comments: Dogs must be kept on leads

Cambridge Camping and Caravanning Club Site

Address: 19 Cabbage Moor, Great Shelford, Cambridge, Cambridgeshire CB2 5NB
Telephone: 01223 841185
Website: www.campingandcaravanningclub.co.uk
Extra charge for dogs? No
Any breed restrictions? No
Dog bins?
Area for walking dogs? Yes (leads Max 2 metres long)
Static caravans? No
Cost of static?
Mobile caravans? Yes
Cost of mobile? £5.15 - £7.60 per adult per night
Tents? Yes
Cost of tent pitch? £5.15 - £7.60 per adult per night
Electricity at the pitch? £2.90 per night
Showers? Yes
Onsite Entertainment? No
Opening times? 13 March - 3 Nov
Comments: Dogs must be kept on leads

Cherry Hinton Caravan Club

Address: Lime Kiln Road, Cherry Hinton, Cambridge, Cambridgeshire CB1 4NQ

Telephone: 01223 244088

Website: www.caravanclub.co.uk

Extra charge for dogs? No

Any breed restrictions? No

Dog bins?

Area for walking dogs? There are dog walks around

Static caravans? No

Cost of static?

Mobile caravans? Yes

Cost of mobile? £4.30 per pitch + £3.95 per adult

Tents? Yes

Cost of tent pitch? £3.00 - £8.00 per pitch + £3.95 per adult

Electricity at the pitch? Yes

Showers? Yes

Onsite Entertainment? No

Opening times? All Year

Comments: Dogs must be kept on leads

Crystal Lakes Caravan Park

Address: Low Road, Fenstanton, St. Ives, Cambridgeshire PE28 9HU

Telephone: 01480 497728

Website: www.crystallakesleisure.com

Extra charge for dogs? No

Any breed restrictions? No

Dog bins?

Area for walking dogs? Adjacent Field to let dogs off leads

Static caravans? No

Cost of static?

Mobile caravans? Yes

Cost of mobile? £9.50 - £15.50

Tents? Yes

Cost of tent pitch? £6.50 - £15.50

Electricity at the pitch? Yes

Showers? Yes

Onsite Entertainment? Fishing Lakes, Boot Sale, Playareas

Opening times? March - October

Comments: Dogs must be kept on leads

Deepings Caravan & Camping Park

Address: Outgang, Towngate East, Market Deeping, Peterborough, Cambridgeshire PE6 8LQ

Telephone: 01778 344335

Website: www.thedeepings.com

Extra charge for dogs? No

Any breed restrictions? No

Dog bins?

Area for walking dogs? Area nearby

Static caravans? Yes

Cost of static? From £200 per week

Mobile caravans? Yes

Cost of mobile? From £12.00 per night

Tents? Yes

Cost of tent pitch? From £10.00 per night

Electricity at the pitch? Yes

Showers? Yes

Onsite Entertainment? Yes

Opening times? All Year

Ferry Meadows Caravan Club Site

Address: Ham Lane, Peterborough, Cambridgeshire PE2 5UU

Telephone: 01733 233526

Website:

Extra charge for dogs? No

Any breed restrictions? No

Dog bins?
Area for walking dogs? Park Nearby
Static caravans? No
Cost of static?
Mobile caravans? Yes
Cost of mobile? ?
Tents? Yes
Cost of tent pitch? ?
Electricity at the pitch? Yes
Showers? Yes
Onsite Entertainment? No
Opening times? All Year (Tents Mar - Sept)

Floods Ferry Marina Park

Address: Floods Ferry, March, Cambridgeshire PE15 0YR
Telephone: 01354 677302
Website: www.floodferrymarina.co.uk
Extra charge for dogs? No
Any breed restrictions? No
Dog bins?
Area for walking dogs? Walks nearby
Static caravans? No
Cost of static?
Mobile caravans? Yes
Cost of mobile? £17.00 per night
Tents? Yes
Cost of tent pitch? £17.00 per night
Electricity at the pitch? Yes
Showers? Yes
Onsite Entertainment? Yes
Opening times? All Year

Highfield Farm Touring Park

Address: Long Road, Comberton, Cambridgeshire CB3 7DG
Telephone: 01223 262308
Website: www.highfieldfarmtouringpark.co.uk
Extra charge for dogs? Yes
Any breed restrictions? No
Dog bins?
Area for walking dogs? Walks around farm
Static caravans? No
Cost of static?
Mobile caravans? Yes
Cost of mobile? £10.50 - £13.50
Tents? Yes
Cost of tent pitch? £10.00 - £13.50
Electricity at the pitch? Yes
Showers? Yes
Onsite Entertainment? No
Opening times? End Mar - End Oct
Comments: Dogs must be kept on leads, maximum of 2 dogs per pitch.

Huntingdon Boathaven & Caravan

Address: The Avenue, Godmanchester, Huntingdon, Cambridgeshire PE29 2AF
Telephone: 01480 411977
Website: www.huntingdonboathaven.co.uk
Extra charge for dogs? No
Any breed restrictions? No
Dog bins?
Area for walking dogs? Field on site for dogs
Static caravans? No
Cost of static?
Mobile caravans? Yes
Cost of mobile? £14.00 - £16.00
Tents? Yes
Cost of tent pitch? £11.00 - £15.00
Electricity at the pitch? Yes
Showers? Yes
Onsite Entertainment? No
Opening times? All Year
Comments: Dogs must be kept on leads

Lazydays

Address: Bridgehill Road, Newborough, Peterborough, Cambridgeshire PE6 7SA
Telephone: 01733 810259
Website:
Extra charge for dogs? No
Any breed restrictions? No
Dog bins?
Area for walking dogs? Dog Walks
Static caravans? No
Cost of static?
Mobile caravans? Yes
Cost of mobile? £10.00 per night
Tents? Yes
Cost of tent pitch? From £5.00
Electricity at the pitch? Yes
Showers? Yes
Onsite Entertainment? No
Opening times? All Year
Comments: Dogs must be kept on leads

Nene Way Caravan Club

Address: 4 Fotheringhay Road, Nassington, Peterborough, Cambridgeshire PE8 6QU
Telephone: 01780 783352
Website:
Extra charge for dogs? No
Any breed restrictions? No
Dog bins?
Area for walking dogs? Dog Walks
Static caravans? No
Cost of static?
Mobile caravans? Yes
Cost of mobile? £10.00 per night
Tents? No
Cost of tent pitch?
Electricity at the pitch? Yes
Showers? No
Onsite Entertainment? No
Opening times? All Year

Northey Lodge

Address: North Bank, Whittlesey Road, Peterborough, Cambridgeshire PE6 7YZ
Telephone: 01733 223918
Website: www.northeylodge.co.uk
Extra charge for dogs? Yes
Any breed restrictions? No
Dog bins?
Area for walking dogs? Field
Static caravans? No
Cost of static?
Mobile caravans? Yes
Cost of mobile? £12.00 - £14.00 for 2 adults per night
Tents? Yes
Cost of tent pitch? £10.00 for 2 people per night
Electricity at the pitch? Yes
Showers? Yes
Onsite Entertainment? No
Opening times? All Year
Comments: Dogs must be kept on leads

Quiet Waters Caravan Park

Address: Hemingford Abbots, Cambridgeshire PE28 9AJ
Telephone: 01480 463405
Website: www.quietwaterscaravanpark.co.uk
Extra charge for dogs? Yes
Any breed restrictions? No
Dog bins?
Area for walking dogs? No
Static caravans? Yes
Cost of static? £14.00 per week
Mobile caravans? No

Cost of mobile?
Tents? Yes
Cost of tent pitch? £2.00 per night
Electricity at the pitch? Yes
Showers? Yes
Onsite Entertainment? No
Opening times? End Mar - End Oct
Comments: Dogs must be kept on leads, maximum of 2 dogs per pitch

Riverside Caravan & Camping Park

Address: 21 New River Bank, Littleport, Ely, Cambridgeshire CB7 4TA
Telephone: 01353 860255
Website: www.riversideccp.co.uk
Extra charge for dogs? No
Any breed restrictions? Legal breeds only
Dog bins?
Area for walking dogs? Riverbank to exercise dogs
Static caravans? No
Cost of static?
Mobile caravans? Yes
Cost of mobile? £10.00 - £17.00 per night
Tents? Yes
Cost of tent pitch? From £5.00
Electricity at the pitch? Yes
Showers? Yes
Onsite Entertainment? No
Opening times? All Year

Roseberry Tourist Park

Address: Earith Road, Willingham, Cambridge, Cambridgeshire CB4 5LT
Telephone: 01954 260346
Website: www.roseberrytouristpark.co.uk
Extra charge for dogs? No
Any breed restrictions? Yes
Dog bins?
Area for walking dogs? Yes where you can let dogs off leads
Static caravans? No
Cost of static?
Mobile caravans? Yes
Cost of mobile? From £12.00 per night
Tents? Yes
Cost of tent pitch? From £8.00
Electricity at the pitch? Yes
Showers? Yes
Onsite Entertainment? No
Opening times? All Year

Sacrewell Farm & Country Centre

Address: Thornhaugh, Peterborough, Cambridgeshire PE8 6HJ
Telephone: 01780 782254
Website: www.sacrewell.org.uk
Extra charge for dogs? No
Any breed restrictions? No
Dog bins?
Area for walking dogs? Dog Walk
Static caravans? Yes
Cost of static? £8.50 per adult £5.50 per child
Mobile caravans? Yes
Cost of mobile? £8.50 per adult £5.50 per child
Tents? Yes
Cost of tent pitch? £8.50 per adult £5.50 per child
Electricity at the pitch? Yes
Showers? Yes
Onsite Entertainment? No
Opening times? March - October
Comments: Dogs must be kept on leads.

St. Neot's Camping & Caravanning Club Site

Address: Hardwick Road, Eynesbury, St. Neots, Cambridgeshire PE19 2PR

Telephone: 01480 474404

Website:

Extra charge for dogs? No

Any breed restrictions? No

Dog bins?

Area for walking dogs? No

Static caravans? No

Cost of static?

Mobile caravans? Yes

Cost of mobile? From £5.15 per adult £2.25 per child

Tents?

Cost of tent pitch? From £5.15 per adult £2.25 per child

Electricity at the pitch? Yes

Showers? Yes

Onsite Entertainment? No

Opening times? Mid Mar - End Oct

Comments: Dogs must be kept on leads.

Stanford Park

Address: Weirs Drove, Burwell, Cambridgeshire CB5 0BP

Telephone: 01638 741547

Website: www.stanfordcaravanparks.co.uk

Extra charge for dogs? No

Any breed restrictions? No

Dog bins? No

Area for walking dogs? Yes

Static caravans? No

Cost of static?

Mobile caravans? Yes

Cost of mobile? From £12.00 per night for 2 adults

Tents? Yes

Cost of tent pitch? From £12.00 per night for 2 adults

Electricity at the pitch? Yes

Showers? Yes

Onsite Entertainment? No

Opening times? All Year

Comments: Dogs must be kept on leads.

Stroud Hill Park

Address: Fen Road, St. Ives, Cambridgeshire PE28 3DE

Telephone: 01487 741365

Website: www.stroudhillpark.co.uk

Extra charge for dogs? Yes

Any breed restrictions? No

Dog bins?

Area for walking dogs? Yes

Static caravans? No

Cost of static?

Mobile caravans? Yes

Cost of mobile? £20.00 per night

Tents? Yes

Cost of tent pitch? £15.00 per night

Electricity at the pitch? Yes

Showers? Yes

Onsite Entertainment? No

Opening times? All Year

Comments: There are bars and restaurants on site.

The Willows Caravan Park

Address: Bromholme Lane, Brampton, Huntingdon, Cambridgeshire PE28 4NE

Telephone: 01480 437566

Website: www.willowscaravanpark.com

Extra charge for dogs? Yes for 2nd dog only

Any breed restrictions? Yes

Dog bins?

Area for walking dogs? Plenty of Dog Walks
Static caravans? No
Cost of static?
Mobile caravans? Yes
Cost of mobile? £14.00 - £16.00 per night
Tents? Yes
Cost of tent pitch? £13.00 - £16.00 per night
Electricity at the pitch? Yes
Showers? Yes
Onsite Entertainment? No
Opening times? All Year
Comments: Do not allow Pitbulls, Staffs, Dobermans or Rottweilers.

Two Acres Caravan & Camping

Address: Ely Road, Little Thetford, Ely, Cambridgeshire CB6 3HH
Telephone: 01353 648870
Website: www.twoacrescaravanand camping.com
Extra charge for dogs? No
Any breed restrictions? No
Dog bins?
Area for walking dogs? No
Static caravans? Yes
Cost of static? No Dogs
Mobile caravans? Yes
Cost of mobile? 12.00
Tents?
Cost of tent pitch? 12.00
Electricity at the pitch? Yes
Showers? Yes
Onsite Entertainment? No
Opening times? All Year
Comments: Dogs are not allowed in the Static's

Westview Marina

Address: High Street, Earith, Cambridgeshire PE28 3PN
Telephone: 01487 841627
Website:
Extra charge for dogs? No
Any breed restrictions? No
Dog bins?
Area for walking dogs? Yes
Static caravans? Yes
Cost of static? From £6.00 for 2 people
Mobile caravans? Yes
Cost of mobile? From £9.00 for 2 people
Tents? Yes
Cost of tent pitch? From £7.00 for 2 people
Electricity at the pitch? Some
Showers? Yes
Onsite Entertainment? No
Opening times? End Mar - End Sept
Comments: Dogs must be kept on leads

Wyton Lakes Holiday Park

Address: Banks End, Wyton, Huntingdon, Cambridgeshire PE28 2AA
Telephone: 01480 412715
Website: www.wytonlakes.com
Extra charge for dogs? Yes
Any breed restrictions? Yes
Dog bins? Yes
Area for walking dogs? Yes
Static caravans? No
Cost of static?
Mobile caravans? Yes
Cost of mobile? From £15.00 per night
Tents? Yes
Cost of tent pitch? From £12.00 per night for 2 people

Electricity at the pitch? Yes (Caravans Only)

Showers? Yes

Onsite Entertainment? No

Opening times? April - End October

Comments: No Rottweilers. A 10% discount is given for bookings longer than 7 days.

Yarwell Mill Caravan Park

Address: Yarwell, Peterborough, Cambridgeshire PE8 6PS

Telephone: 01780 782344

Website: www.yarwellmill.co.uk

Extra charge for dogs? Yes

Any breed restrictions? Yes

Dog bins?

Area for walking dogs? Yes

Static caravans? Yes

Cost of static? From £100 per week

Mobile caravans? Yes

Cost of mobile? £13.00 - £17.50 per night

Tents? Yes

Cost of tent pitch? From £10.00 - £12.00 per night

Electricity at the pitch? Yes

Showers? Yes

Onsite Entertainment? No

Opening times? March - October

Comments: No dangerous breeds

Arrowebrook Farm

Address: Arrowebrook Lane, Greasby, Wirral, Cheshire, CH49 3NZ

Telephone: 0151 677 1615

Website:

Extra charge for dogs? No

Any breed restrictions? No

Dog bins?

Area for walking dogs? Yes

Static caravans? No

Cost of static?

Mobile caravans? Yes

Cost of mobile? £10.00 per night

Tents? Yes

Cost of tent pitch? £10.00 per night

Electricity at the pitch? Yes

Showers? Yes

Onsite Entertainment? No

Opening times? March - October

Cheshire

Birch Bank Farm,

Address: Stamford Lane, Christleton, Chester, CH3 7QD
Telephone: 01244 335233
Website: www.birchbankfarm.co.uk
Extra charge for dogs? No
Any breed restrictions? No
Dog bins?
Area for walking dogs? Yes
Static caravans? No
Cost of static?
Mobile caravans? Yes
Cost of mobile? £12.50 per night
Tents? Yes
Cost of tent pitch? From £9.00
Electricity at the pitch? Yes
Showers? Yes
Onsite Entertainment? No
Opening times? May - October

Cheshire Broads Caravan Site

Address: Winsford, Cheshire, CW7 4EF
Telephone: 01606 861043
Website: www.thornleyleisure.co.uk
Extra charge for dogs? Yes
Any breed restrictions? No
Dog bins?
Area for walking dogs? Yes
Static caravans? Yes
Cost of static? From £140.00 - £400.00 per week
Mobile caravans?
Cost of mobile?
Tents?
Cost of tent pitch?
Electricity at the pitch? Yes
Showers? No
Onsite Entertainment? Yes
Opening times? March - Mid January

Cotton Arms

Address: Cholmondeley Road, Wrenbury, Cheshire, CW5 8HG
Telephone: 01270 780377
Website: www.cottonarms.co.uk
Extra charge for dogs? No
Any breed restrictions? No
Dog bins?
Area for walking dogs? Field and a Canal
Static caravans? No
Cost of static?
Mobile caravans? Yes
Cost of mobile? £14.00 per night
Tents? Yes
Cost of tent pitch? £8.00
Electricity at the pitch? Yes
Showers? Yes
Onsite Entertainment? Bowling green, Pub and Pavillon
Opening times? Beg Feb - End Dec

Daneside Country Park

Address: Holmes Chapel Road, Somerford, Congleton, CW12 4SL
Telephone: 01260 291486
Website: www.danesidecountrypark.com
Extra charge for dogs? No
Any breed restrictions? No
Dog bins?

Area for walking dogs? Yes
Static caravans? Yes
Cost of static? From £295.00 per week
Mobile caravans? No
Cost of mobile?
Tents? No
Cost of tent pitch?
Electricity at the pitch? Yes
Showers? Yes
Onsite Entertainment? No
Opening times? Beg Mar - Mid Jan

Elm Beds Caravan Park

Address: Poyntont, Cheshire, SK12 1TG
Telephone: 01625 872370
Website:
Extra charge for dogs? No
Any breed restrictions? No
Dog bins?
Area for walking dogs? Fields and Canal
Static caravans? No
Cost of static?
Mobile caravans? Yes
Cost of mobile? £14.00 per night
Tents? Yes
Cost of tent pitch? From £7.00
Electricity at the pitch? Yes
Showers? Yes
Onsite Entertainment? No
Opening times? March - October

Elm Cottage

Address: Chester Lane, Winsford, Cheshire, CW7 2QJ
Telephone: 01829 760544
Website: www.elmcottagecp.co.uk
Extra charge for dogs? No
Any breed restrictions? No
Dog bins?
Area for walking dogs? Yes
Static caravans? No
Cost of static?
Mobile caravans? Yes
Cost of mobile? £14.00 - £16.00 per night
Tents? Yes
Cost of tent pitch? £11.00 per night
Electricity at the pitch? Yes
Showers? Yes
Onsite Entertainment? No
Opening times? All Year

Fairoaks

Address: Rake Lane, Little Sanney, Chester, CH2 4HS
Telephone: 01513 551600
Website:
Extra charge for dogs? No
Any breed restrictions? No
Dog bins?
Area for walking dogs? Dog Walk on Site
Static caravans? No
Cost of static?
Mobile caravans? Yes
Cost of mobile? From £14.90 per night
Tents? Yes
Cost of tent pitch? From £14.90 for 2 people per night
Electricity at the pitch? Yes
Showers? Yes
Onsite Entertainment? No
Opening times? All Year

Holly Bank Caravan Park

Address: Warburton Bridge Rd, Rixton, Warrington, WA3 6HU
Telephone: 0161 775 2842
Website:
Extra charge for dogs? No
Any breed restrictions? No

Dog bins?
Area for walking dogs? Yes
Static caravans? No
Cost of static?
Mobile caravans? Yes
Cost of mobile? £17.00 per night
Tents? Yes
Cost of tent pitch? £6.00
Electricity at the pitch? Yes
Showers? Yes
Onsite Entertainment? No
Opening times? All Year
Comments: Dogs must be kept on a lead.

Lamb Cottage Camping & Caravan Park,

Address: Daleford Lane, Whitegate, Nr Northwich, CW8 2BN
Telephone: 01606 882302
Website: www.lambcottage.co.uk
Extra charge for dogs? Yes
Any breed restrictions? No
Dog bins?
Area for walking dogs? Dog walk
Static caravans? No
Cost of static?
Mobile caravans? Yes
Cost of mobile? £18.00 per night
Tents? No
Cost of tent pitch?
Electricity at the pitch? Yes
Showers? Yes
Onsite Entertainment? No
Opening times? March - October
Comments: Dogs must be kept on a lead. Only 2 dogs per pitch. Adults only, no children or teenagers.

Lymefield Farm

Address: Hyde, Chester, SK14 6HS
Telephone: 01457 764094
Website:
Extra charge for dogs? No
Any breed restrictions? No
Dog bins? No
Area for walking dogs? Off Site
Static caravans? No
Cost of static?
Mobile caravans? Yes
Cost of mobile? From £10.00 per night
Tents? Yes
Cost of tent pitch? From £10.00 per night
Electricity at the pitch? Yes
Showers? Yes
Onsite Entertainment? No
Opening times? March - November
Comments: Dogs must be kept on a lead at all times.

Manor Wood Country Caravan Park

Address: Coddington, Chester, CH3 9EN
Telephone: 07762 817827
Website: www.cheshirecaravansites.co.uk
Extra charge for dogs? Yes
Any breed restrictions? No
Dog bins?
Area for walking dogs? Yes
Static caravans? Yes
Cost of static? £250.00 - £450.00 per week
Mobile caravans? Yes
Cost of mobile? £16.00 - 19.00 per night
Tents? Yes
Cost of tent pitch? £16.00 - £19.00 per night
Electricity at the pitch? Yes

Showers? Yes

Onsite Entertainment? No

Opening times? All Year

Comments: Maximum of 2 dogs per pitch.

Netherwood Touring Site

Address: Netherwood House, Whitchurch Rd Nr Chester, CH3 6AF

Telephone: 01244 335583

Website: www.netherwoodtouringsite.co.uk

Extra charge for dogs? No

Any breed restrictions? No

Dog bins?

Area for walking dogs? Yes

Static caravans? No

Cost of static?

Mobile caravans? Yes

Cost of mobile? £14.00 - £17.00 for 2 adults

Tents? Yes

Cost of tent pitch? £14.00 - £17.00 for 2 adults

Electricity at the pitch? Yes

Showers? Yes

Onsite Entertainment? No

Opening times? Beg March - End October

Comments: No Children allowed Adults only

New Farm

Address: Long Lane, Wettenhall, Winsford, Cheshire, CW7 4DW

Telephone: 01270 528213

Website: www.newfarmbbandcaravanpark.co.uk

Extra charge for dogs? No

Any breed restrictions? Yes

Dog bins?

Area for walking dogs? Yes

Static caravans? No

Cost of static?

Mobile caravans? Yes

Cost of mobile? £16.00

Tents? Yes

Cost of tent pitch? £13.00

Electricity at the pitch? Yes

Showers? Yes

Onsite Entertainment? No

Opening times? All Year

Comments: Not Rottweilers

Northwood Hall Country Touring Park,

Address: Frodsham St, Kelsall, Chester, CW6 0RP

Telephone: 01829 752569

Website:

Extra charge for dogs? No

Any breed restrictions? Yes

Dog bins?

Area for walking dogs? Yes

Static caravans? No

Cost of static?

Mobile caravans? Yes

Cost of mobile? From £14.00 per night

Tents? Yes

Cost of tent pitch? From £10.00 per night

Electricity at the pitch? Yes (Caravans only)

Showers? Yes

Onsite Entertainment? No

Opening times? All Year

Comments: Not Rottweilers or Pittbulls unless muzzled. There is a park on site for the children.

Raby Park Paddock Camp Site

Address: Raby Park, Neston, Cheshire, CH64 9FX

Telephone: 07956 534035

Website:

Extra charge for dogs? No

Any breed restrictions? No

Dog bins?

Area for walking dogs? Yes

Static caravans? No

Cost of static?

Mobile caravans? Yes

Cost of mobile? £5.00 per person per night

Tents? No

Cost of tent pitch?

Electricity at the pitch? Yes

Showers? Yes

Onsite Entertainment? No

Opening times? All Year

Comments: Dogs must be kept on lead. No children. No visitors

Ridgeway Country Holiday Park

Address: The Ridgeway, Frodsham, WA6 6XQ

Telephone: 01928 734981

Website: www.ridgewaypark.com

Extra charge for dogs? Yes

Any breed restrictions? Yes

Dog bins?

Area for walking dogs? Dog area just adjacent to the Park

Static caravans? Yes

Cost of static? From £214.00 - £577.00 per week

Mobile caravans?

Cost of mobile?

Tents?

Cost of tent pitch?

Electricity at the pitch? N/A

Showers? N/A

Onsite Entertainment? No

Opening times? Beg March - Begin January

Strawberry Wood

Address: Lower Withington, Macclesfield, SK11 9DU

Telephone: 01477 571407

Website: http://uk.geocities.com/strawberrywoodcaravanpark

Extra charge for dogs? No

Any breed restrictions? No

Dog bins?

Area for walking dogs? No

Static caravans? No

Cost of static?

Mobile caravans? Yes

Cost of mobile? £14.00 per night

Tents? No

Cost of tent pitch?

Electricity at the pitch? Yes

Showers? Yes

Onsite Entertainment? No

Opening times? March - October

The Antrobus Arms

Address: Warrington Road,Antrtobus, Northwich, Cheshire, CW9 6JD

Telephone: 01606 891333

Website:

Extra charge for dogs? No

Any breed restrictions? No

Dog bins?

Area for walking dogs? Yes

Static caravans? No

Cost of static?

Mobile caravans? Yes

Cost of mobile? £5.00 per night

Tents? Yes

Cost of tent pitch? £5.00 per night

Electricity at the pitch? No
Showers? No
Onsite Entertainment? Yes
Opening times? All Year

The Hollies

Address: Little Budworth, Tarporley,Cheshire, CW6 9ES
Telephone: 01829 760171
Website: www.thehollies farmshop.co.uk
Extra charge for dogs? No
Any breed restrictions? No
Dog bins?
Area for walking dogs? Yes
Static caravans? No
Cost of static?
Mobile caravans? Yes
Cost of mobile? From £17.50 per night
Tents? No
Cost of tent pitch?
Electricity at the pitch? Yes
Showers? Yes
Onsite Entertainment? No
Opening times? March - October

The Wild Boar Inn

Address: Wincle, Macclesfield, Cheshire, SK11 0QL
Telephone: 01260 227219
Website: www.thewildboar.co.uk
Extra charge for dogs? Yes
Any breed restrictions? No
Dog bins?
Area for walking dogs? Yes
Static caravans? No
Cost of static?
Mobile caravans? Yes
Cost of mobile?
Tents? Yes
Cost of tent pitch? £5.00 - £6.00 per adult

Electricity at the pitch? No
Showers? Yes
Onsite Entertainment? Yes
Opening times? All Year
Comments: Entertainment stops from November to March

Thornleigh Park Farm

Address: Ferry Lane, Higher Ferry, Chester, CH1 6QF
Telephone: 01244 371718
Website:
Extra charge for dogs? No
Any breed restrictions? No
Dog bins? No
Area for walking dogs? Yes
Static caravans? No
Cost of static?
Mobile caravans? Yes
Cost of mobile? From £8.00 per night
Tents? Yes
Cost of tent pitch? From £3.50 per adult £2.00 per child per night
Electricity at the pitch? Yes
Showers? Yes
Onsite Entertainment? No
Opening times? All Year

Woodbine Cottage Caravan Park,

Address: Warrington Rd, Acton Bridge, Nr Northwich, CW8 3QB
Telephone: 01606 852319/77900
Website:
Extra charge for dogs? No
Any breed restrictions? Yes
Dog bins?
Area for walking dogs? Yes
Static caravans? No
Cost of static?
Mobile caravans? Yes

Cost of mobile? From £16.50 per night up to 4 people
Tents? Yes
Cost of tent pitch? From £10.00 per night
Electricity at the pitch? Yes
Showers? Yes
Onsite Entertainment? No
Opening times? 1st March - 1st November
Comments: Maximum 2 dogs per pitch. No dangerous breeds.

Woodlands Caravan Park

Address: Wash Lane, Allostock, Knutsford, WA16 9LG
Telephone: 01565 723307/722628
Website:
Extra charge for dogs? No
Any breed restrictions? No
Dog bins?
Area for walking dogs? Yes
Static caravans? No
Cost of static?
Mobile caravans? Yes
Cost of mobile? £13.00 per night
Tents? Yes
Cost of tent pitch? £12.00 per night
Electricity at the pitch? Yes
Showers? Yes
Onsite Entertainment? No
Opening times? 1st March - 7th January

A J Inch

Address: Fair View, Poughill, Bude, Cornwall EX23 9HH
Telephone: 01288 353018
Website:
Extra charge for dogs? No
Any breed restrictions? No
Dog bins? Yes
Area for walking dogs? Yes
Static caravans? No
Cost of static?
Mobile caravans? Yes
Cost of mobile? From £11.00 per night
Tents? No
Cost of tent pitch?
Electricity at the pitch? Yes
Showers? Yes
Onsite Entertainment? No
Opening times? All Year

Atlantic Coast Caravan Park

Address: 53, Upton Towans, Hayle, Cornwall TR27 5BL
Telephone: 01736 752071
Website: www.atlanticcoast-caravan park.co.uk
Extra charge for dogs? Yes
Any breed restrictions? Yes
Dog bins?
Area for walking dogs? No
Static caravans? Yes
Cost of static? From £245.00 per week
Mobile caravans? Yes
Cost of mobile? From £12.00 per night
Tents? Yes
Cost of tent pitch? From £12.00 per night
Electricity at the pitch? Yes
Showers? Yes
Onsite Entertainment? No
Opening times? Easter - End October
Comments: No dangerous breeds including Rottweilers and Dobermans

Ayr Holiday Park

Address: Ayr, St Iver, Cornwall, TR26 1EJ
Telephone: 01736 795855
Website: www.ayrholidaypark.co.uk
Extra charge for dogs? Yes
Any breed restrictions? No
Dog bins?
Area for walking dogs? Yes
Static caravans? Yes
Cost of static? From £300.00 per week
Mobile caravans? Yes
Cost of mobile? From £14.00 per night
Tents? Yes
Cost of tent pitch? From £14.00 per night
Electricity at the pitch? Yes
Showers? Yes
Onsite Entertainment? No
Opening times? All Year

Ayr Holiday Park and Trevalgan Touring Park

Address: St Ives, Cornwall, TR26 3BJ
Telephone: 01736 796433
Website: www.ayrholidaypark.co.uk
Extra charge for dogs? Yes
Any breed restrictions? No

Dog bins? Yes
Area for walking dogs? Yes
Static caravans? Yes
Cost of static? From £310.00 per week
Mobile caravans? Yes
Cost of mobile? From £14.00 per night for 2 People
Tents? Yes
Cost of tent pitch? From £14.00 per night for 2 People
Electricity at the pitch? Yes
Showers? Yes
Onsite Entertainment? No
Opening times? All Year

Badgers Folly

Address: Hicks Mill, Truro, Cornwall, TR4 8RE
Telephone: 01872 865211
Website: www.5van.co.uk
Extra charge for dogs? No
Any breed restrictions? No
Dog bins? No
Area for walking dogs? Off Site
Static caravans? No
Cost of static?
Mobile caravans? Yes
Cost of mobile? From £8.50 with electric
Tents? No
Cost of tent pitch?
Electricity at the pitch? Yes
Showers? No
Onsite Entertainment? No
Opening times? April - End September

Balnoon Camping Site

Address: Halsetown, St.Ives, Cornwall, TR26 3JA
Telephone: 01736 795431
Website:
Extra charge for dogs? No
Any breed restrictions? Yes
Dog bins?
Area for walking dogs? No
Static caravans? No
Cost of static?
Mobile caravans? Yes
Cost of mobile? From £9.00 - £13.00 per night for 2 people
Tents? Yes
Cost of tent pitch? From £9.00 - £13.00 per night for 2 people
Electricity at the pitch? Yes
Showers? Yes
Onsite Entertainment? No
Opening times? Easter - October
Comments: No dangerous breeds, dogs must be kept on a lead.

Bay View Farm

Address: St Martins, Looe, Cornwall, PL13 1NZ
Telephone: 01503 265922
Website: www.looebaycaravans.co.uk
Extra charge for dogs? No
Any breed restrictions? No
Dog bins?
Area for walking dogs? Yes
Static caravans? No
Cost of static?
Mobile caravans? Yes
Cost of mobile? From £10.00 - £17.50 per night
Tents? Yes
Cost of tent pitch? From £10.00 - £17.50 per night
Electricity at the pitch? Yes
Showers? Yes
Onsite Entertainment? No
Opening times? March - October

Comments: There are Shire Horses on the farm that people can watch

Beacon Cottage Farm Touring Park

Address: Beacon Cottage, St. Agnes, Cornwall TR5 0NU

Telephone: 01872 552347

Website: www.beaconcottagefarm holidays.co.uk

Extra charge for dogs? Yes

Any breed restrictions? No

Dog bins?

Area for walking dogs? Yes

Static caravans? No

Cost of static?

Mobile caravans? Yes

Cost of mobile? From £16.00 - £21.00 per night

Tents? Yes

Cost of tent pitch? From £16.00 - £21.00 per night

Electricity at the pitch? Yes

Showers? Yes

Onsite Entertainment? No

Opening times? Easter - October

Comments: Dogs must be kept on a lead.

Boleigh Farm Site

Address: Boleigh Farm, Lamorna, Penzance, Cornwall

Telephone: 01736 810305

Website:

Extra charge for dogs? No

Any breed restrictions? No

Dog bins?

Area for walking dogs? No

Static caravans? No

Cost of static?

Mobile caravans? Yes

Cost of mobile? From £8.00 per night

Tents? Yes

Cost of tent pitch? From £8.00 per night

Electricity at the pitch? Yes

Showers? Yes

Onsite Entertainment? No

Opening times? Easter - October

Bone Valley Caravan Park

Address: Heamoor, Penzance, Cornwall TR20 8UJ

Telephone: 01736 360313

Website: www.cornwalltouristboard.co.uk/bonevalleycaravancampingpark

Extra charge for dogs? No

Any breed restrictions? No

Dog bins?

Area for walking dogs? No

Static caravans? Yes

Cost of static? From £175.00 - £400.00 per week

Mobile caravans? Yes

Cost of mobile? £6.50 per night + £3.00 per adult

Tents? Yes

Cost of tent pitch? £6.50 per night + £3.00 per adult

Electricity at the pitch? Yes (£3.50 per night)

Showers? Yes

Onsite Entertainment? No

Opening times? All Year

Comments: Dogs must be kept on a lead at all times. Dogs must not be left unattended in statics. There is a Campers Lounge and Kitchen. There are baby changing facilities available.

Broad Meadow House

Address: Quay Road Charlestown, St Austell, Cornwall, PL25 3NX

Telephone: 01726 76636

Website: www.broadmeadowhouse.com
Extra charge for dogs? No
Any breed restrictions? No
Dog bins? Yes
Area for walking dogs? Yes
Static caravans? Yes (see Comments)
Cost of static? From £18.00 per adult £15.00 per child
Mobile caravans? No
Cost of mobile?
Tents? Yes
Cost of tent pitch? £6.00 per adult £3.00 per child per night
Electricity at the pitch? Yes (£2.00 per night)
Showers? Yes
Onsite Entertainment? No
Opening times? Easter - September
Comments: These are tents that are already erected with beds made, and breakfast brought to you. There are two types of packs available the Luxury Bedroom Pack and the Budget Bedroom Pack.

Budemeadows Touring Park

Address: Poundstock, Bude, Cornwall EX23 0NA
Telephone: 01288 361646
Website: www.budemeadows.com
Extra charge for dogs? Yes
Any breed restrictions? No
Dog bins? No
Area for walking dogs? No
Static caravans? No
Cost of static?
Mobile caravans? Yes
Cost of mobile? From £4.60 - £10.50 per adult per night
Tents? Yes
Cost of tent pitch? From £4.60 - £10.50 per adult per night
Electricity at the pitch? Yes
Showers? Yes
Onsite Entertainment? Bar, Shop and Swimming Pool
Opening times? All Year

Calloose Caravan Park

Address: Calloose Lane, Leedstown, Hayle, Cornwall TR27 5ET
Telephone: 01736 850431
Website: www.calloose.co.uk
Extra charge for dogs? Yes
Any breed restrictions? No
Dog bins?
Area for walking dogs? Yes
Static caravans? No
Cost of static?
Mobile caravans? Yes
Cost of mobile? From £14.00 - £20.00 per night
Tents? Yes
Cost of tent pitch? From £14.00 - £20.00 per night
Electricity at the pitch? Yes
Showers? Yes
Onsite Entertainment? Yes
Opening times? Easter – End September

Cambrose Touring Park

Address: Portreath Road, Redruth, Cornwall, TR16 4HT
Telephone: 01209 890747
Website: www.cambrosetouringpark.co.uk
Extra charge for dogs? Yes
Any breed restrictions? Yes
Dog bins?
Area for walking dogs? Yes

Static caravans? No
Cost of static?
Mobile caravans? Yes
Cost of mobile? From £9.00 - £14.50 per pitch for 2 people
Tents? Yes
Cost of tent pitch? From £9.00 - £14.50 per pitch for 2 people
Electricity at the pitch? Yes
Showers? Yes
Onsite Entertainment? No
Opening times? April - End October
Comments: No Dangerous Breeds

Cardinney Caravan And Camping Park

Address: Crows-an-wra, Penzance, Cornwall, TR19 6HX
Telephone: 01736 810880
Website: www.cardinney-camping-park.co.uk
Extra charge for dogs? No
Any breed restrictions? No
Dog bins?
Area for walking dogs? Off Site
Static caravans? No
Cost of static?
Mobile caravans? Yes
Cost of mobile? £15.50 per pitch for 2 people (Peak Season)
Tents?
Cost of tent pitch?
Electricity at the pitch? Yes
Showers? Yes
Onsite Entertainment? No
Opening times? 1st Feb - End Nov

Carlyon Bay Camping Park

Address: Cypress Avenue, Carlyon Bay, St Austell, Cornwall, PL25 3RE
Telephone: 01726 812735
Website: www.carlyonbay.net
Extra charge for dogs? Yes
Any breed restrictions? Yes
Dog bins? Yes
Area for walking dogs? Yes
Static caravans? No
Cost of static?
Mobile caravans? Yes
Cost of mobile? From £10.00 - £22.00 per pitch
Tents? Yes
Cost of tent pitch? From £10.00 - £22.00 per pitch
Electricity at the pitch? Yes
Showers? Yes
Onsite Entertainment? Childrens Entertainment
Opening times? Easter - October
Comments: No Dangerous Breeds including Rottweilers and Dobermans

Carnevas Holiday Park

Address: Carnevas Farm, St Merryn, Padstow, Cornwall, PL28 8PN
Telephone: 01841 520230
Website: www.carnevasholidaypark.co.uk
Extra charge for dogs? Yes
Any breed restrictions? Yes
Dog bins? No
Area for walking dogs? Yes
Static caravans? Yes
Cost of static? From £180.00 per week
Mobile caravans? Yes
Cost of mobile? From £9.00 per night
Tents? Yes
Cost of tent pitch? From £9.00 per night
Electricity at the pitch? Yes
Showers? Yes

Onsite Entertainment? Limited
Opening times? 1st April - End October
Comments: No Dangerous Breeds

Carnmoggas Holiday Park

Address: Little Polgooth, Mevagissey, Cornwall, PL26 7DD
Telephone: 01726 74070
Website: www.carnmoggas.com
Extra charge for dogs? Yes
Any breed restrictions? No
Dog bins? Yes
Area for walking dogs? Yes
Static caravans? Yes
Cost of static? From £390.00 per week
Mobile caravans? No
Cost of mobile?
Tents? No
Cost of tent pitch?
Electricity at the pitch? Yes
Showers? No
Onsite Entertainment? Yes
Opening times? All Year

Carnon Downs Caravan & Camping Site

Address: Carnon Downs, Truro, Cornwall, TR3 6JJ
Telephone: 01872 862283
Website: www.carnon-downs-caravan park.co.uk
Extra charge for dogs? No
Any breed restrictions? No
Dog bins?
Area for walking dogs? Yes
Static caravans? No
Cost of static?
Mobile caravans? Yes
Cost of mobile? £17.00 per night
Tents? Yes
Cost of tent pitch? £14.00 per night
Electricity at the pitch? Yes
Showers? Yes
Onsite Entertainment? No
Opening times? All Year

Chiverton Park

Address: East Hill, Chiverton Cross, Blackwater, Truro, Cornwall TR4 8HS
Telephone: 01872 560667
Website: www.chivertonpark.co.uk
Extra charge for dogs? Yes
Any breed restrictions? No
Dog bins? No
Area for walking dogs? No
Static caravans? Yes
Cost of static? From £150.00 - £600.00 per week
Mobile caravans? Yes
Cost of mobile? From £14.00 - £22.00 per night
Tents? Yes
Cost of tent pitch? From £14.00 - £22.00 per night
Electricity at the pitch? Yes
Showers? Yes
Onsite Entertainment? No
Opening times? Beg March - End October

Cosawes Caravan Park

Address: Perranarworthal. Truro. Cornwall. TR3 7QS
Telephone: 01872 863724
Website: www.cosawestouringand camping.co.uk
Extra charge for dogs? No
Any breed restrictions? No
Dog bins? No
Area for walking dogs? Yes
Static caravans? No
Cost of static?

Mobile caravans? Yes
Cost of mobile? From £9.00 - £16.00
Tents? Yes
Cost of tent pitch? From £9.00 - £16.00
Electricity at the pitch? Yes
Showers? Yes
Onsite Entertainment? No
Opening times? All Year
Comments: Dogs must be kept on a lead.

Court Farm Caravan & Camping Holidays

Address: St Stephen. St Austell. Cornwall. PL26 7LE
Telephone: 01726 823 684
Website: www.courtfarmcornwall.co.uk
Extra charge for dogs? No
Any breed restrictions? Yes
Dog bins?
Area for walking dogs? Yes
Static caravans? No
Cost of static?
Mobile caravans? Yes
Cost of mobile? From £9.50 per night
Tents? Yes
Cost of tent pitch? From £9.50 per night
Electricity at the pitch? Yes
Showers? Yes
Onsite Entertainment? No
Opening times? April - September
Comments: No Dangerous Breeds

Coxford Meadow Campsite

Address: Coxford Meadow St Gennys, Bude, Cornwall, EX23 0NS
Telephone: 01840 230707
Website:
Extra charge for dogs? Yes
Any breed restrictions? Yes
Dog bins?
Area for walking dogs? Yes
Static caravans? No
Cost of static?
Mobile caravans? Yes
Cost of mobile? £5.50 - £6.50 per person per night
Tents? Yes
Cost of tent pitch? £4.50 - £5.50 per person per night
Electricity at the pitch? Yes
Showers? Yes
Onsite Entertainment? No
Opening times? All Year
Comments: No Rottweilers

Crantock Beach Holiday Park

Address: Crantock, Newquay, Cornwall, TR8 5RH
Telephone: 0871 641 0323
Website: www.parkdeanholidays.co.uk
Extra charge for dogs? Yes
Any breed restrictions? Yes
Dog bins?
Area for walking dogs? Yes
Static caravans? Yes
Cost of static? From £159.00 per week
Mobile caravans? No
Cost of mobile?
Tents? No
Cost of tent pitch?
Electricity at the pitch? No
Showers? No
Onsite Entertainment? Yes
Opening times? 14 March - 3rd November

Crantock Plains Touring Park

Address: Crantock Plains, Crantock, Newquay, Cornwall TR8 5PH
Telephone: 01637 830955
Website: www.crantock-plains.co.uk

Extra charge for dogs? Yes
Any breed restrictions? No
Dog bins? Yes
Area for walking dogs? Off Site
Static caravans? No
Cost of static?
Mobile caravans? Yes
Cost of mobile? From £5.50 - £7.50 per adult per night
Tents? Yes
Cost of tent pitch? From £5.50 - £7.50 per adult per night
Electricity at the pitch? Yes
Showers? Yes
Onsite Entertainment? No
Opening times? Easter - September
Comments: Dogs must be kept on a lead.

Dennis Cove Camping Ltd

Address: Dennis Lane, Padstow, Cornwall, PL28 8DR
Telephone: 01841 532349
Website: www.denniscove.co.uk
Extra charge for dogs? Yes
Any breed restrictions? Yes
Dog bins? No
Area for walking dogs? Yes
Static caravans? No
Cost of static?
Mobile caravans? Yes
Cost of mobile? From £12.70 per night for 2 people
Tents? Yes
Cost of tent pitch? From £12.70 per night for 2 people
Electricity at the pitch? Yes
Showers? Yes
Onsite Entertainment? No
Opening times? April - End September

Dinham Farm Caravan & Camping Park

Address: St. Minver, Wadebridge, Cornwall PL27 6RH
Telephone: 01208 812878
Website: www.dinhamfarm.co.uk
Extra charge for dogs? Yes
Any breed restrictions? Yes
Dog bins? No
Area for walking dogs? Yes
Static caravans? Yes
Cost of static? From £270.00 - £480.00
Mobile caravans? Yes
Cost of mobile? £16.00 for 2 adults + Pitch
Tents? Yes
Cost of tent pitch? £16.00 for 2 adults + Pitch
Electricity at the pitch? Yes (£2.00 - £4.00)
Showers? Yes
Onsite Entertainment? No
Opening times? Easter - Mid October
Comments: No Dangerous Breeds

Dolbeare Caravan Park

Address: St. Ive Rd, Landrake, Saltash, Cornwall PL12 5AF
Telephone: 01752 851332
Website: www.dolbeare.co.uk
Extra charge for dogs? Yes
Any breed restrictions? Yes
Dog bins? Yes
Area for walking dogs? Yes
Static caravans? No
Cost of static?
Mobile caravans? Yes
Cost of mobile? From £11.40 - £17.00
Tents? Yes
Cost of tent pitch? From £11.40 - £17.00

Electricity at the pitch? Yes
Showers? Yes
Onsite Entertainment? No
Opening times? All Year
Comments: No Dangerous Breeds. They have a laundry room.

DoubleTrees Farm Caravan & Camping site

Address: Luxulyan Road, St Blazey Gate, Par, St Austell, Cornwall, PL24 2EH
Telephone: 01726 812266
Website: www.eids.co.uk/doublethrees
Extra charge for dogs? No
Any breed restrictions? No
Dog bins? No
Area for walking dogs? Yes
Static caravans? No
Cost of static?
Mobile caravans? Yes
Cost of mobile? From £12.00 per night for 2 adults including electricity
Tents? Yes
Cost of tent pitch? From £12.00 per night for 2 adults including electricity
Electricity at the pitch? Yes
Showers? Yes
Onsite Entertainment? No
Opening times? Beg March - End December

Dove Meadows

Address: Green Lane West, Marazion, Cornwall TR17 0HH
Telephone: 01736 710854
Website:
Extra charge for dogs? No
Any breed restrictions? No
Dog bins? No
Area for walking dogs? Off Site
Static caravans? No
Cost of static?
Mobile caravans? Yes
Cost of mobile? From £6.00 - £15.00
Tents? Yes
Cost of tent pitch? From £6.00 - £15.00
Electricity at the pitch? Yes
Showers? Yes
Onsite Entertainment? No
Opening times? All Year
Comments: Dogs must be kept on leads during Summer months.

East Crinnis Caravan & Camping

Address: Lantyan, Par Moor Rd, Par, Cornwall PL24 2SQ
Telephone: 01726 813023
Website: www.crinniscamping.co.uk
Extra charge for dogs? Not for 1 dog
Any breed restrictions? No
Dog bins? Yes
Area for walking dogs? Yes
Static caravans? No
Cost of static?
Mobile caravans? Yes
Cost of mobile? From £8.00 - £15.00 per pitch for 2 people per night
Tents? Yes
Cost of tent pitch? From £8.00 - £15.00 per pitch for 2 people per night
Electricity at the pitch? Yes
Showers? Yes
Onsite Entertainment? No
Opening times? Easter - End October
Comments: Dogs must be well behaved.

Franchies Holidays

Address: Cury Cross Lanes, Near Mullion, Helston, Cornwall, TR12
Telephone: 01326 240301

Website: www.franchies.co.uk
Extra charge for dogs? Yes
Any breed restrictions? No
Dog bins? Yes
Area for walking dogs? Yes
Static caravans? Yes
Cost of static? From £170.00 - £460.00 per week
Mobile caravans? Yes
Cost of mobile? From £10.00 - £16.00 per night
Tents? Yes
Cost of tent pitch? From £10.00 - £16.00 per night
Electricity at the pitch? Yes
Showers? Yes
Onsite Entertainment? No
Opening times? Easter - End October
Comments: Dogs must be kept on a lead. Maximum of 2 dogs per party. There is a small shop on site and a launderette.

Glenmorris Park

Address: Longstone Rd, St. Mabyn, Bodmin, Cornwall PL30 3BY
Telephone: 01208 841677
Website: www.glenmorris.co.uk
Extra charge for dogs? Yes
Any breed restrictions? No
Dog bins? Yes
Area for walking dogs? Yes
Static caravans? Yes
Cost of static? From £175.00 per week
Mobile caravans? Yes
Cost of mobile? From £10.00 per night
Tents? Yes
Cost of tent pitch? From £10.00 per night
Electricity at the pitch? Yes
Showers? Yes
Onsite Entertainment? No
Opening times? March - End October
Comments: There is a games room on site for the children.

Globe Vale Holiday Park

Address: Sinns Common, Redruth, Cornwall TR16 4BH
Telephone: 01209 891183
Website: www.globevale.co.uk
Extra charge for dogs? Yes
Any breed restrictions? No
Dog bins? Yes
Area for walking dogs? Yes
Static caravans? Yes
Cost of static? From £160.00 - £390.00 per week
Mobile caravans? Yes
Cost of mobile? From £8.50 - £17.00 per night
Tents? Yes
Cost of tent pitch? From £8.50 - £17.00 per night
Electricity at the pitch? Yes
Showers? Yes
Onsite Entertainment? No
Opening times? Mid March - End October
Comments: Maximum 2 dogs. Dogs have to be kept on a lead. Dogs cannot be left unattended in the Static Caravans. There is a Launderette and a childrens play area on site.

Gnome World Holiday Park

Address: Moorland Road, Indian Queens, St. Columb, Cornwall TR9 6HN
Telephone: 01726 860812
Website: www.gnomesworld@btconnect.com

Extra charge for dogs? No
Any breed restrictions? Yes
Dog bins? Yes
Area for walking dogs? Yes
Static caravans? Yes
Cost of static? From £175.00 - £475.00 per week
Mobile caravans? Yes
Cost of mobile? From £3.50 - £4.15 per adult
Tents? Yes
Cost of tent pitch?
Electricity at the pitch? Yes (£2.00 per night)
Showers? Yes
Onsite Entertainment? No
Opening times? March - December
Comments: Dogs must be kept on a lead. No dangerous breeds.

Golden Lion Inn Lakeside Camping.

Address: Stithians Lake, Menherion, Redruth, Cornwall, TR16 6NW
Telephone: 01209 860332
Website: www.golden-lion-inn.co.uk
Extra charge for dogs? No
Any breed restrictions? No
Dog bins? No
Area for walking dogs? Yes
Static caravans? No
Cost of static?
Mobile caravans? Yes
Cost of mobile? From £12.00 per night
Tents? Yes
Cost of tent pitch? From £10.00 per night
Electricity at the pitch? Yes
Showers? Yes
Onsite Entertainment? Bar, Pub and Restaurant
Opening times? All Year

Gwithian Farm Campsite

Address: 1 Churchtown Rd. Gwithian, Hayle. St Ives. Cornwall. TR27 5BX
Telephone: 01736 753127
Website: www.gwithianfarm.co.uk
Extra charge for dogs? Yes
Any breed restrictions? No
Dog bins? No
Area for walking dogs? No
Static caravans? No
Cost of static?
Mobile caravans? Yes
Cost of mobile? From £13.00 - £22.00 per night with electric
Tents? Yes
Cost of tent pitch? From £10.00 - £18.00 per night
Electricity at the pitch? Yes
Showers? Yes
Onsite Entertainment? No
Opening times? Easter - Beg October
Comments: There is a pub opposite.

Harlyn Sands Holiday Park

Address: Lighthouse Rd, Trevose Head, Padstow, Cornwall PL28 8SQ
Telephone: 01841 520720
Website: www.harlynsands.co.uk
Extra charge for dogs? Yes
Any breed restrictions? Yes
Dog bins? Yes
Area for walking dogs? No
Static caravans? Yes
Cost of static? From £100.00 per week
Mobile caravans? Yes
Cost of mobile? From £6.00 per night
Tents? Yes
Cost of tent pitch? From £6.00 per night
Electricity at the pitch? Yes
Showers? Yes
Onsite Entertainment? Yes

Opening times? March - End October

Comments: No Dangerous Breeds.

Health Farm Camping

Address: Ponsongath, Coverack, Cornwall, TR12 6SQ

Telephone: 01326 280521

Website: www.heath_farm_holidays.co.uk

Extra charge for dogs? No

Any breed restrictions? No

Dog bins? No

Area for walking dogs? Yes

Static caravans? No

Cost of static?

Mobile caravans? Yes

Cost of mobile? From £10.00 per night

Tents? Yes

Cost of tent pitch? From £10.00 per night

Electricity at the pitch? Yes

Showers? Yes

Onsite Entertainment? No

Opening times? All Year

Heligan Woods

Address: St Ewe, Mevagissey, Cornwall, PL26 6EZ

Telephone: 01726 843485

Website: www.heliganpark.co.uk

Extra charge for dogs? Yes

Any breed restrictions? No

Dog bins? Yes

Area for walking dogs? No

Static caravans? Yes

Cost of static? From £195.00 - £695.00 per week

Mobile caravans? Yes

Cost of mobile? From £10.25 - £23.85 for 2 people

Tents? Yes

Cost of tent pitch? From £10.25 - £23.85 for 2 people

Electricity at the pitch? Yes

Showers? Yes

Onsite Entertainment? No

Opening times? 12th Jan - 22nd Nov

Comments: Dogs must be kept on a lead.

Hellesveor Caravan & Camping site

Address: Hellesveor Farm, St Ives, Cornwall, TR26 3AD

Telephone: 01736 795738

Website: www.intocornwall.com

Extra charge for dogs? No

Any breed restrictions? No

Dog bins? No

Area for walking dogs? No

Static caravans? Yes

Cost of static? From £200.00 - £400.00 per week

Mobile caravans? Yes

Cost of mobile? From £10.00 - £25.00 per night for 2 People

Tents? Yes

Cost of tent pitch? From £10.00 - £25.00 per night for 2 People

Electricity at the pitch? Yes

Showers? Yes

Onsite Entertainment? No

Opening times? All Year

Comments: Dogs must be kept on a lead.

Hendra Holiday Park

Address: Lane, Newquay, Cornwall TR8 4NY

Telephone: 01637 875778

Website: www.hendra-holidays.com
Extra charge for dogs? Yes
Any breed restrictions? Yes
Dog bins? Yes
Area for walking dogs? Yes
Static caravans? Yes
Cost of static? From £129.00 for short break/From £235.00 per week
Mobile caravans? Yes
Cost of mobile? From £4.55 - £8.25 per adult per night
Tents? Yes
Cost of tent pitch? From £4.55 - £8.25 per adult per night
Electricity at the pitch? Yes
Showers? Yes
Onsite Entertainment? Yes
Opening times? Easter - November
Comments: No dangerous breeds.

Hentervene Holiday Park

Address: Crackington Haven, Bude, Cornwall EX23 0LF
Telephone: 01840 230065
Website: www.hentervene.co.uk
Extra charge for dogs? Yes
Any breed restrictions? Yes
Dog bins? Yes
Area for walking dogs? Yes
Static caravans? Yes
Cost of static? From £190.00 - £460.00 per week
Mobile caravans? Yes
Cost of mobile? From £12.00 - £24.00 per night
Tents? No
Cost of tent pitch?
Electricity at the pitch? Yes
Showers? Yes
Onsite Entertainment? No
Opening times? March - October
Comments: No dangerous breeds.

Higher Chellew Touring site

Address: Higher Trenowin, Nancledra, Penzance, Cornwall, TR20 8BD
Telephone: 01736 364532
Website: www.higherchellewcamping.co.uk
Extra charge for dogs? Yes
Any breed restrictions? No
Dog bins? No
Area for walking dogs? Yes
Static caravans? No
Cost of static?
Mobile caravans? Yes
Cost of mobile? From £9.00 - £14.00 per night
Tents? No
Cost of tent pitch? From £9.00 - £14.00 per night
Electricity at the pitch? Yes
Showers? Yes
Onsite Entertainment? No
Opening times? March - End October

Higher Harlyn Park

Address: St Merryn, Padstow, Cornwall, PL28 8SG
Telephone: 01841 520022
Website: www.higherharlynpark.co.uk
Extra charge for dogs? Yes
Any breed restrictions? No
Dog bins? Yes
Area for walking dogs? Yes
Static caravans? Yes
Cost of static? From £250.00 - £600.00 per week
Mobile caravans? Yes

Cost of mobile? From £8.00 - £18.00 per night
Tents? Yes
Cost of tent pitch? From £8.00 - £18.00 per night
Electricity at the pitch? Yes
Showers? Yes
Onsite Entertainment? Bar, Live Music (once a week)
Opening times? Easter - Mid September
Comments: Dogs must be kept on a lead.

Praa Sands

Address: Praa Sands, Penzance, Cornwall TR20 9TL
Telephone: 01736 763222
Website:
Extra charge for dogs? No
Any breed restrictions? No
Dog bins? No
Area for walking dogs? Yes
Static caravans? No
Cost of static?
Mobile caravans? Yes
Cost of mobile? From £11.50
Tents? Yes
Cost of tent pitch? From £9.50 - £11.50
Electricity at the pitch? Yes (£3.00 per day)
Showers? Yes
Onsite Entertainment? No
Opening times? Easter - End October
Comments: Dogs must be kept on a lead.

Higher Trevaskis Caravan & Camping Park

Address: Gwinear Rd, Connor Downs, Hayle, Cornwall TR27 5JQ
Telephone: 01209 831736
Website:
Extra charge for dogs? No
Any breed restrictions? Yes
Dog bins? No
Area for walking dogs? Off Site
Static caravans? No
Cost of static?
Mobile caravans? Yes
Cost of mobile? From £10.00 - £22.00 per night for 2 adults & 2 Children
Tents? Yes
Cost of tent pitch? From £10.00 - £22.00 per night for 2 adults & 2 Children
Electricity at the pitch? Yes
Showers? Yes
Onsite Entertainment? No
Opening times? Mid April - End September
Comments: Maximum 2 Dogs.

Kelynack Caravan And Camping Park

Address: St Just, Penzance, Cornwall, TR19 7RE
Telephone: 01736 787633
Website: www.kelynackholidays.co.uk
Extra charge for dogs? Yes
Any breed restrictions? No
Dog bins? Yes
Area for walking dogs? Off Site
Static caravans? Yes
Cost of static? From £155.00 - £410.00
Mobile caravans? Yes
Cost of mobile? From £5.50 - £6.50 per adult per night
Tents? Yes
Cost of tent pitch? From £5.50 - £6.50 per adult per night
Electricity at the pitch? Yes
Showers? Yes
Onsite Entertainment? No

Opening times? 1st April - 1st November

Comments: Dogs must be kept on a lead.

Kenneggy Cove Holiday Park

Address: Higher Kenneggy, Rosudgeon, Penzance, TR20 9AU

Telephone: 01736 763453

Website: www.keneggycove.co.uk

Extra charge for dogs? Yes

Any breed restrictions? No

Dog bins? No

Area for walking dogs? No

Static caravans? Yes

Cost of static? From £270.00 - £515.00 per week

Mobile caravans? Yes

Cost of mobile? From £14.50 - £19.00 per night

Tents? Yes

Cost of tent pitch? From £14.50 - £19.00 per night

Electricity at the pitch? Yes

Showers? Yes

Onsite Entertainment? No

Opening times? May - October

Comments: Dogs must be kept on a lead.

Killiwerris Touring Park

Address: Penstraze, Chacewater, Truro, Cornwall, TR4 8PF

Telephone: 01872 561356

Website: www.killiwerris.co.uk

Extra charge for dogs? Yes

Any breed restrictions? No

Dog bins? Yes

Area for walking dogs? Off Site

Static caravans? No

Cost of static?

Mobile caravans? Yes

Cost of mobile? From £12.00 - £16.00 per night

Tents? Yes

Cost of tent pitch? From £12.00 - £16.00 per night

Electricity at the pitch? Yes

Showers? Yes

Onsite Entertainment? No

Opening times? Easter - End October

Lakefield Caravan Park

Address: Lower Pendavey Farm, Camelford, Cornwall PL32 9TX

Telephone: 01840 213279

Website: www.lakefieldequestrian centre.co.uk

Extra charge for dogs? No

Any breed restrictions? No

Dog bins? No

Area for walking dogs? Yes

Static caravans? No

Cost of static?

Mobile caravans? Yes

Cost of mobile? From £6.00 - £10.00 per night for 2 people

Tents? Yes

Cost of tent pitch? From £6.00 - £10.00 per night for 2 people

Electricity at the pitch? Yes

Showers? Yes

Onsite Entertainment? No

Opening times? Easter - September

Comments: Dogs must be kept on a lead. There is a small shop on site.

Lanyon Holiday Park

Address: Loscombe Lane Four Lanes, Redruth, Cornwall, TR16 6LP

Telephone: 01209 313474

Website: www.lanyonholidaypark.co.uk

Extra charge for dogs? Yes
Any breed restrictions? No
Dog bins? Yes
Area for walking dogs? Yes
Static caravans? Yes
Cost of static? From £230.00 - £840.00 per week
Mobile caravans? Yes
Cost of mobile? From £10.00 - £21.00 for 2 people
Tents? Yes
Cost of tent pitch? From £10.00 - £21.00 for 2 people
Electricity at the pitch? Yes
Showers? Yes
Onsite Entertainment? Yes (High Season)
Opening times? Statics 14th Feb - End Dec Touring March - October

Liskey Holiday Park

Address: Greenbottom, Truro, Cornwall, TR4 8QN
Telephone: 01872 560274
Website: www.liskey.co.uk
Extra charge for dogs? Yes
Any breed restrictions? No
Dog bins? Yes
Area for walking dogs? Yes
Static caravans? No
Cost of static?
Mobile caravans? Yes
Cost of mobile? From £14.00 - £22.00 per night
Tents? Yes
Cost of tent pitch? From £14.00 - £22.00 per night
Electricity at the pitch? Yes
Showers? Yes
Onsite Entertainment? No
Opening times? All Year

Comments: There is a laundry room and shop on site.

Little Bodieve Holiday Park

Address: Bodieve Rd, Wadebridge, Cornwall PL27 6EG
Telephone: 01208 812323
Website: www.littlebodieve.co.uk
Extra charge for dogs? Yes
Any breed restrictions? No
Dog bins? No
Area for walking dogs? Yes
Static caravans? No Dogs Allowed in Statics
Cost of static?
Mobile caravans? Yes
Cost of mobile? From £4.60 per night per adult - £7.00 per night per adult
Tents? Yes
Cost of tent pitch? From £4.60 per night per adult - £7.00 per night per adult
Electricity at the pitch? Yes
Showers? Yes
Onsite Entertainment? Yes (Peak Season, Easter & Whitsun)
Opening times? Easter - End October

Little Treginges

Address: Little Treginges St Keverne, Helston, Cornwall, TR12 6QS
Telephone: 01326 280580
Website:
Extra charge for dogs? No
Any breed restrictions? No
Dog bins? Yes
Area for walking dogs? Off Site
Static caravans? No
Cost of static?
Mobile caravans? Yes
Cost of mobile? From £8.00 - £12.00 per

pitch
Tents? Yes
Cost of tent pitch? From £8.00 - £12.00 per pitch
Electricity at the pitch? Yes
Showers? Yes
Onsite Entertainment? No
Opening times? March - End September

Little Trevarrack Tourist Park

Address: Laity Lane, St. Ives, Cornwall TR26 3HW
Telephone: 01736 797580
Website: www.littletrevarrack.co.uk
Extra charge for dogs? Yes
Any breed restrictions? No
Dog bins? Yes
Area for walking dogs? Yes
Static caravans? No
Cost of static?
Mobile caravans? Yes
Cost of mobile? From £11.50 - £26.50 per night
Tents? Yes
Cost of tent pitch? From £11.50 - £26.50 per night
Electricity at the pitch? Yes
Showers? Yes
Onsite Entertainment? No
Opening times? April - End September

Looe Bay Holiday Park

Address: East Looe, Looe, Cornwall, PL14 1NX
Telephone: 0870 444 7774
Website: www.parkdeanholidays.co.uk
Extra charge for dogs? Yes
Any breed restrictions? Yes
Dog bins? Yes
Area for walking dogs? Yes
Static caravans? Yes
Cost of static? From 199.00 - £500.00 per week
Mobile caravans? No
Cost of mobile?
Tents? No
Cost of tent pitch?
Electricity at the pitch? No
Showers? No
Onsite Entertainment? Yes
Opening times? February - December
Comments: No Dangerous Breeds

Lower Treave Caravan and camping site

Address: Crows-an-wra, St. Buryan, Penzance, Cornwall, TR19 6HZ
Telephone: 01736 810559
Website: www.lowertreave.co.uk
Extra charge for dogs? No
Any breed restrictions? No
Dog bins? No
Area for walking dogs? Off Site
Static caravans? Yes
Cost of static? From £230.00 - £330.00 per week
Mobile caravans? Yes
Cost of mobile? £13.00 per night for 2 Adults in High Season
Tents? Yes
Cost of tent pitch? £13.00 per night for 2 Adults in High Season
Electricity at the pitch? Yes
Showers? Yes
Onsite Entertainment? No
Opening times? Easter - October

Lundynant Caravan Site

Address: St. Minver, Wadebridge, Cornwall PL27 6QX

Telephone: 01208 862268
Website:
Extra charge for dogs? No
Any breed restrictions? Yes
Dog bins? No
Area for walking dogs? Off Site
Static caravans? Yes
Cost of static? From £195.00 - £460.00 per week
Mobile caravans? Yes
Cost of mobile? From £13.00 - £19.00 with electric per night
Tents? Yes
Cost of tent pitch? From £13.00 - £19.00 with electric per night
Electricity at the pitch? Yes
Showers? Yes
Onsite Entertainment? No
Opening times? Easter - End October
Comments: No Dangerous Breeds

Magic Cove Touring Park

Address: Mawgan Porth, Newquay, Cornwall, TR8 4BD
Telephone: 01637 860263
Website: www.redcove.co.uk
Extra charge for dogs? Yes
Any breed restrictions? No
Dog bins? No
Area for walking dogs? Yes
Static caravans? No
Cost of static?
Mobile caravans? Yes
Cost of mobile? From £8.00 per night for 2 people
Tents? Yes
Cost of tent pitch? From £8.00 per night for 2 people
Electricity at the pitch? Yes
Showers? Yes
Onsite Entertainment? No
Opening times? March - End September
Comments: Dogs must be kept on a lead.

Magor Farm Caravan and Camp Site

Address: Tehidy, Camborne, Cornwall, TR1 0JF
Telephone: 01209 713367
Website: www.magorfarm.co.uk
Extra charge for dogs? Yes
Any breed restrictions? No
Dog bins? No
Area for walking dogs? Yes
Static caravans? No
Cost of static?
Mobile caravans? Yes
Cost of mobile? From £8.00 - £10.00 per night for 2 people + vehicle
Tents? Yes
Cost of tent pitch? From £8.00 - £10.00 per night for 2 people + vehicle
Electricity at the pitch? Yes (£2.50 per night)
Showers? Yes
Onsite Entertainment? No
Opening times? Easter - End October

Maribou Holiday Park & Campsite

Address: St Merryn, Padstow, Cornwall, PL28 8QA
Telephone: 01841 520520
Website: www.maribouholidaypark.co.uk
Extra charge for dogs? Yes
Any breed restrictions? No
Dog bins? No
Area for walking dogs? Yes
Static caravans? Yes
Cost of static? From £130.00 per week
Mobile caravans? No

Cost of mobile?
Tents? No
Cost of tent pitch?
Electricity at the pitch? No
Showers? Yes
Onsite Entertainment? Yes
Opening times? Easter - End October

Marver Holiday Park

Address: Mawgan Porth, Newquay, Cornwall, TR8 4BB
Telephone: 01637 860493
Website: www.marverholidaypark.co.uk
Extra charge for dogs? Statics - No Charge Touring 1st Dog Free
Any breed restrictions? No
Dog bins? No
Area for walking dogs? No
Static caravans? Yes
Cost of static? From £175.00 per week
Mobile caravans? Yes
Cost of mobile? From £8.50 per night
Tents? Yes
Cost of tent pitch? From £8.50 per night
Electricity at the pitch? Yes
Showers? Yes
Onsite Entertainment? No
Opening times? March - October
Comments: Dogs must be kept on a lead.

Mena Caravan & Camping Park

Address: Lanivet, Bodmin, Cornwall, PL30 5HW
Telephone: 01208 831845
Website: www.campsitesincornwall.co.uk
Extra charge for dogs? Yes
Any breed restrictions? No
Dog bins? No
Area for walking dogs? Yes
Static caravans? Yes
Cost of static? From £150.00 per week
Mobile caravans? Yes
Cost of mobile? From £9.00 per night
Tents? Yes
Cost of tent pitch? From £9.00 per night
Electricity at the pitch? Yes
Showers? Yes
Onsite Entertainment? No
Opening times? All Year
Comments: Dogs cannot be left unattended in the Static Caravans. They are having Dog bins and daytime kennels put in later this year.

Merrose Farm

Address: Portscatho, Truro, Cornwall, TR7 5EL
Telephone: 01872 580380
Website: www.caravanclub.co.uk
Extra charge for dogs? No
Any breed restrictions? No
Dog bins? Yes
Area for walking dogs? Yes
Static caravans? No
Cost of static?
Mobile caravans? Yes
Cost of mobile? From £14.00 per pitch per night for 2 people
Tents? Yes
Cost of tent pitch? From £14.00 per pitch per night for 2 people
Electricity at the pitch? Yes
Showers? Yes
Onsite Entertainment? No
Opening times? Mid Mar - Beg Nov

Monkey Tree Holiday Park

Address: Hendra Croft,Scotland Rd, Rejerrah, Newquay, Cornwall TR8 5QR
Telephone: 01872 572032

Website: www.monkeytreeholidaypark.co.uk
Extra charge for dogs? Yes
Any breed restrictions? No
Dog bins? Yes
Area for walking dogs? Yes
Static caravans? Yes
Cost of static? From £150.00 - £550.00 per week
Mobile caravans? Yes
Cost of mobile? From £4.50 - £7.20 per adult per night
Tents? Yes
Cost of tent pitch?
Electricity at the pitch? Yes
Showers? Yes
Onsite Entertainment? Clubhouse, Café, Restaurant, Childrens Activites
Opening times? March - Beg Nov
Comments: They are open all year but all facilites shut apart from Showers.

Mother Iveys Bay Caravan Park

Address: Trevose Head, Padstow, Cornwall, PL28 8SL
Telephone: 01841 520990
Website: www.motheriveysbay.com
Extra charge for dogs? Yes
Any breed restrictions? No
Dog bins? Yes
Area for walking dogs? Off Site
Static caravans? Yes
Cost of static? From £215.00 - £995.00 per week
Mobile caravans? Yes
Cost of mobile? From £8.00 - £46.00 per night
Tents? Yes
Cost of tent pitch? From £8.00 - £46.00 per night
Electricity at the pitch? Yes
Showers? Yes
Onsite Entertainment? No
Opening times? Easter - End October

Mullion Holiday Park

Address: Mullion. Cornwall. TR12 7LJ
Telephone: 0870 444 5344
Website: www.parkdeanholidays.co.uk
Extra charge for dogs? Yes
Any breed restrictions? Yes
Dog bins? Yes
Area for walking dogs? Yes
Static caravans? Yes
Cost of static? From £159.00 per week
Mobile caravans? Yes
Cost of mobile? From £12.00 per night
Tents? Yes
Cost of tent pitch?
Electricity at the pitch? Yes
Showers? Yes
Onsite Entertainment? Yes
Opening times? Easter - End October
Comments: No dangerous breeds

Namparra Campsite

Address: Kuggar, Helston, Cornwall, TR12 7LY
Telephone: 01326 290040
Website: www.namparracampsite.co.uk
Extra charge for dogs? No
Any breed restrictions? No
Dog bins? No
Area for walking dogs? Yes
Static caravans? No
Cost of static?
Mobile caravans? Yes
Cost of mobile? From £10.00 per night
Tents? Yes
Cost of tent pitch? From £8.00

Electricity at the pitch? Yes
Showers? Yes
Onsite Entertainment? No
Opening times? Easter - October

Newperran Holiday Park

Address: Rejerrah, Newquay, Cornwall TR8 5QJ
Telephone: 01872 572407
Website: www.newperran.co.uk
Extra charge for dogs? Yes
Any breed restrictions? No
Dog bins? Yes
Area for walking dogs? Yes
Static caravans? No
Cost of static?
Mobile caravans? Yes
Cost of mobile? From £4.45 - £7.75 per adult per night + £1.30 for car
Tents? Yes
Cost of tent pitch?
Electricity at the pitch? Yes
Showers? Yes
Onsite Entertainment? Yes
Opening times? March - End October
Comments: Dogs must be kept on leads at all times.

Newquay Holiday Park

Address: Newquary, Cornwall, TR8 4HS
Telephone: 01637 871 111
Website: www.parkdeanholidays.co.uk
Extra charge for dogs? Yes
Any breed restrictions? Yes
Dog bins? Yes
Area for walking dogs? Yes
Static caravans? Yes
Cost of static? From £159.00 per week
Mobile caravans? Yes
Cost of mobile? From £12.00 per night
Tents? Yes
Cost of tent pitch? From £12.00 per night
Electricity at the pitch? Yes
Showers? Yes
Onsite Entertainment? Yes
Opening times? March - End October
Comments: No dangerous breeds.

Noongallas Campsite

Address: Gulval, Penzance, Cornwall, TR20 8YR
Telephone: 01736 366698
Website: www.noongallas.com
Extra charge for dogs? No
Any breed restrictions? No
Dog bins? No
Area for walking dogs? Yes
Static caravans? No
Cost of static?
Mobile caravans? No
Cost of mobile?
Tents? Yes
Cost of tent pitch? From £5.00 per person per night
Electricity at the pitch? No
Showers? Yes
Onsite Entertainment? Sometimes
Opening times? July & August

Old Kerrow Farm Holiday Park

Address: Stenalees, St Austell, Cornwall, PL26 8GD
Telephone: 01726 851651
Website: www.oldkerrowfarmholiday park.co.uk
Extra charge for dogs? Yes
Any breed restrictions? No
Dog bins? No
Area for walking dogs? Yes

Static caravans? Yes
Cost of static? From £190.00 - £465.00 per week
Mobile caravans? Yes
Cost of mobile? From £14.00 - £21.00 per night
Tents? Yes
Cost of tent pitch? From £14.00 - £21.00 per night
Electricity at the pitch? Yes
Showers? Yes
Onsite Entertainment? Bar
Opening times? All Year

Old Macdonalds Farm

Address: Porthcothan Bay, Padstow, Cornwall, PL28 8LW
Telephone: 01841 540829
Website: www.oldmacdonalds.co.uk
Extra charge for dogs? Yes
Any breed restrictions? No
Dog bins? No
Area for walking dogs? Yes
Static caravans? No
Cost of static?
Mobile caravans? Yes
Cost of mobile? From £6.00 per adult £5.00 per child in High Season
Tents? Yes
Cost of tent pitch? From £6.00 per adult £5.00 per child in High Season
Electricity at the pitch? Yes
Showers? Yes
Onsite Entertainment? No
Opening times? Easter - End October
Comments: Dogs must be kept on leads and must be friendly dogs.

Padstow Touring Park

Address: Trerethern, Padstow, Cornwall, PL28 8LE
Telephone: 01841 532061
Website: www.padstowtouringpark.co.uk
Extra charge for dogs? Yes
Any breed restrictions? No
Dog bins? No
Area for walking dogs? Yes
Static caravans? No
Cost of static?
Mobile caravans? Yes
Cost of mobile? From £10.00 per night
Tents? Yes
Cost of tent pitch? From £10.00 per night
Electricity at the pitch? Yes
Showers? Yes
Onsite Entertainment? No
Opening times? All Year

Par Sands Holiday Park

Address: Par Beach, Par, Cornwall PL24 2AS
Telephone: 01726 812868
Website: www.parsands.co.uk
Extra charge for dogs? Yes
Any breed restrictions? Yes
Dog bins? No
Area for walking dogs? Yes
Static caravans? Yes
Cost of static? From £220.00 per week
Mobile caravans? No
Cost of mobile?
Tents? No
Cost of tent pitch?
Electricity at the pitch?
Showers?
Onsite Entertainment? No
Opening times? Easter - October
Comments: No illegal dogs.

Penderleath Caravan & Camping site

Address: Towednack, Penderleath,

St Ives, Cornwall, TR26 3AF
Telephone: 01736 798403
Website: www.penderleath.co.uk
Extra charge for dogs? Yes
Any breed restrictions? No
Dog bins? Yes
Area for walking dogs? Yes
Static caravans? No
Cost of static?
Mobile caravans? Yes
Cost of mobile? From £11.50 per night
Tents? Yes
Cost of tent pitch? From £11.50 per night
Electricity at the pitch? Yes
Showers? Yes
Onsite Entertainment? No
Opening times? Easter - End October

Pengoon Farm Touring Park

Address: Nancegollan, Helston, Cornwall, TR13 0BH
Telephone: 01326 561219
Website: www.pengoon.co.uk
Extra charge for dogs? No
Any breed restrictions? No
Dog bins? Yes
Area for walking dogs? Yes
Static caravans? No
Cost of static?
Mobile caravans? Yes
Cost of mobile? From £7.00 - £11.00 per night
Tents? Yes
Cost of tent pitch? From £6.00 - £10.00
Electricity at the pitch? Yes
Showers? Yes
Onsite Entertainment? No
Opening times? All Year

Penhale Caravan and Camping Park

Address: Fowey Cornwall PL23 1JU
Telephone: 01726 833425
Website: www.penhale-fowey.co.uk
Extra charge for dogs? Yes
Any breed restrictions? No
Dog bins? No
Area for walking dogs? Yes
Static caravans? Yes
Cost of static? From £155.00 per week
Mobile caravans? Yes
Cost of mobile? From £1.00 per pitch + cost of adult/children
Tents? Yes
Cost of tent pitch? From £1.00 per pitch + cost of adults/children
Electricity at the pitch? Yes
Showers? Yes
Onsite Entertainment? No
Opening times? Easter - October

Penhaven Touring Park

Address: The Camp Site, Pentewan, St Austell, Cornwall, PL26 6DL
Telephone: 01726 843687
Website: www.penhaventouring.co.uk
Extra charge for dogs? Yes
Any breed restrictions? No
Dog bins? No
Area for walking dogs? Yes
Static caravans? No
Cost of static?
Mobile caravans? Yes
Cost of mobile? From £9.00 per night
Tents? Yes
Cost of tent pitch? From £9.00 per night
Electricity at the pitch? Yes
Showers? Yes
Onsite Entertainment? No

Opening times? Easter - End October

Penlee Caravan Park

Address: Cliff Rd, Mousehole, Penzance, Cornwall TR19 6QT
Telephone: 01736 732861
Website:
Extra charge for dogs? Yes
Any breed restrictions? Yes
Dog bins? No
Area for walking dogs? Off Site
Static caravans? Yes
Cost of static? From £159.00 - £399.00 per week
Mobile caravans? No
Cost of mobile?
Tents? No
Cost of tent pitch?
Electricity at the pitch? No
Showers? No
Onsite Entertainment? No
Opening times? All Year
Comments: No Dangerous Breeds

Penmarlam Caravan & Camping Park

Address: Bodinnick-by-fowey, Fowey, Cornwall, PL23 1LZ
Telephone: 01726 870088
Website: www.penmarlampark.co.uk
Extra charge for dogs? No
Any breed restrictions? No
Dog bins? Yes
Area for walking dogs? Yes
Static caravans? No
Cost of static?
Mobile caravans? Yes
Cost of mobile? From £12.00 - £19.00 per night for 2 people with electric
Tents? Yes
Cost of tent pitch? From £12.00 - £19.00 per night for 2 people with electric
Electricity at the pitch? Yes
Showers? Yes
Onsite Entertainment? No
Opening times? Easter - End October
Comments: They have an Off License and Laundry room on site.

Penmillard Farm

Address: Rame, Torpoint, Cornwall, PL10 1LG
Telephone: 01752 822215
Website: www.penmillard.co.uk
Extra charge for dogs? No
Any breed restrictions? No
Dog bins? No
Area for walking dogs? No
Static caravans? No
Cost of static?
Mobile caravans? Yes
Cost of mobile? From £10.00 per night
Tents? Yes
Cost of tent pitch? From £10.00 per night
Electricity at the pitch? Yes
Showers? No
Onsite Entertainment? No
Opening times? All Year

Pennance Mill Farm

Address: Maenporth Rd, Maenporth, Falmouth, Cornwall TR11 5HJ
Telephone: 01326 317431
Website: www.pennancemill.co.uk
Extra charge for dogs? Yes
Any breed restrictions? No
Dog bins? No
Area for walking dogs? Yes
Static caravans? No
Cost of static?
Mobile caravans? Yes

Cost of mobile? From £14.00 - £17.00 per night for 2 people + Car

Tents? Yes

Cost of tent pitch? From £14.00 - £17.00 per night for 2 people + Car

Electricity at the pitch? Yes

Showers? Yes

Onsite Entertainment? No

Opening times? Easter - End October

Penrose Farm Touring Park

Address: Goonhavern. Truro. Cornwall. TR4 9QF

Telephone: 01872 573185

Website: www.penrosefarm.co.uk

Extra charge for dogs? Yes (July & August)

Any breed restrictions? No

Dog bins? Yes

Area for walking dogs? Yes

Static caravans? No

Cost of static?

Mobile caravans? Yes

Cost of mobile? From £12.00 - £28.50 fully serviced per night

Tents? Yes

Cost of tent pitch? From £12.00 - £28.50 fully serviced per night

Electricity at the pitch? Yes

Showers? Yes

Onsite Entertainment? No

Opening times? Mid March - End October

Comments: There is a Take Away and an Off License.

Penvose Farm

Address: Tregurrian, Newquay, Cornwall TR8 4AE

Telephone: 01637 860277

Website: www.cornwallonline.co.uk

Extra charge for dogs? Yes

Any breed restrictions? No

Dog bins? No

Area for walking dogs? Yes

Static caravans? Yes

Cost of static? From £200.00 per week

Mobile caravans? Yes

Cost of mobile? From £6.00 per adult per night £4.00 per child per night

Tents? Yes

Cost of tent pitch? From £6.00 per adult per night £4.00 per child per night

Electricity at the pitch? Yes

Showers? Yes

Onsite Entertainment? No

Opening times? Mid March - End October

Comments: They have Course Fishing available here.

Penwarne Camping & Caravan Park

Address: Penwarne Barton Farm, Penwarne, Mawnan Smith, Falmouth, Cornwall TR11 5PH

Telephone: 01326 250136

Website:

Extra charge for dogs? No

Any breed restrictions? No

Dog bins? No

Area for walking dogs? Yes

Static caravans? No

Cost of static?

Mobile caravans? Yes

Cost of mobile? £10.00 per night

Tents? Yes

Cost of tent pitch? £10.00 per night

Electricity at the pitch? Yes

Showers? Yes

Onsite Entertainment? No

Opening times? All Year

Comments: Dogs must be kept on leads.

Perran Quay Touring Park

Address: Hendra Croft, Rejerrah, Newquay, Cornwall TR8 5QP

Telephone: 01872 572561

Website: www.perran-quay.co.uk

Extra charge for dogs? Yes

Any breed restrictions? No

Dog bins? No

Area for walking dogs? Off Site

Static caravans? Yes

Cost of static? From £150.00 - £425.00 per week

Mobile caravans? Yes

Cost of mobile? From £8.00 - £26.00 No Electric. From £12.00 - £29.00 With Electric

Tents? Yes

Cost of tent pitch? From £8.00 - £26.00 No Electric. From £12.00 - £29.00 With Electric

Electricity at the pitch? Yes

Showers? Yes

Onsite Entertainment? Yes (Peak Season)

Opening times? All Year

Perran Sands

Address: Perran Sands, Perranporth, Cornwall, TR6 0AQ

Telephone: 01872 573551

Website: www.haven.com

Extra charge for dogs? Yes

Any breed restrictions? Yes

Dog bins? Yes

Area for walking dogs? Yes

Static caravans? Yes

Cost of static? From £208.00 per week

Mobile caravans? Yes

Cost of mobile? From £98.20 per week for 2 people

Tents? Yes

Cost of tent pitch? From £98.20 per week for 2 people

Electricity at the pitch? Yes

Showers? Yes

Onsite Entertainment? Yes

Opening times? Mid March - November

Comments: No Dangerous Breeds

Perran View Holiday Park John Fowler Holidays

Address: Trevellas, St Agnes, Cornwall, TR5 0XS

Telephone: 01271 866 766

Website: www.johnfowlerholidays.com

Extra charge for dogs? Yes

Any breed restrictions? No

Dog bins? No

Area for walking dogs? Off Site

Static caravans? Yes

Cost of static? From £105.00 per week

Mobile caravans? Yes

Cost of mobile? From £6.00 no electric £10.00 with electric

Tents? Yes

Cost of tent pitch? From £6.00 no electric £10.00 with electric

Electricity at the pitch? Yes

Showers? Yes

Onsite Entertainment? Nightly Entertainment, Kids Clubs, Tennis Courts

Opening times? Beg March - Begin November

Perranporth Camping And Touring Park

Address: Budnick, Perranporth, Cornwall, TR6 0DB

Telephone: 01872 572174

Website:

Extra charge for dogs? Yes
Any breed restrictions? No
Dog bins? No
Area for walking dogs? Yes
Static caravans? Yes
Cost of static?
Mobile caravans? Yes
Cost of mobile? From £5.00 per night
Tents? Yes
Cost of tent pitch? From £5.00 per night
Electricity at the pitch? Yes
Showers? Yes
Onsite Entertainment? Clubhouse and Outdoor Swimming Pool
Opening times? Easter - End September

Pine Green Caravan Park

Address: Doublebois, Liskeard, Cornwall PL14 6LE
Telephone: 01579 320183
Website: www.pinegreenpark.co.uk
Extra charge for dogs? No
Any breed restrictions? No
Dog bins? Yes
Area for walking dogs? Yes
Static caravans? No
Cost of static?
Mobile caravans? Yes
Cost of mobile? From £12.00 - £16.00 per night
Tents? No
Cost of tent pitch?
Electricity at the pitch? Yes
Showers? Yes
Onsite Entertainment? No
Opening times? All Year

Polborder House Caravan & Camping Park

Address: Polborder House, St.Martin, Looe, Cornwall PL13 1NZ
Telephone: 01503 240265
Website: www.peaceful-polborder.co.uk
Extra charge for dogs? Yes
Any breed restrictions? Yes
Dog bins? No
Area for walking dogs? Off Site
Static caravans? Yes
Cost of static? From £190.00 - £480.00
Mobile caravans? Yes
Cost of mobile? From £10.00 - £19.00 for 2 Adults + Electric
Tents? Yes
Cost of tent pitch? From £10.00 - £19.00 for 2 Adults + Electric
Electricity at the pitch? Yes
Showers? Yes
Onsite Entertainment? No
Opening times? All Year
Comments: No Dangerous Breeds. There is a Shop and a Laundry room on site.

Poldown Caravan Park

Address: Primrose Cottage, Breage, Helston, Cornwall TR13 9NN
Telephone: 01326 574560
Website: www.poldown.co.uk
Extra charge for dogs? Yes
Any breed restrictions? No
Dog bins? No
Area for walking dogs? Yes
Static caravans? Yes
Cost of static? From £150.00 per week
Mobile caravans? Yes
Cost of mobile? From £9.00 per night
Tents? Yes
Cost of tent pitch?
Electricity at the pitch? Yes
Showers? Yes
Onsite Entertainment? No
Opening times? Easter - September
Comments: Maximum 1 dog.

Polmanter Tourist Park

Address: Halsetown. St Ives. Cornwall. TR26 3LX
Telephone: 01736 795640
Website: www.polmanter.com
Extra charge for dogs? Yes
Any breed restrictions? No
Dog bins? Yes
Area for walking dogs? Yes
Static caravans? No
Cost of static?
Mobile caravans? Yes
Cost of mobile? From £12.00 - £29.00 per pitch per night
Tents? Yes
Cost of tent pitch?
Electricity at the pitch? Yes
Showers? Yes
Onsite Entertainment? Yes (High Season)
Opening times? Easter - End October
Comments: Maximum 2 Dogs

Polruan Holidays-Camping & Caravaning

Address: Townsend, Polruan, Fowey, Cornwall PL23 1QH
Telephone: 01726 870263
Website: www.polruanholidays.co.uk
Extra charge for dogs? Yes
Any breed restrictions? No
Dog bins? Yes
Area for walking dogs? Yes
Static caravans? Yes
Cost of static? From £190.00 - £420.00 per week
Mobile caravans? Yes
Cost of mobile? From £10.25 per night
Tents? Yes
Cost of tent pitch? From £8.00 per night
Electricity at the pitch? Yes
Showers? Yes
Onsite Entertainment? No
Opening times? Easter - 1st November

Porth Beach Tourist Park

Address: Porth, Newquay, Newquay, Cornwall, TR7 3NH
Telephone: 01637 876 531
Website: www.porthbeach.co.uk
Extra charge for dogs? Yes
Any breed restrictions? Yes
Dog bins? No
Area for walking dogs? Off Site
Static caravans? No
Cost of static?
Mobile caravans? Yes
Cost of mobile? From £14.00 - £29.00 per night
Tents? Yes
Cost of tent pitch? From £14.00 - £29.00 per night
Electricity at the pitch? Yes
Showers? Yes
Onsite Entertainment? No
Opening times? Beg March - End October
Comments: No Dangerous Breeds

Porthtowan Tourist Park

Address: Mile Hill, Porthtowan, Truro, Cornwall, TR4 8TY
Telephone: 01209 890256
Website: www.porthtowantouristpark.co.uk
Extra charge for dogs? Yes
Any breed restrictions? No
Dog bins? Yes
Area for walking dogs? Yes
Static caravans? No

Cost of static?
Mobile caravans? Yes
Cost of mobile? From £8.50 - £15.00 per night for 2 people + 1 car
Tents? Yes
Cost of tent pitch? From £8.50 - £15.00 per night for 2 people + 1 car
Electricity at the pitch? Yes
Showers? Yes
Onsite Entertainment? Kids Playground
Opening times? April - End September

Powderham Castle Caravan & Tourist Park

Address: Powderham Castle, Lanlivery, Bodmin, Cornwall PL30 5BU
Telephone: 01208 872277
Website: www.powderhamcastletouristpark.co.uk
Extra charge for dogs? Yes
Any breed restrictions? Yes
Dog bins? Yes
Area for walking dogs? Yes
Static caravans? No
Cost of static?
Mobile caravans? Yes
Cost of mobile? From £11.00 - £15.00 for 2 people per night
Tents? Yes
Cost of tent pitch? From £11.00 - £15.00 for 2 people per night
Electricity at the pitch? Yes
Showers? Yes
Onsite Entertainment? No
Opening times? Easter - End October
Comments: No Dangerous Breeds

Presingoll Farm

Address: Presingoll Farm, St Agnes, Cornwall, TR5 0PB
Telephone: 01872 552 333
Website: www.presingollfarm.fsbusiness.co.uk
Extra charge for dogs? No
Any breed restrictions? No
Dog bins? Yes
Area for walking dogs? Yes
Static caravans? No
Cost of static?
Mobile caravans? Yes
Cost of mobile? From £6.00 per adult per night £1.50 per child per night
Tents? Yes
Cost of tent pitch? From £6.00 per adult per night £1.50 per child per night
Electricity at the pitch? Yes
Showers? Yes
Onsite Entertainment? No
Opening times? Easter - End October
Comments: No Dangerous Breeds. Dogs must be kept on a lead.

Quarryfield Caravan And Camping Park

Address: Tretheress Road, Crantock,Newquay, Cornwall, TR7 2TG
Telephone: 01637 872792
Website: www.quarryfield.co.uk
Extra charge for dogs? Yes
Any breed restrictions? No
Dog bins? No
Area for walking dogs? Yes
Static caravans? Yes
Cost of static? From £170.00 per week
Mobile caravans? Yes
Cost of mobile? From £6.00 per adult per night £4.00 per child per night
Tents? Yes
Cost of tent pitch? From £6.00 per adult

per night £4.00 per child per night
Electricity at the pitch? Yes
Showers? Yes
Onsite Entertainment? Licensed Bar with some entertainment
Opening times? Easter - End October

River Valley Holiday Park

Address: London Apprentice, St Austell, Cornwall, PL267AP
Telephone: 01726 73533
Website: www.cornwall-holidays.co.uk
Extra charge for dogs? Yes
Any breed restrictions? No
Dog bins? No
Area for walking dogs? Yes
Static caravans? Yes
Cost of static? From £240.00 - £550.00 per week
Mobile caravans? Yes
Cost of mobile? From £12.50 - £25.00 per night
Tents? Yes
Cost of tent pitch? From £12.50 - £25.00 per night
Electricity at the pitch? Yes
Showers? Yes
Onsite Entertainment? No
Opening times? April - End September

Riverside Holiday Park

Address: Lane, Newquay, Cornwall, TR8 4PE
Telephone: 01637 873617
Website: www.riversideholidaypark.co.uk
Extra charge for dogs? Yes
Any breed restrictions? No
Dog bins? Yes
Area for walking dogs? Yes
Static caravans? No
Cost of static?
Mobile caravans? Yes
Cost of mobile? £26.00 for 2 adults, 2 children, car and electric per night
Tents? Yes
Cost of tent pitch? £26.00 for 2 adults, 2 children, car and electric per night
Electricity at the pitch? Yes
Showers? Yes
Onsite Entertainment? No
Opening times? Easter - End October

Rosebud Farm Touring Park

Address: Rosebud Farm, St Teath, Bodmin, Cornwall, PL30 3LB
Telephone: 01840 211487
Website: www.rosebudfarmtouringpark.co.uk
Extra charge for dogs? Yes
Any breed restrictions? No
Dog bins? Yes
Area for walking dogs? Yes
Static caravans? No
Cost of static?
Mobile caravans? Yes
Cost of mobile? From £10.00 for Family of Four and a Car
Tents? Yes
Cost of tent pitch? From £10.00 for Family of Four and a Car
Electricity at the pitch? Yes
Showers? Yes
Onsite Entertainment? No
Opening times? Easter - October
Comments: Dogs must be kept on a lead.

Roselands Caravan Park

Address: Dowran, St Just, Penzance, Cornwall, TR19 7RS
Telephone: 01736 788571

Website: www.roselands.co.uk
Extra charge for dogs? No
Any breed restrictions? No
Dog bins? No
Area for walking dogs? Yes
Static caravans? Yes
Cost of static? From £135.00 - £530.00 per week
Mobile caravans? Yes
Cost of mobile? From £8.00 - £10.00 per night
Tents? Yes
Cost of tent pitch? From £8.00 - £10.00 per night
Electricity at the pitch? Yes
Showers? Yes
Onsite Entertainment? No
Opening times? January - October

Roseville Holiday Park

Address: Goonhavern, Truro, Cornwall TR4 9LA
Telephone: 01872 572448
Website: www.rosevilleholidaypark.co.uk
Extra charge for dogs? Yes
Any breed restrictions? Yes
Dog bins? Yes
Area for walking dogs? Yes
Static caravans? Yes
Cost of static? From £200.00 - £500.00 per week
Mobile caravans? Yes
Cost of mobile? From £5.00 - £10.50 per person per night
Tents? Yes
Cost of tent pitch? From £5.00 - £10.50 per person per night
Electricity at the pitch? Yes
Showers? Yes
Onsite Entertainment? No
Opening times? Easter - October
Comments: No Dangerous Breeds

Ruthern Valley Holidays

Address: Ruthernbridge Bodmin Cornwall PL30 5LU
Telephone: 01208 831395
Website: www.ruthernvalley.com
Extra charge for dogs? Yes
Any breed restrictions? Yes
Dog bins? No
Area for walking dogs? Off Site
Static caravans? Yes
Cost of static? From £200.00 per week
Mobile caravans? Yes
Cost of mobile? From £11.50 per night
Tents? Yes
Cost of tent pitch? From £11.50 per night
Electricity at the pitch? Yes
Showers? Yes
Onsite Entertainment? No
Opening times? April - October
Comments: No Dangerous Dogs and no large, hairy dogs.

Sea Acres Holiday Park

Address: Kennack Sands, Ruan Minor, Helston, Cornwall TR12 7LT
Telephone: 01326 290064
Website: www.parkdeanholidays.co.uk
Extra charge for dogs? Yes
Any breed restrictions? Yes
Dog bins? Yes
Area for walking dogs? Off Site
Static caravans? Yes
Cost of static? From £149.00 - £829.00 per week
Mobile caravans? No

Cost of mobile?
Tents? No
Cost of tent pitch?
Electricity at the pitch? No
Showers? No
Onsite Entertainment? Yes
Opening times? Easter - October
Comments: No Dangerous Breeds. Maximum of 2 dogs per van. There is a bar on site.

Seagull Tourist Park

Address: St.Merryn, Padstow, Cornwall, PL28 8PT
Telephone: 01841 520117
Website:
Extra charge for dogs? No
Any breed restrictions? No
Dog bins? No
Area for walking dogs? Yes
Static caravans? No
Cost of static?
Mobile caravans? Yes
Cost of mobile? From £11.00 per night with electric
Tents? Yes
Cost of tent pitch? From £11.00 per night with electric
Electricity at the pitch? Yes
Showers? Yes
Onsite Entertainment? No
Opening times? 1st April - End September
Comments: There is a Laundry room on site.

Seaview International Holiday Park

Address: Boswinger, Gorran, St Austell, PL26 6LL
Telephone: 01726 843 425
Website: www.seaviewinternational.com
Extra charge for dogs? Yes
Any breed restrictions? Yes
Dog bins? Yes
Area for walking dogs? Yes
Static caravans? No
Cost of static?
Mobile caravans? Yes
Cost of mobile? From £7.00 per night
Tents? Yes
Cost of tent pitch? From £7.00 per night
Electricity at the pitch? Yes
Showers? Yes
Onsite Entertainment? No
Opening times? April - October
Comments: No Dangerous Breeds

Silver Sands Holiday Park

Address: Ruan Minor, Helston, Cornwall TR12 7LZ
Telephone: 01326 290631
Website: www.silversandsholidaypark.co.uk
Extra charge for dogs? Yes
Any breed restrictions? No
Dog bins? No
Area for walking dogs? Yes
Static caravans? Yes
Cost of static? From £99.00 per week
Mobile caravans? Yes
Cost of mobile? From £10.00 without Electric £12.00 with Electric
Tents? Yes
Cost of tent pitch? From £10.00 without Electric £12.00 with Electric
Electricity at the pitch? Yes
Showers? Yes
Onsite Entertainment? No
Opening times? Easter - Mid September

Silverbow Park

Address: Perranwell, Goonhavern, Truro, Cornwall TR4 9NX

Telephone: 01872 572347

Website:

Extra charge for dogs? Yes

Any breed restrictions? No

Dog bins? Yes

Area for walking dogs? Yes

Static caravans? No

Cost of static?

Mobile caravans? Yes

Cost of mobile? From £12.00 - £22.00 per night for 2 people

Tents? Yes

Cost of tent pitch? From £12.00 - £22.00 per night for 2 people

Electricity at the pitch? Yes

Showers? Yes

Onsite Entertainment? Yes

Opening times? Beg May - End September

Comments: They have a Swimming Pool and Tennis Courts on site

South Winds

Address: Old Polzeath Road, Polzeath, Cornwall, PL27 6QU

Telephone: 01208 863267

Website: www.polzeathcamping.co.uk

Extra charge for dogs? Yes

Any breed restrictions? No

Dog bins? No

Area for walking dogs? Off Site

Static caravans? No

Cost of static?

Mobile caravans? Yes

Cost of mobile? From £12.00 per night per pitch

Tents? Yes

Cost of tent pitch? From £12.00 per night per pitch

Electricity at the pitch? Yes

Showers? Yes

Onsite Entertainment? No

Opening times? Easter - End October

Comments: Dogs must be kept on a lead.

St Agnes Beacon Caravan Club Site

Address: Beacon Drive, St Agnes, Cornwall, TR5 0NU

Telephone: 01872 552543

Website: www.caravanclub.co.uk

Extra charge for dogs? No

Any breed restrictions? No

Dog bins? No

Area for walking dogs? Yes

Static caravans? No

Cost of static?

Mobile caravans? Yes

Cost of mobile? From £10.30 per night

Tents? No

Cost of tent pitch?

Electricity at the pitch? Yes

Showers? No

Onsite Entertainment? No

Opening times? March - October

St Day Holiday Park

Address: St. Day, Redruth, Cornwall TR16 5JR

Telephone: 01209 820459

Website: www.holidaysatsameday.co.uk

Extra charge for dogs? Yes

Any breed restrictions? No

Dog bins? Yes

Area for walking dogs? Off Site

Static caravans? No

Cost of static?

Mobile caravans? Yes

Cost of mobile? From £12.00 per night

Tents? Yes

Cost of tent pitch?
Electricity at the pitch? Yes
Showers? Yes
Onsite Entertainment? No
Opening times? Easter - October

St Ives Holiday Village

Address: Lelant, St Ives, Cornwall, TR26 3HX
Telephone: 01271 866 766
Website: www.johnfowlerholidays.com
Extra charge for dogs? Yes
Any breed restrictions? No
Dog bins? Yes
Area for walking dogs? Yes
Static caravans? Yes
Cost of static? From £145.00 per week
Mobile caravans? No
Cost of mobile?
Tents? No
Cost of tent pitch?
Electricity at the pitch? No
Showers? No
Onsite Entertainment? Yes
Opening times? March - End October

St Minver Holiday Park

Address: Near Rock. Wadebridge. Cornwall. PL27 6RR
Telephone: 0871 641 0323
Website: www.parkdeanholidays.co.uk
Extra charge for dogs? Yes
Any breed restrictions? Yes
Dog bins? Yes
Area for walking dogs? No
Static caravans? Yes
Cost of static? From £96.00 for weekend
Mobile caravans? No
Cost of mobile?
Tents? No
Cost of tent pitch?
Electricity at the pitch? No
Showers? No
Onsite Entertainment? Yes
Opening times? March - Beg November
Comments: No Dangerous Breeds

St. Tinney Farm

Address: Otterham, Cornwall, PL32 9TA
Telephone: 01840 261274
Website: www.st-tinney.co.uk
Extra charge for dogs? Yes
Any breed restrictions? No
Dog bins? No
Area for walking dogs? Yes
Static caravans? No
Cost of static?
Mobile caravans? Yes
Cost of mobile? From £4.50 - £8.00 per person
Tents? Yes
Cost of tent pitch?
Electricity at the pitch? Yes
Showers? Yes
Onsite Entertainment? Yes
Opening times? Easter - End September
Comments: There is a Public House and heated swimming pool on site.

Summer Lodge Holiday Park

Address: Whitecross, Newquay, Cornwall, TR8 4LW
Telephone: 01726 860 415
Website: www.summerlodge.co.uk
Extra charge for dogs? Yes
Any breed restrictions? Yes
Dog bins? No
Area for walking dogs? Yes
Static caravans? Yes
Cost of static? From £125.00 per week
Mobile caravans? Yes
Cost of mobile? From £12.00 for

standard pitch per night
Tents? Yes
Cost of tent pitch? From £12.00 for standard pitch per night
Electricity at the pitch? Yes
Showers? Yes
Onsite Entertainment? Yes
Opening times? March - November
Comments: No Dangerous Breeds

Sun Haven Holiday park

Address: Mawgan Porth, Newquay, Cornwall, TR8 4BQ
Telephone: 01637 860 373
Website: www.sunhavenvalley.com
Extra charge for dogs? Yes
Any breed restrictions? No
Dog bins? No
Area for walking dogs? Off Site
Static caravans? Yes
Cost of static? From £255.00 - £665.00
Mobile caravans? Yes
Cost of mobile? From £11.00 - £21.50 per night
Tents? Yes
Cost of tent pitch? From £11.00 - £21.50 per night
Electricity at the pitch? Yes
Showers? Yes
Onsite Entertainment? No
Opening times? April - October
Comments: Maximum of 2 dogs Off Peak and maximum of 1 dog during Peak Season

Sun Valley Holiday Park

Address: Pentewan Road, Mevagissey, St. Austell, Cornwall, PL26 6DJ
Telephone: 01726 843266
Website: www.sunvalleyholidays.co.uk
Extra charge for dogs? Yes
Any breed restrictions? No
Dog bins? No
Area for walking dogs? Yes
Static caravans? Yes
Cost of static? From £175.00 per week
Mobile caravans? Yes
Cost of mobile? From £16.50 per night
Tents? Yes
Cost of tent pitch? From £16.50 per night
Electricity at the pitch? Yes
Showers? Yes
Onsite Entertainment? Yes
Opening times? All Year
Comments: There is a Bar on site

Sunny Meadows Holiday Park

Address: Lelant Downs, Hayle, Cornwall TR27 6LL
Telephone: 01736 752243
Website: www.chycor.co.uk
Extra charge for dogs? Yes
Any breed restrictions? No
Dog bins? No
Area for walking dogs? Off Site
Static caravans? Yes
Cost of static? From £180.00 per week
Mobile caravans? Yes
Cost of mobile? From £9.00 per night
Tents? Yes
Cost of tent pitch? From £9.00 per night
Electricity at the pitch? Yes
Showers? Yes
Onsite Entertainment? No
Opening times? All Year
Comments: They do not take puppies.

Tamar Lake Farm

Address: Thurdon, Kilkhampton, Bude, Cornwall, EX23 9SA

Telephone: 01288 321426

Website: www.caravancampingsites.co.uk

Extra charge for dogs? No

Any breed restrictions? No

Dog bins? No

Area for walking dogs? Yes

Static caravans? No

Cost of static?

Mobile caravans? Yes

Cost of mobile? From £3.00 - £8.00 per night

Tents? Yes

Cost of tent pitch? From £3.00 - £8.00 per night

Electricity at the pitch? Yes

Showers? Yes

Onsite Entertainment? No

Opening times? March - End October

Comments: Take Away Chinese food cooked on site.

Tencreek Holiday Park

Address: Polperro Road, Looe, Cornwall, PL13 2JR

Telephone: 01726 65511

Website: www.dolphinholidays.co.uk

Extra charge for dogs? Yes

Any breed restrictions? No

Dog bins? Yes

Area for walking dogs? Yes

Static caravans? Yes

Cost of static? From £90.00 - £755.00 per week

Mobile caravans? Yes

Cost of mobile? From £9.50 - £25.50 for 2 people + Pitch

Tents? Yes

Cost of tent pitch? From £9.50 - £25.50 for 2 people + Pitch

Electricity at the pitch? Yes

Showers? Yes

Onsite Entertainment? Yes

Opening times? All Year

Comments: Dogs must be kept on a lead.

The Caravan Club Ltd

Address: Godrevy Park, Upton Towans, Gwithian, Hayle, Cornwall TR27 5BL

Telephone: 01736 753100

Website: www.caravanclub.co.uk

Extra charge for dogs? No

Any breed restrictions? No

Dog bins? No

Area for walking dogs? No

Static caravans? No

Cost of static?

Mobile caravans? Yes

Cost of mobile? From £4.40 per adult £1.50 per child £4.80 per pitch per night

Tents? Yes

Cost of tent pitch? From £4.40 per adult £1.50 per child £4.80 per pitch per night

Electricity at the pitch? Yes

Showers? Yes

Onsite Entertainment? No

Opening times? Mid March - Mid November

The Caravan Club Ltd,

Address: Trewethet Farm, Trethevy, Tintagel, Cornwall PL34 0BQ

Telephone: 01840 770222

Website: www.caravanclub.co.uk

Extra charge for dogs? No

Any breed restrictions? No

Dog bins? No

Area for walking dogs? Yes

Static caravans? No

Cost of static?

Mobile caravans? Yes
Cost of mobile? From £4.40 per adult £1.50 per child £4.80 per pitch per night
Tents? Yes
Cost of tent pitch? From £4.40 per adult £1.50 per child £4.80 per pitch per night
Electricity at the pitch? Yes
Showers? Yes
Onsite Entertainment? No
Opening times? Mid March - Mid November

The Caravan Club Site

Address: Merrose Farm, Portscatho, Truro, Cornwall TR2 5EL
Telephone: 01872 580380
Website: www.caravanclub.co.uk
Extra charge for dogs? No
Any breed restrictions? No
Dog bins? Yes
Area for walking dogs? Yes
Static caravans? No
Cost of static?
Mobile caravans? Yes
Cost of mobile? From £4.60 per adult £1.50 per child £4.80 per pitch per night
Tents? Yes
Cost of tent pitch? From £4.60 per adult £1.50 per child £4.80 per pitch per night
Electricity at the pitch? Yes
Showers? Yes
Onsite Entertainment? No
Opening times? March - November

The Friendly Camp

Address: Tregullas Farm, Penhale, Ruan Minor, Helston, Cornwall TR12 7LJ
Telephone: 01326 240387
Website:
Extra charge for dogs? Yes
Any breed restrictions? No
Dog bins? No
Area for walking dogs? Yes
Static caravans? Yes
Cost of static? From £120.00 - £360.00 per week
Mobile caravans? Yes
Cost of mobile? From £8.00 - £10.00 per night
Tents? Yes
Cost of tent pitch? From £8.00 - £10.00 per night
Electricity at the pitch? Yes
Showers? Yes
Onsite Entertainment? No
Opening times? Easter - End October

The Headland Caravan & Camping Park

Address: Atlantic Rd, Tintagel, Cornwall PL34 0DE
Telephone: 01840 770239
Website: www.headlandcaravanpark.co.uk
Extra charge for dogs? Yes
Any breed restrictions? No
Dog bins? No
Area for walking dogs? Off Site
Static caravans? Yes
Cost of static? From £180.00 - £595.00 per week
Mobile caravans? Yes
Cost of mobile? From £11.00 - £14.00 per night
Tents? Yes
Cost of tent pitch? From £12.00 - £15.50 for car and family per night
Electricity at the pitch? Yes
Showers? Yes
Onsite Entertainment? No
Opening times? Easter - October

The Laurels Holiday Park

Address: Whitecross, Wadebridge, Cornwall PL27 7JQ

Telephone: 01209 313474

Website: www.lanyonholidaypark.co.uk

Extra charge for dogs? Yes

Any breed restrictions? No

Dog bins? Yes

Area for walking dogs? Yes

Static caravans? Yes

Cost of static? From £250.00 - £850.00 per week

Mobile caravans? Yes

Cost of mobile? From £10.00 - £16.00 per night

Tents? Yes

Cost of tent pitch? From £10.00 - £16.00 per night

Electricity at the pitch? Yes

Showers? Yes

Onsite Entertainment? No

Opening times? March - October

The Meadow Caravan Park

Address: Holywell Bay, Newquay, Cornwall TR8 5PP

Telephone: 01872 572752

Website: www.holywellbeachholidays.co.uk

Extra charge for dogs? Yes

Any breed restrictions? Yes

Dog bins? No

Area for walking dogs? Yes

Static caravans? Yes

Cost of static? From £145.00 per week

Mobile caravans? Yes

Cost of mobile? From £5.50 per night for 1 person

Tents?

Cost of tent pitch?

Electricity at the pitch? Yes

Showers? Yes

Onsite Entertainment? No

Opening times? May - October

Comments: Only allow small dogs.

The Meadows Campsite

Address: Pentewan Rd, St Austell, Cornwall, PL26 6DL

Telephone: 01726 842547

Website: www.themeadowspentewanvalley.co.uk

Extra charge for dogs? No

Any breed restrictions? No

Dog bins? No

Area for walking dogs? Yes

Static caravans? Yes

Cost of static? From £100.00 - £350.00 per week

Mobile caravans? Yes

Cost of mobile? From £9.00 - £14.00 for 2 people per night

Tents? Yes

Cost of tent pitch? From £9.00 - £14.00 for 2 people per night

Electricity at the pitch? Yes

Showers? Yes

Onsite Entertainment? No

Opening times? Easter - End October

The North Inn

Address: Pendeen, Penzance, Cornwall, TR19 7DN

Telephone: 01736 788417

Website: www.thenorthinnpendeen.co.uk

Extra charge for dogs?

Any breed restrictions? No

Dog bins? No

Area for walking dogs? Off Site

Static caravans? No

Cost of static?

Mobile caravans? Yes

Cost of mobile? From £4.00 per night

Tents? Yes

Cost of tent pitch? From £4.00 per night

Electricity at the pitch? Yes

Showers? No

Onsite Entertainment? No

Opening times? All Year

Comments: There are showers available in the pub.

Tower Park Caravan and Camping

Address: St Buryan, Penzance, Cornwall, TR19 6BZ

Telephone: 01736 810286

Website: www.towerparkcamping.co.uk

Extra charge for dogs? Yes

Any breed restrictions? No

Dog bins? No

Area for walking dogs? Yes

Static caravans? Yes

Cost of static? From £160.00 per week

Mobile caravans? Yes

Cost of mobile? From £10.25 per night for 1 dog and 2 people

Tents? Yes

Cost of tent pitch? From £10.25 per night for 1 dog and 2 people

Electricity at the pitch? Yes

Showers? Yes

Onsite Entertainment? No

Opening times? March - January

Comments: Maximum 2 Dogs

Treago Farm Camping & Caravan Park

Address: Treago Farm, Crantock, Newquay, Cornwall, TR8 5QS

Telephone: 01637 830277

Website: www.treagofarm.co.uk

Extra charge for dogs? Yes

Any breed restrictions? No

Dog bins? No

Area for walking dogs? Off Site

Static caravans? Yes

Cost of static? From £310.00 - £600.00 per week

Mobile caravans? Yes

Cost of mobile? From £6.00 - £8.00 per person per night

Tents? Yes

Cost of tent pitch? From £6.00 - £8.00 per person per night

Electricity at the pitch? Yes

Showers? Yes

Onsite Entertainment? No

Opening times? Easter - End October

Trebellan Camping & Caravan Park

Address: Cubert, Newquay, Cornwall TR8 5PY

Telephone: 01637 830522

Website: www.trebellan.co.uk

Extra charge for dogs? Yes

Any breed restrictions? No

Dog bins? Yes

Area for walking dogs? Yes

Static caravans? Yes

Cost of static? From £310.00 - £600.00 per week

Mobile caravans? Yes

Cost of mobile? From £6.00 - £8.00 per person per night

Tents? Yes

Cost of tent pitch? From £6.00 - £8.00 per person per night

Electricity at the pitch? Yes

Showers? Yes

Onsite Entertainment? No

Opening times? May - October

Treen Farm Campsite

Address: St Buryan, Penzance, Cornwall
Telephone: 01736 810273
Website: www.treenfarmcampsite.co.uk
Extra charge for dogs? No
Any breed restrictions? No
Dog bins? No
Area for walking dogs? Off Site
Static caravans? No
Cost of static?
Mobile caravans? Yes
Cost of mobile? From £4.00 per adult
Tents? Yes
Cost of tent pitch? From £4.00 per adult
Electricity at the pitch? Yes
Showers? Yes
Onsite Entertainment? No
Opening times? Easter - End October

Tregarton Park

Address: Gorran, Nr Mevagissey, St Austell, PL26 6NF
Telephone: 01726 843666
Website: www.tregarton.co.uk
Extra charge for dogs? Yes
Any breed restrictions? No
Dog bins? Yes
Area for walking dogs? Yes
Static caravans? No
Cost of static?
Mobile caravans? Yes
Cost of mobile? From £4.95 - £21.95 per night
Tents? Yes
Cost of tent pitch? From £4.95 - £21.95 per night
Electricity at the pitch? Yes
Showers? Yes
Onsite Entertainment? No
Opening times? April - End October

Tregavone Farm Touring Park

Address: St.Merryn, Padstow, Cornwall, PL28 8JZ
Telephone: 01841 520148
Website: www.tregavonefarm.co.uk
Extra charge for dogs? Yes
Any breed restrictions? No
Dog bins? Yes
Area for walking dogs? Yes
Static caravans? No
Cost of static?
Mobile caravans? Yes
Cost of mobile? From £6.50 per night
Tents? Yes
Cost of tent pitch? From £6.50 per night
Electricity at the pitch? Yes
Showers? Yes
Onsite Entertainment? No
Opening times? March - October

Tregedna Farm Holidays

Address: Maenporth, Falmouth, Cornwall, TR11 5HL
Telephone: 01326 250529
Website: www.tregednafarmholidays.co.uk
Extra charge for dogs? No
Any breed restrictions? No
Dog bins? No
Area for walking dogs? Yes
Static caravans? No
Cost of static?
Mobile caravans? Yes
Cost of mobile? From £6.00 - £6.50 per person per night
Tents? Yes
Cost of tent pitch?
Electricity at the pitch? Yes
Showers? Yes
Onsite Entertainment? No

Opening times? April - October

Comments: Dogs must be kept on a lead at all times.

Treglisson Touring Park

Address: Wheal Alfred Rd, Hayle, Cornwall TR27 5JT

Telephone: 01736 753141

Website: www.treglisson.co.uk

Extra charge for dogs? No

Any breed restrictions? No

Dog bins? No

Area for walking dogs? Yes

Static caravans? No

Cost of static?

Mobile caravans? Yes

Cost of mobile? From £9.00 - £15.50 per night for 2 people

Tents? Yes

Cost of tent pitch? From £9.00 - £15.50 per night for 2 people

Electricity at the pitch? Yes

Showers? Yes

Onsite Entertainment? No

Opening times? Easter - End October

Tregoad Park Quality Touring Park

Address: St Martins, Looe, Cornwall, PL13 1PB

Telephone: 01503 262718

Website: www.tregoadpark.co.uk

Extra charge for dogs? Yes

Any breed restrictions? No

Dog bins? Yes

Area for walking dogs? Yes

Static caravans? Yes

Cost of static? From £110.00 per week

Mobile caravans? Yes

Cost of mobile? From £8.50 per night

Tents? Yes

Cost of tent pitch? From £8.50 per night

Electricity at the pitch? Yes

Showers? Yes

Onsite Entertainment? Yes (High Season)

Opening times? All Year

Tregurrian Camping And Caravanning Club Site

Address: Tregurrian, Newquary, Cornwall, TR8 4AE

Telephone: 01637 860448

Website: www.thecampingand caravanningclub.co.uk

Extra charge for dogs? No

Any breed restrictions? No

Dog bins? Yes

Area for walking dogs? Off Site

Static caravans? No

Cost of static?

Mobile caravans? Yes

Cost of mobile? From £5.15 - £8.60 per adult per night. From £2.25 -£2.35 per child per night

Tents? Yes

Cost of tent pitch? From £5.15 - £8.60 per adult per night. From £2.25 -£2.35 per child per night

Electricity at the pitch? Yes

Showers? Yes

Onsite Entertainment? No

Opening times? End April - October

Comments: Dogs must be kept on a lead.

Trekenning Tourist Park

Address: Trekenning, Newquay, Cornwall, TR8 4JF

Telephone: 01637 880462

Website: www.trekenning.co.uk

Extra charge for dogs? Yes

Any breed restrictions? No

Dog bins? No

Area for walking dogs? No
Static caravans? No
Cost of static?
Mobile caravans? Yes
Cost of mobile? From £12.00 per night for 2 people
Tents? Yes
Cost of tent pitch? From £12.00 per night for 2 people
Electricity at the pitch? Yes
Showers? Yes
Onsite Entertainment? Yes
Opening times? All Year
Comments: Bar with in house entertainment.

Trelawne Manor Holiday Park

Address: Looe, Cornwall PL13 2NA
Telephone: 01271 866766
Website: www.johnfowlerholidays.com
Extra charge for dogs? Yes
Any breed restrictions? No
Dog bins? No
Area for walking dogs? No
Static caravans? Yes
Cost of static? From £145.00 per week
Mobile caravans? No
Cost of mobile?
Tents? No
Cost of tent pitch?
Electricity at the pitch? No
Showers? No
Onsite Entertainment? Yes
Opening times? 1st March - 1st November

Trelispen Caravan & Camping Park

Address: Gorran Haven, St Austell, Cornwall, PL26 6NT
Telephone: 01726 843501
Website: www.trelispen.co.uk
Extra charge for dogs? No
Any breed restrictions? No
Dog bins? No
Area for walking dogs? Off Site
Static caravans? No
Cost of static?
Mobile caravans? Yes
Cost of mobile? From £10.00 - £18.00 per night
Tents? Yes
Cost of tent pitch? From £10.00 - £18.00 per night
Electricity at the pitch? Yes
Showers? Yes
Onsite Entertainment? No
Opening times? Easter - End October

Treloan Coastal Farm Holidays

Address: Treloan Lane, Portscatho, The Roseland, Truro, Cornwall. TR2 5EF
Telephone: 01872 580989
Website: www.coastalfarmholidays.co.uk
Extra charge for dogs? Yes
Any breed restrictions? No
Dog bins? No
Area for walking dogs? Off Site
Static caravans? Yes
Cost of static? From £180.00 - £590.00 per week
Mobile caravans? Yes
Cost of mobile? From £9.50 - £19.50 per night
Tents? Yes
Cost of tent pitch? From £9.50 - £19.50 per night
Electricity at the pitch? Yes
Showers? Yes
Onsite Entertainment? No

Opening times? All Year

Treloy Tourist Park

Address: Newquay, Cornwall TR8 4JN
Telephone: 01637 872063
Website: www.treloy.co.uk
Extra charge for dogs? Yes
Any breed restrictions? Yes
Dog bins? Yes
Area for walking dogs? Yes
Static caravans? No
Cost of static?
Mobile caravans? Yes
Cost of mobile? From £10.00 per night
Tents? Yes
Cost of tent pitch? From £10.00 per night
Electricity at the pitch? Yes
Showers? Yes
Onsite Entertainment? Yes
Opening times? May - Mid September
Comments: They do not allow Rottweilers, Alastians, Dobermens, Pitbull Terriers or Ridgebacks.

Trencreek Farm Holiday Park

Address: Hewaswater, St Austell, Cornwall, PL26 7JG
Telephone: 01726 882540
Website: www.surfbayholidays.co.uk
Extra charge for dogs? Yes
Any breed restrictions? Yes
Dog bins? Yes
Area for walking dogs? Yes
Static caravans? Yes
Cost of static? From £155.00 per week
Mobile caravans? Yes
Cost of mobile? From £8.50 per night
Tents? Yes
Cost of tent pitch? From £8.50 per night
Electricity at the pitch? Yes
Showers? Yes
Onsite Entertainment? Children's Entertainment
Opening times? March - January
Comments: No Dangerous Breeds.

Trethem Mill Touring Park

Address: Trethem, St. Just in Roseland, Truro, Cornwall TR2 5JF
Telephone: 01872 580504
Website: www.trethem.com
Extra charge for dogs? Yes
Any breed restrictions? No
Dog bins? Yes
Area for walking dogs? Yes
Static caravans? No
Cost of static?
Mobile caravans? Yes
Cost of mobile? From £15.00 - £21.00 per night
Tents? Yes
Cost of tent pitch? From £15.00 - £21.00 per night
Electricity at the pitch? Yes
Showers? Yes
Onsite Entertainment? No
Opening times? 1st April - Beg October

Trethias Farm Caravan Park

Address: St. Merryn, Padstow, Cornwall PL28 8PL
Telephone: 01841 520323
Website:
Extra charge for dogs? Yes
Any breed restrictions? No
Dog bins? Yes
Area for walking dogs? Yes
Static caravans? No
Cost of static?
Mobile caravans? Yes

Cost of mobile? From £12.00 per night for 2 adults
Tents? Yes
Cost of tent pitch?
Electricity at the pitch? Yes
Showers? Yes
Onsite Entertainment? No
Opening times? 1st April - 30th September
Comments: Fully booked from 26th July - 30th August 2008

Trethiggey Touring Park

Address: Quintrell Downs, Newquary, Cornwall, TR8 4QR
Telephone: 01637 877 672
Website: www.trethiggey.co.uk
Extra charge for dogs? Yes
Any breed restrictions? No
Dog bins? No
Area for walking dogs? Yes
Static caravans? Yes
Cost of static? From £180.00 - £660.00 per week
Mobile caravans? Yes
Cost of mobile? From £4.45 - £7.35 per adult per night
Tents? Yes
Cost of tent pitch? From £4.45 - £7.35 per adult per night
Electricity at the pitch? Yes
Showers? Yes
Onsite Entertainment? Bar
Opening times? March - December

Trevair Touring site

Address: South Treveneague, St Hilary, Goldsithney, Penzance, Cornwall, TR20 9BY
Telephone: 01736 740647
Website: www.trevairtouringpark.co.uk
Extra charge for dogs? No
Any breed restrictions? No
Dog bins? No
Area for walking dogs? Off Site
Static caravans? No
Cost of static?
Mobile caravans? Yes
Cost of mobile? From £5.00 per person per night
Tents?
Cost of tent pitch?
Electricity at the pitch? Yes
Showers? Yes
Onsite Entertainment? No
Opening times? Easter - End October
Comments: Dogs must be kept on a lead.

Trevarrian Holiday Park

Address: Mawgan Porth, Newquary, Cornwall, TR8 4AQ
Telephone: 01637 860 381
Website: www.trevarrian.co.uk
Extra charge for dogs? Yes
Any breed restrictions? No
Dog bins? Yes
Area for walking dogs? Yes
Static caravans? No
Cost of static?
Mobile caravans? Yes
Cost of mobile? From £9.00 - £20.50 per night for 2 people
Tents? Yes
Cost of tent pitch? From £9.00 - £20.50 per night for 2 people
Electricity at the pitch? Yes
Showers? Yes
Onsite Entertainment? Yes
Opening times? Easter - 1st October

Trevarth Holiday Park

Address: Blackwater. Truro. Cornwall. TR4 8HR

Telephone: 01872 560266

Website: www.trevarth.co.uk

Extra charge for dogs? Yes

Any breed restrictions? Yes

Dog bins? No

Area for walking dogs? No

Static caravans? No

Cost of static?

Mobile caravans? Yes

Cost of mobile? From £10.00 per night for 2 People

Tents? Yes

Cost of tent pitch? From £10.00 per night for 2 People

Electricity at the pitch? Yes

Showers? Yes

Onsite Entertainment? Games Room

Opening times? April - October

Comments: No Dangerous Breeds.

Trevaylor Touring Park

Address: Bottallack, St Just, Penzance, Cornwall, TR19 7PU

Telephone: 01736 787016

Website: www.cornishcamping.co.uk

Extra charge for dogs? Yes(Peak Season)

Any breed restrictions? No

Dog bins? No

Area for walking dogs? Yes

Static caravans? Yes

Cost of static? From £200.00 per week

Mobile caravans? Yes

Cost of mobile? From £10.00 per night for 2 People

Tents? Yes

Cost of tent pitch? From £10.00 per night for 2 People

Electricity at the pitch? Yes

Showers? Yes

Onsite Entertainment? No

Opening times? All Year

Treveague Farm

Address: Gorran, Nr Mevagissey, St Austell, PL26 6NY

Telephone: 01726 842295

Website: www.treveaguefarm.co.uk

Extra charge for dogs? No

Any breed restrictions? No

Dog bins? Yes

Area for walking dogs? Yes

Static caravans? No

Cost of static?

Mobile caravans? Yes

Cost of mobile? From £6.00 - £15.00 per night

Tents? Yes

Cost of tent pitch? From £6.00 - £15.00 per night

Electricity at the pitch? Yes

Showers? Yes

Onsite Entertainment? No

Opening times? April - October

Trevean & Camping Park

Address: St. Merryn, Padstow, Cornwall PL28 8PR

Telephone: 01841 520772

Website:

Extra charge for dogs? Yes

Any breed restrictions? No

Dog bins? No

Area for walking dogs? Yes

Static caravans? No

Cost of static?

Mobile caravans? Yes

Cost of mobile? From £8.00 per night for 2 people

Tents? Yes

Cost of tent pitch? From £8.00 per night for 2 people

Electricity at the pitch? Yes

Showers? Yes
Onsite Entertainment? No
Opening times? Easter - End October

Trevelgue Holiday Park

Address: Trevelgue Rd, Porth, Newquay, Cornwall TR8 4AS
Telephone: 01637 851851
Website: www.trevelgue.co.uk
Extra charge for dogs? Yes
Any breed restrictions? No
Dog bins?
Area for walking dogs? Yes
Static caravans? Yes
Cost of static? From £145.00 per week
Mobile caravans? Yes
Cost of mobile? From £3.10 per adult per night
Tents? Yes
Cost of tent pitch? From £3.10 per adult per night
Electricity at the pitch? Yes
Showers? Yes
Onsite Entertainment? Yes
Opening times? All Year
Comments: Dogs are not allowed in July and August.

Trevella Park

Address: Crantock, Newquay, Cornwall, TR8 5EW
Telephone: 01637 830 308
Website: www.trevella.co.uk
Extra charge for dogs? Yes
Any breed restrictions? No
Dog bins? Yes
Area for walking dogs? Yes
Static caravans? Yes
Cost of static? From £273.00 per week
Mobile caravans? Yes
Cost of mobile? From £4.45 per adult per night
Tents? Yes
Cost of tent pitch? From £4.45 per adult per night
Electricity at the pitch? Yes
Showers? Yes
Onsite Entertainment? No
Opening times? Easter - October

Treveor Farm

Address: Gorran, St Austell, Cornwall, PL26 6LW
Telephone: 01726 842387
Website: www.treveorfarm.co.uk
Extra charge for dogs? Yes
Any breed restrictions? Yes
Dog bins? No
Area for walking dogs? Off Site
Static caravans? No
Cost of static?
Mobile caravans? Yes
Cost of mobile? From £7.00 - £15.00 per night
Tents? Yes
Cost of tent pitch? From £6.00 - £13.00 per night
Electricity at the pitch? Yes
Showers? Yes
Onsite Entertainment? No
Opening times? Easter - End October
Comments: No Dangerous Breeds

Treverven Touring Caravan & Camping Site

Address: St Buryan, Penzance, Cornwall, TR19 6DL
Telephone: 01736 810200
Website:www.shycor/camping/treveren.co.uk
Extra charge for dogs? No
Any breed restrictions? Yes
Dog bins? Yes

Area for walking dogs? Yes
Static caravans? No
Cost of static?
Mobile caravans? Yes
Cost of mobile? From £8.50 per night
Tents? Yes
Cost of tent pitch? From £8.50 per night
Electricity at the pitch? Yes
Showers? Yes
Onsite Entertainment? No
Opening times? April - End October
Comments: No Dangerous Breeds. Dogs must be kept on a lead. Maximum of 2 dogs.

Trevornick

Address: Holywell Bay, Newquay, Cornwall TR8 5PW
Telephone: 01637 830531
Website: www.trevernick.co.uk
Extra charge for dogs? Yes
Any breed restrictions? No
Dog bins? Yes
Area for walking dogs? Yes
Static caravans? No
Cost of static?
Mobile caravans? Yes
Cost of mobile? From £4.95 per adult - £9.30 per adult per day
Tents? Yes
Cost of tent pitch? From £4.95 per adult - £9.30 per adult per day
Electricity at the pitch? Yes
Showers? Yes
Onsite Entertainment? Yes
Opening times? 17th May - 13th Sept

Trevorry Caravan Park

Address: Cornwall, Lostwithiel, Cornwall PL22 0JH
Telephone: 01208 872279
Website: www.caravanclub.co.uk
Extra charge for dogs? No
Any breed restrictions? No
Dog bins? No
Area for walking dogs? Yes
Static caravans? No
Cost of static?
Mobile caravans? Yes
Cost of mobile? From £7.00 per night
Tents? Yes
Cost of tent pitch? From £7.00 per night
Electricity at the pitch? Yes
Showers? Yes
Onsite Entertainment? No
Opening times? All Year

Trewethett Farm Caravan Club

Address: Trethevy. Tintagel. Cornwall. PL34 0BQ
Telephone: 01840 770222
Website: www.caravanclub.co.uk
Extra charge for dogs? No
Any breed restrictions? No
Dog bins? Yes
Area for walking dogs? Off Site
Static caravans? No
Cost of static?
Mobile caravans? Yes
Cost of mobile? From £4.60 - £6.00 per adult, £1.50 - £2.50 per child, £4.80 - £7.60 per pitch per night
Tents? Yes
Cost of tent pitch? From £4.60 - £6.00 per adult, £1.50 - £2.50 per child, £4.80 - £7.60 per pitch per night
Electricity at the pitch? Yes
Showers? Yes
Onsite Entertainment? No
Opening times? March - November
Comments: Dogs must be kept on a lead.

Trewince Farm Holiday Park

Address: St Issey, Wadebridge, Cornwall, PL27 7RL

Telephone: 01208 812830

Website: www.trewincefarmholidaypark.co.uk

Extra charge for dogs? Yes

Any breed restrictions? Yes

Dog bins? Yes

Area for walking dogs? Yes

Static caravans? No

Cost of static?

Mobile caravans? Yes

Cost of mobile? From £15.00 per pitch for 2 people per night

Tents? Yes

Cost of tent pitch? From £15.00 per pitch for 2 people per night

Electricity at the pitch? Yes

Showers? Yes

Onsite Entertainment? No

Opening times? Easter - End October

Comments: Dogs must be kept on a lead. No Dangerous Breeds. This is a very young family site there is a no noise policy after 10pm.

Treworgans Holiday Park

Address: Cubert, Newquay, Cornwall TR8 5HH

Telephone: 01637 830200

Website: www.treworgansholidaypark.co.uk

Extra charge for dogs? Yes

Any breed restrictions? No

Dog bins? No

Area for walking dogs? Off Site

Static caravans? Yes

Cost of static? From £200.00 - £555.00 per week

Mobile caravans? No

Cost of mobile?

Tents? No

Cost of tent pitch?

Electricity at the pitch?

Showers?

Onsite Entertainment? No

Opening times? Easter - End October

Comments: Maximum of 2 Dogs.

Treyarnon Bay Camping And Caravan Site

Address: Treyarnon Bay, St. Merryn, Padstow, Cornwall PL28 8JR

Telephone: 01841 520681

Website: www.treyaronbay.co.uk

Extra charge for dogs? Yes

Any breed restrictions? Yes

Dog bins? No

Area for walking dogs? No

Static caravans? No

Cost of static?

Mobile caravans? Yes

Cost of mobile? From £7.00 - £13.00 per night

Tents? Yes

Cost of tent pitch? From £7.00 - £13.00 per night

Electricity at the pitch? Yes

Showers? Yes

Onsite Entertainment? No

Opening times? 1st April - End September

Comments: Only Average and small size dogs.

Tristram Caravan & Camping Site

Address: Polzeath, Wadebridge, Cornwall PL27 6UG

Telephone: 01208 862215

Website: www.polzeathcamping.co.uk

Extra charge for dogs? Yes

Any breed restrictions? No

Dog bins? No
Area for walking dogs? No
Static caravans? No
Cost of static?
Mobile caravans? Yes
Cost of mobile? From £12.00 per night per pitch
Tents? Yes
Cost of tent pitch? From £12.00 per night per pitch
Electricity at the pitch? Yes
Showers? Yes
Onsite Entertainment? No
Opening times? Easter - End October
Comments: Dogs must be kept on a lead.

Veryan Camping & Caravanning site

Address: Tretheake Manor, Veryan, Truro, Cornwall, TR2 5PP
Telephone: 01872 501658
Website: www.campingandcaravanningclub.co.uk
Extra charge for dogs? No
Any breed restrictions? No
Dog bins? Yes
Area for walking dogs? Yes
Static caravans? No
Cost of static?
Mobile caravans? Yes
Cost of mobile? From £5.15 - £7.60 per adult per night
Tents? Yes
Cost of tent pitch? From £5.15 - £7.60 per adult per night
Electricity at the pitch? Yes
Showers? Yes
Onsite Entertainment? No
Opening times? End March - Begin November
Comments: Dogs must be kept on a lead at all times.

Watergate Bay Touring Park

Address: Tregurrian, Newquay, Cornwall TR8 4AD
Telephone: 01637 860387
Website: www.watergatebaytouringpark.co.uk
Extra charge for dogs? Yes
Any breed restrictions? No
Dog bins? Yes
Area for walking dogs? Yes
Static caravans? No
Cost of static?
Mobile caravans? Yes
Cost of mobile? From £10.00 for 2 adults per night
Tents?
Cost of tent pitch?
Electricity at the pitch? Yes
Showers? Yes
Onsite Entertainment? Yes
Opening times? March - October

Wheal Rodney Holiday Park

Address: Gwallon, Marazion, Penzance, Cornwall, TR17 0HL
Telephone: 01736 710605
Website: www.whealrodney.co.uk
Extra charge for dogs? Yes
Any breed restrictions? No
Dog bins? No
Area for walking dogs? Off Site
Static caravans? No
Cost of static?
Mobile caravans? Yes
Cost of mobile? From £12.00 per night for 2 adults
Tents? Yes
Cost of tent pitch? From £10.00 per night for 2 adults

Electricity at the pitch? Yes
Showers? Yes
Onsite Entertainment? No
Opening times? Easter - End October

Wheal Rose Caravan Parks

Address: Chynoweth Wheal Rose Caravan, Wheal Rose, Scorrier, Redruth, Cornwall TR16 5DD
Telephone: 01209 891496
Website: www.whealrosecaravanpark.co.uk
Extra charge for dogs? No
Any breed restrictions? No
Dog bins? No
Area for walking dogs? Off Site
Static caravans? Yes
Cost of static? From £120.00 - £300.00 per week
Mobile caravans? Yes
Cost of mobile? From £9.00 - £15.00 per night
Tents? Yes
Cost of tent pitch? From £9.00 - £15.00 per night
Electricity at the pitch? Yes
Showers? Yes
Onsite Entertainment? No
Opening times? March - December
Comments: Dogs must be kept on a lead.

White Acres Country Park

Address: White Cross, Newquay, Cornwall TR8 4LW
Telephone: 01726 862 100
Website: www.parkdeanholidays.co.uk
Extra charge for dogs? Yes
Any breed restrictions? Yes
Dog bins? Yes
Area for walking dogs? Yes
Static caravans? Yes
Cost of static? From £300.00 per week
Mobile caravans? No
Cost of mobile?
Tents? No
Cost of tent pitch?
Electricity at the pitch? No
Showers? No
Onsite Entertainment? Yes
Opening times? March - November
Comments: No Dangerous Breeds

Whitsand Bay Holiday Park

Address: Millbrook, Torpoint, Cornwall, PL10 1JZ
Telephone: 01752 822597
Website: www.whitsandbayholidays.co.uk
Extra charge for dogs? Yes
Any breed restrictions? No
Dog bins? No
Area for walking dogs? No
Static caravans? No
Cost of static?
Mobile caravans? Yes
Cost of mobile? From £10.00 - £30.00 per night
Tents? No
Cost of tent pitch?
Electricity at the pitch? Yes
Showers? Yes
Onsite Entertainment? No
Opening times? All Year
Comments: There is an Indoor Swimming Pool, Sauna and a licensed bar.

Willow Valley Camping Park

Address: Dyehouse, Bush, Bude, Cornwall, EX23 9LB

Telephone: 01288 353104
Website: www.willowvalley.co.uk
Extra charge for dogs? Yes
Any breed restrictions? No
Dog bins? Yes
Area for walking dogs? Yes
Static caravans? No
Cost of static?
Mobile caravans? Yes
Cost of mobile? From £8.00 per night
Tents? Yes
Cost of tent pitch? From £8.00 per night
Electricity at the pitch? Yes
Showers? Yes
Onsite Entertainment? No
Opening times? Begin March - End October

Wooda Farm Park

Address: Poughill, Bude, Cornwall, EX23 9HJ
Telephone: 01288 352069
Website: www.wooda.co.uk
Extra charge for dogs? Yes
Any breed restrictions? Yes
Dog bins? Yes
Area for walking dogs? Yes
Static caravans? No
Cost of static?
Mobile caravans? Yes
Cost of mobile? From £12.00 - £26.00 per night
Tents? Yes
Cost of tent pitch? From £12.00 - £26.00 per night
Electricity at the pitch? Yes
Showers? Yes
Onsite Entertainment? No
Opening times? 1st April - 31st October
Comments: There is a bar and a take away.

Woodbury

Address: Kea Downs Road. Penstraze. Truro. Cornwall. TR4 8PF
Telephone: 01872 560932
Website:
Extra charge for dogs? No
Any breed restrictions? No
Dog bins? Yes
Area for walking dogs? Yes
Static caravans? No
Cost of static?
Mobile caravans? Yes
Cost of mobile? From £5.00 per night for 2 People
Tents?
Cost of tent pitch?
Electricity at the pitch? No
Showers? No
Onsite Entertainment? No
Opening times? All Year
Comments: No Children allowed.

Zoar Camp Site

Address: Lizland, St Keverne, Cornwall, TR12 6RH
Telephone: 01326 280397
Website: www.zoar.co.uk
Extra charge for dogs? No
Any breed restrictions? No
Dog bins? No
Area for walking dogs? Yes
Static caravans? Yes
Cost of static? From £5.00 per night per adult
Mobile caravans? Yes
Cost of mobile? From £5.00 per night per adult
Tents? Yes
Cost of tent pitch? From £5.00 per night per adult

Electricity at the pitch? Yes
Showers? Yes
Onsite Entertainment? No
Opening times? May - September

Blue Hills Touring Park

Address: Cross Combe, Trevellas, St Agnes, Cornwall, TR5 0XP
Telephone: 01872 552999
Website: www.bluehillscamping.co.uk
Extra charge for dogs? No
Any breed restrictions? No
Dog bins? No
Area for walking dogs? Yes
Static caravans? No
Cost of static?
Mobile caravans? Yes
Cost of mobile? From £6.00 per night
Tents? Yes
Cost of tent pitch? From £5.00 per night
Electricity at the pitch? Yes
Showers? Yes
Onsite Entertainment? No
Opening times? All Year

Carbeil Naturist Holiday Park

Address: Treliddon Lane, Downderry, Torpoint, Cornwall, P11 3LS
Telephone: 01503 250636
Website: www.carbeil.co.uk
Extra charge for dogs? No
Any breed restrictions? No
Dog bins? Yes
Area for walking dogs? Yes
Static caravans? No
Cost of static?
Mobile caravans? Yes
Cost of mobile? From £15.00 per night
Tents? Yes
Cost of tent pitch? From £15.00 per night
Electricity at the pitch? Yes
Showers? Yes
Onsite Entertainment? Yes
Opening times? All Year
Comments: Bar which has quiz nights.

East Thorne Touring Park

Address: Kilkhampton, Bude, Cornwall, EX23 9RY
Telephone: 01288 321654
Website:
Extra charge for dogs? No
Any breed restrictions? No
Dog bins? No
Area for walking dogs? Yes
Static caravans? No
Cost of static?
Mobile caravans? Yes
Cost of mobile? From £6.80 per night
Tents? Yes
Cost of tent pitch? From £4.80 per night
Electricity at the pitch? Yes
Showers? Yes
Onsite Entertainment? No
Opening times? March - October

Higher Golla Caravan Park

Address: HIGHER GOLLA FARM, PENHALLOW, Truro, TR4 9LZ
Telephone: 01872 572116
Website: www.highergollatouringpark.co.uk
Extra charge for dogs? Yes
Any breed restrictions? Yes
Dog bins? No
Area for walking dogs? Yes
Static caravans? Yes
Cost of static? From £150.00 per week

Mobile caravans? Yes
Cost of mobile? From £8.00 - £12.00 per pitch + 2 adults + 2 Children (Under 12) per night with electric
Tents? No
Cost of tent pitch?
Electricity at the pitch? Yes
Showers? No
Onsite Entertainment? No
Opening times? Easter - End October
Comments: No dangerous breeds, dogs must be kept on a lead. Maximum 2 dogs.

Little Dinham Woodland Caravan Park

Address: St. Minver, Wadebridge, Cornwall PL27 6RH
Telephone: 01208 812538
Website: www.littledinham.co.uk
Extra charge for dogs? Yes
Any breed restrictions? No
Dog bins? No
Area for walking dogs? Yes
Static caravans? Yes
Cost of static? From £220.00 - £550.00 per week
Mobile caravans? No
Cost of mobile?
Tents? No
Cost of tent pitch?
Electricity at the pitch? No
Showers? No
Onsite Entertainment? No
Opening times? Easter - End October
Comments: Do not take dogs from 19th July - 23rd August.

Polglaze Farm

Address: Polglaze Farm, Fowey, Cornwall, PL23 1JZ
Telephone: 01726 833642
Website: www.polglaze.co.uk
Extra charge for dogs? No
Any breed restrictions? Yes
Dog bins? No
Area for walking dogs? Off Site
Static caravans? Yes
Cost of static? From £150.00 per week
Mobile caravans? Yes
Cost of mobile? From £8.00 per night
Tents? Yes
Cost of tent pitch? From £8.00 per night
Electricity at the pitch? Yes
Showers? Yes
Onsite Entertainment? No
Opening times? July & August
Comments: No Dangerous Breeds and No Large Dogs.

Sennen Cove Camping And Caravanning Club Site

Address: Higher Tregiffian Farm, St Buryan, Penzance, Cornwall, TR19 6JB
Telephone: 01736 871588
Website: www.thecampingandcaravanningclub.co.uk
Extra charge for dogs? No
Any breed restrictions? No
Dog bins? Yes
Area for walking dogs? Yes
Static caravans? No
Cost of static?
Mobile caravans? Yes
Cost of mobile? From £4.40 per person + £6.00 if non member per night
Tents? No
Cost of tent pitch? From £4.40 per person + £6.00 if non member per night
Electricity at the pitch? Yes
Showers? Yes
Onsite Entertainment? No

Opening times? End April - End September

Comments: Dogs must be kept on a lead.

Tollgate Farm Caravan & Camping Park

Address: Toll Gate Farm, Budnick Hill, Perranporth, Cornwall TR6 0AD

Telephone: 01872 572130

Website: www.tollgatefarm.co.uk

Extra charge for dogs? No

Any breed restrictions? No

Dog bins? Yes

Area for walking dogs? Yes

Static caravans? No

Cost of static?

Mobile caravans? Yes

Cost of mobile? From £7.50 per night

Tents? Yes

Cost of tent pitch? From £7.50 per night

Electricity at the pitch? Yes

Showers? Yes

Onsite Entertainment? No

Opening times? Easter - End September

Summer Valley Touring Park

Address: Shortlanesand, Truro, Cornwall, TR4 9DW

Telephone: 01872 277878

Website: www.summervalley.co.uk

Extra charge for dogs? Yes

Any breed restrictions? ?

Dog bins? ?

Area for walking dogs? Yes

Static caravans? No

Cost of static?

Mobile caravans? Yes

Cost of mobile? From £12.50 per night for 2 adults with electric

Tents? Yes

Cost of tent pitch? From £12.50 per night for 2 adults with electric

Electricity at the pitch? Yes

Showers? Yes

Onsite Entertainment? No

Opening times? March - October

Comments: Dogs must be kept on a lead. There is a children's play area on site.

Black Beck Caravan Park

Address: Bouth, Ulverston, Cumbria LA12 8JN

Telephone: 01229 861274

Website: www.blackbeck.com

Extra charge for dogs? No

Any breed restrictions? No

Dog bins? No

Area for walking dogs? Off Site

Static caravans? No

Cost of static?

Mobile caravans? Yes

Cost of mobile? From £12.50 - £18.00 per night

Tents? No

Cost of tent pitch?

Electricity at the pitch? Yes

Showers? Yes

Onsite Entertainment? No

Opening times? 1st March - 15th November

Comments: There is a sauna, gym and spa area.

Chapel Farm Caravan Park

Address: Little Asby, Appleby-In-Westmorland, Cumbria CA16 6QE

Telephone: 015396 23665

Website: www.chapelfarmcaravanpark.co.uk

Extra charge for dogs? No

Any breed restrictions? No

Dog bins? No

Area for walking dogs? Off Site

Static caravans? Yes

Cost of static? From £170.00 - £280.00 per week

Mobile caravans? No

Cost of mobile?

Tents? No

Cost of tent pitch?

Electricity at the pitch? No

Showers? No

Onsite Entertainment? No

Opening times? 1st March - 14th November

Croft Caravan & Camp Site

Address: North Lonsdale Rd, Hawkshead, Ambleside, Cumbria LA22 0QS

Telephone: 015394 36374

Website: www.hawkshead-croft.com

Extra charge for dogs? Yes (Statics only)

Any breed restrictions? No

Dog bins? No

Area for walking dogs? Yes

Static caravans? Yes

Cost of static? From £290.00 per week

Mobile caravans? Yes

Cost of mobile? From £17.50 per night

Tents? Yes

Cost of tent pitch? From £14.00 per night

Electricity at the pitch? Yes

Showers? Yes

Onsite Entertainment? No

Opening times? March - November

Cross Hall Caravan Park

Address: Cautley, Sedbergh, Cumbria LA10 5LY

Telephone: 015396 20668

Website: www.cautleycaravans.co.uk

Extra charge for dogs? No

Any breed restrictions? No

Dog bins? No

Area for walking dogs? Off Site

Static caravans? Yes

Cost of static? From £195.00 per week

Mobile caravans? Yes

Cost of mobile? From £12.50 per night

Tents? Yes

Cost of tent pitch? From £5.00 per person per night

Electricity at the pitch? Yes

Showers? Yes

Onsite Entertainment? No

Opening times? 1st April - End October

Dalston Hall Caravan Park

Address: Dalston, Carlisle, Cumbria CA5 7JX

Telephone: 01228 710165

Website: www.dalstonholidaypark.com

Extra charge for dogs? Yes

Any breed restrictions? No

Dog bins? No

Area for walking dogs? Yes

Static caravans? No

Cost of static?

Mobile caravans? Yes

Cost of mobile? From £12.00 per night

Tents? Yes

Cost of tent pitch? From £8.00 per night

Electricity at the pitch? Yes

Showers? Yes

Onsite Entertainment? Yes

Opening times? March - January

Comments: There is a Golf Course, with club house and bar.

Fell End Caravan Park

Address: Slackhead Rd, Hale, Milnthorpe, Cumbria LA7 7BS

Telephone: 015395 62122

Website: www.pureleisuregroup.co.uk

Extra charge for dogs? Yes

Any breed restrictions? No

Dog bins? Yes

Area for walking dogs? Yes

Static caravans? No

Cost of static?

Mobile caravans? Yes

Cost of mobile? From £15.00 - £17.00 per night

Tents? Yes

Cost of tent pitch? From £10.50 - £12.50 per night

Electricity at the pitch? Yes

Showers? Yes

Onsite Entertainment? Occasionally

Opening times? All Year

Flusco Wood

Address: Flusco, Penrith, Cumbria CA11 0JB

Telephone: 017684 80020

Website: www.fluscowood.co.uk

Extra charge for dogs? Yes

Any breed restrictions? No

Dog bins? Yes

Area for walking dogs? Yes

Static caravans? No

Cost of static?

Mobile caravans? Yes

Cost of mobile? From £16.00 - £19.00 per night for 2 adults

Tents? No
Cost of tent pitch?
Electricity at the pitch? Yes
Showers? Yes
Onsite Entertainment? No
Opening times? Easter - End October

Gill Head Farm Caravan Park

Address: Gill Head Farm, Troutbeck, Penrith, Cumbria CA11 0ST
Telephone: 017684 86363
Website: www.gillheadfarm.co.uk
Extra charge for dogs? Yes
Any breed restrictions? No
Dog bins? Yes
Area for walking dogs? Yes
Static caravans? No
Cost of static?
Mobile caravans? Yes
Cost of mobile? From £16.00 per pitch per night
Tents? Yes
Cost of tent pitch? From £6.00 per person per night
Electricity at the pitch? Yes
Showers? Yes
Onsite Entertainment? No
Opening times? March - October
Comments: Dog must be kept on leads at all times.

Greaves Farm Caravan site

Address: Prospect House, Barber Green, Ayside, Grange-Over-Sands, Cumbria LA11 6HU
Telephone: 015395 36329
Website:
Extra charge for dogs? No
Any breed restrictions? No
Dog bins? No
Area for walking dogs? Off Site
Static caravans? Yes
Cost of static? From £275.00 - £375.00 per week
Mobile caravans? Yes
Cost of mobile? From £12.00 - £16.00 per night
Tents? Yes
Cost of tent pitch? From £12.00 - £16.00 for tent and 2 people per night
Electricity at the pitch? Yes
Showers? Yes
Onsite Entertainment? No
Opening times? March - October

Green Acres Caravan Park

Address: Green Acres, High Knells, Carlisle, Cumbria CA6 4JW
Telephone: 01228 675418
Website: www.caravanpark-cumbria.com
Extra charge for dogs? No
Any breed restrictions? No
Dog bins? No
Area for walking dogs? Yes
Static caravans? No
Cost of static?
Mobile caravans? Yes
Cost of mobile? From £11.00 per night
Tents? Yes
Cost of tent pitch? From £8.00 per night
Electricity at the pitch? Yes
Showers? Yes
Onsite Entertainment? No
Opening times? April - End October

HIGH FELL GATE

Address: High Fellgate, Cartmel Road, Grange-Over-Sands, Cumbria LA11 7QA
Telephone: 0153 9536231
Website:

Extra charge for dogs? No
Any breed restrictions? No
Dog bins? No
Area for walking dogs? Yes
Static caravans? No
Cost of static?
Mobile caravans? Yes
Cost of mobile? From £10.00 - £15.00 per night
Tents? Yes
Cost of tent pitch? From £10.00 - £15.00 per night
Electricity at the pitch? Yes
Showers? Yes
Onsite Entertainment? No
Opening times? March - October

High Gaitle Caravan Park

Address: Longtown, Carlisle, Cumbria CA6 5LU
Telephone: 01228 791819
Website:
Extra charge for dogs? No
Any breed restrictions? Yes
Dog bins? No
Area for walking dogs? Yes
Static caravans? No
Cost of static?
Mobile caravans? Yes
Cost of mobile? From £15.00 per night
Tents? Yes
Cost of tent pitch? From £15.00 per night
Electricity at the pitch? Yes(Caravans only)
Showers? Yes
Onsite Entertainment? No
Opening times? All Year
Comments: No Dangerous Breeds. Maximum 2 Dogs.

Hillcroft Park

Address: Pooley Bridge, Penrith, Cumbria CA10 2LT
Telephone: 01768 486363
Website: www.hillcroftcaravanpark.co.uk
Extra charge for dogs? Yes
Any breed restrictions? Yes
Dog bins? Yes
Area for walking dogs? Yes
Static caravans? No
Cost of static?
Mobile caravans? Yes
Cost of mobile? From £20.00 per night with electric
Tents? Yes
Cost of tent pitch? From £16.00 per night
Electricity at the pitch? Yes
Showers? Yes
Onsite Entertainment? No
Opening times? 1st March - January
Comments: No Dangerous Breeds.

Inglenook Caravan Park

Address: Fitz Bridge, Lamplugh, Workington, Cumbria CA14
Telephone: 01946 861240
Website:
Extra charge for dogs? No
Any breed restrictions? No
Dog bins? No
Area for walking dogs? Off Site
Static caravans? Yes
Cost of static? From £300.00 per week
Mobile caravans? Yes
Cost of mobile? From £14.00 per night for 2 people
Tents? Yes
Cost of tent pitch? From £10.00 - £15.00 for 2 people

Electricity at the pitch? Yes
Showers? Yes
Onsite Entertainment? No
Opening times? All Year

Lakeland Caravan Park

Address: Moor Lane, Flookburgh, Grange-Over-Sands, Cumbria LA11 7LT
Telephone: 01539 558556
Website: www.haven.com
Extra charge for dogs? Yes
Any breed restrictions? Yes
Dog bins? Yes
Area for walking dogs? Yes
Static caravans? Yes
Cost of static?
Mobile caravans? Yes
Cost of mobile?
Tents? Yes
Cost of tent pitch?
Electricity at the pitch? Yes
Showers? Yes
Onsite Entertainment? Yes
Opening times? March - End October
Comments: No Dangerous Breeds

Low Briery Holiday Village

Address: Keswick, Cumbria CA12 4RN
Telephone: 017687 72044
Website: www.keswick.uk.com
Extra charge for dogs? Yes
Any breed restrictions? Yes
Dog bins? No
Area for walking dogs? Off Site
Static caravans? Yes
Cost of static? From £265.00 - £560.00 per week
Mobile caravans? No
Cost of mobile?
Tents? No
Cost of tent pitch?
Electricity at the pitch? No
Showers? No
Onsite Entertainment? No
Opening times? 15th March - 1st November
Comments: No Puppies, Poop scoop is given on arrival

Low Manesty Caravan Club Site

Address: Low Manesty, Borrowdale, Keswick, Cumbria CA12 5UG
Telephone: 017687 77275
Website: www.campingandcaravanningclub.co.uk
Extra charge for dogs? No
Any breed restrictions? No
Dog bins? Yes
Area for walking dogs? Off Site
Static caravans? No
Cost of static?
Mobile caravans? Yes
Cost of mobile? From £9.30 - £13.70 per night for 2 people
Tents? No
Cost of tent pitch?
Electricity at the pitch? Yes
Showers? No
Onsite Entertainment? No
Opening times? March - November

Low Moor Caravan & Camping Site

Address: Low Moor, Penrith, Cumbria CA10
Telephone: 017683 61231
Website: www.lowmoorpark.co.uk
Extra charge for dogs? No
Any breed restrictions? No
Dog bins? No
Area for walking dogs? Off Site

Static caravans? Yes

Cost of static? From £180.00 per week

Mobile caravans? Yes

Cost of mobile? From £12.00 per night for 2 people

Tents? Yes

Cost of tent pitch? From £10.00 per night for 2 People

Electricity at the pitch? Yes (Caravans only)

Showers? Yes

Onsite Entertainment? No

Opening times? April - October

Newby Bridge Caravan Park

Address: Canny Hill, Newby Bridge, Ulverston, Cumbria LA12 8NF

Telephone: 015395 31030

Website: www.cumbriancaravans.co.uk

Extra charge for dogs? No

Any breed restrictions? No

Dog bins? No

Area for walking dogs? Off Site

Static caravans? Yes

Cost of static? From £195.00 per week

Mobile caravans? No

Cost of mobile?

Tents? No

Cost of tent pitch?

Electricity at the pitch? No

Showers? Yes

Onsite Entertainment? No

Opening times? March - October

Comments: Maximum 1 dog per caravan

North Lakes Caravan Park

Address: Bewaldeth, Cockermouth, Cumbria CA13 9SY

Telephone: 017687 76510

Website: www.northlakesholidays.co.uk

Extra charge for dogs? No

Any breed restrictions? No

Dog bins? No

Area for walking dogs? Off Site

Static caravans? No

Cost of static?

Mobile caravans? Yes

Cost of mobile? From £15.00 per night for 2 people

Tents? Yes

Cost of tent pitch? From £15.00 per night for family sized tent

Electricity at the pitch? Yes

Showers? Yes

Onsite Entertainment? No

Opening times? Easter - 14th November

Comments: There is a bar and a games room but are only opened on demand. There is a dog show every year in July.

Park Cliffe Caravan & Camping Estate

Address: Birks Rd, Windermere, Cumbria LA23 3PG

Telephone: 015395 31344

Website: www.parkcliffe.co.uk

Extra charge for dogs? Yes

Any breed restrictions? No

Dog bins? Yes

Area for walking dogs? Yes

Static caravans? No

Cost of static?

Mobile caravans? Yes

Cost of mobile? From £23.00 per night

Tents? Yes

Cost of tent pitch? From £19.00 per night

Electricity at the pitch? Yes

Showers? Yes

Onsite Entertainment? Bar and Restaurant

Opening times? March - Mid November

Park Foot Caravan Park & Camping Park

Address: Howtown, Penrith, Cumbria CA10 2NA

Telephone: 017684 86309

Website: www.parkfootullswater.co.uk

Extra charge for dogs? Yes

Any breed restrictions? No

Dog bins? No

Area for walking dogs? Yes

Static caravans? No

Cost of static?

Mobile caravans? Yes

Cost of mobile? From £12.00 per night for 2 people

Tents? Yes

Cost of tent pitch? From £12.00 per night for 2 people

Electricity at the pitch? Yes

Showers? Yes

Onsite Entertainment? Yes

Opening times? 1st March - 15th November

Pound Farm

Address: Crook, Kendal, Cumbria LA8 8JZ

Telephone: 01539 821220

Website: www.northdales.co.uk

Extra charge for dogs? Yes

Any breed restrictions? No

Dog bins? No

Area for walking dogs? Yes

Static caravans? No

Cost of static?

Mobile caravans? Yes

Cost of mobile? From £16.00 per night for 2 people

Tents? Yes

Cost of tent pitch? From £16.00 per night for 2 people

Electricity at the pitch? Yes

Showers? Yes

Onsite Entertainment? No

Opening times? Mid March - Begin November

Riverside Tourer Park

Address: Rose Garth, Millhouse, Hesket Newmarket, Wigton, Cumbria CA7

Telephone: 016974 78571

Website: www.riverside-tourer-park.co.uk

Extra charge for dogs? No (for 2 dogs)

Any breed restrictions? No

Dog bins? No

Area for walking dogs? Yes

Static caravans? No

Cost of static?

Mobile caravans? Yes

Cost of mobile? From £10.00 per night

Tents? No

Cost of tent pitch?

Electricity at the pitch? Yes

Showers? Yes

Onsite Entertainment? No

Opening times? All Year

Comments: Adults only

Scotgate Holiday Park

Address: Braithwaite, Keswick, Cumbria CA12 5TF

Telephone: 017687 78343

Website: www.scotgateholidaypark.co.uk

Extra charge for dogs? No

Any breed restrictions? No
Dog bins? No
Area for walking dogs? No
Static caravans? Yes
Cost of static? From £225.00 per week
Mobile caravans? Yes
Cost of mobile? From £15.50 per night
Tents? Yes
Cost of tent pitch? From £7.00 per night for 1 person no vehicle
Electricity at the pitch? Yes
Showers? Yes
Onsite Entertainment? No
Opening times? All Year
Comments: Maximum 1 dog. Dogs must be kept on a lead at all times.

Seven Acres Caravan Park

Address: Holmrook, Cumbria CA19 1YD
Telephone: 019467 25480
Website: www.seacote.com
Extra charge for dogs? Yes
Any breed restrictions? No
Dog bins? No
Area for walking dogs? Off Site
Static caravans? Yes
Cost of static? From £196.00 per week
Mobile caravans? Yes
Cost of mobile? From £17.00 - £20.00 per night
Tents? Yes
Cost of tent pitch? From £14.00 - £17.00 per night
Electricity at the pitch? Yes (Caravans only)
Showers? Yes
Onsite Entertainment? Yes
Opening times? All Year

Silecroft Caravan Park

Address: Silecroft, Whicham, Millom, Cumbria LA18 4NX
Telephone: 01229 772659
Website: www.caravanholidayhomes.com
Extra charge for dogs? No
Any breed restrictions? No
Dog bins? No
Area for walking dogs? Off Site
Static caravans? No
Cost of static?
Mobile caravans? Yes
Cost of mobile? From £15.00 per night
Tents? Yes
Cost of tent pitch? From £15.00 per night
Electricity at the pitch? Yes
Showers? Yes
Onsite Entertainment? No
Opening times? 1st March - 31st October
Comments: Dogs must be kept on a lead. There is a swimming pool on site.

South End Caravan Park

Address: Walney, Barrow-In-Furness, Cumbria LA14 3YQ
Telephone: 01229 472823
Website: www.walneyislandcaravanpark.co.uk
Extra charge for dogs? No
Any breed restrictions? No
Dog bins? Yes
Area for walking dogs? Yes
Static caravans? No
Cost of static?
Mobile caravans? Yes
Cost of mobile? From £10.00 - £20.00 per night
Tents? No
Cost of tent pitch?

Electricity at the pitch? Yes
Showers? Yes
Onsite Entertainment? Yes
Opening times? March - October
Comments: There an indoor heated swimming pool on site.

Stanwix Park Holiday Centre

Address: Greenrow, Silloth, Wigton, Cumbria CA7 4HH
Telephone: 016973 32666
Website: www.stanwix.com
Extra charge for dogs? Yes
Any breed restrictions? No
Dog bins? No
Area for walking dogs? No
Static caravans? Yes
Cost of static? From £170.00 per week
Mobile caravans? Yes
Cost of mobile? From £11.50 per pitch per night with electric + £3.60 per adult per night
Tents? Yes
Cost of tent pitch? From £11.50 per pitch per night with electric + £3.60 per adult per night
Electricity at the pitch? Yes
Showers? Yes
Onsite Entertainment? Yes
Opening times? All Year

Tanglewood Caravan Park

Address: Causewayhead, Silloth, Wigton, Cumbria CA7 4PE
Telephone: 016973 31253
Website: www.tanglewoodcaravan park.co.uk
Extra charge for dogs? No
Any breed restrictions? No
Dog bins? No
Area for walking dogs? Off Site
Static caravans? Yes
Cost of static? From £230.00 - £390.00 per week
Mobile caravans? Yes
Cost of mobile? From £15.00 per night including electric
Tents? Yes
Cost of tent pitch? From £15.00 per night including electric
Electricity at the pitch? Yes
Showers? Yes
Onsite Entertainment? Pub
Opening times? March - End January
Comments: Dogs must be kept on a lead.

The Camping & Caravanning Club

Address: Hutton Moor End, Troutbeck, Penrith, Cumbria CA11 0SX
Telephone: 017687 79149
Website: www.campingandcaravanning club.co.uk
Extra charge for dogs? No
Any breed restrictions? No
Dog bins? Yes
Area for walking dogs? Yes
Static caravans? Yes
Cost of static? From £297.00 - £491.00 per week
Mobile caravans? Yes
Cost of mobile? From £6.60 - £7.60 per adult per night
Tents? Yes
Cost of tent pitch? From £6.60 - £7.60 per adult per night
Electricity at the pitch? Yes
Showers? Yes
Onsite Entertainment? Small Play area
Opening times? 1st March - 15th November & 2 weeks Christmas/ New Year

Ullswater Caravan & Camping Park

Address: Watermillock, Penrith, Cumbria CA11 0LR
Telephone: 017684 86666
Website: www.uccmp.co.uk
Extra charge for dogs? Yes
Any breed restrictions? Yes
Dog bins? No
Area for walking dogs? Yes
Static caravans? Yes
Cost of static? From £340.00 per week
Mobile caravans? Yes
Cost of mobile? From £18.00 per pitch with electric
Tents? Yes
Cost of tent pitch? From £15.50 per night
Electricity at the pitch? Yes
Showers? Yes
Onsite Entertainment? No
Opening times? March - Mid November
Comments: No Dangerous Breeds

White Cross Bay Holiday Park

Address: Ambleside Rd, Troutbeck Bridge, Windermere, Cumbria LA23 1LF
Telephone: 015394 43937
Website: www.southlakelandparks.co.uk
Extra charge for dogs? Yes
Any breed restrictions? No
Dog bins? Yes
Area for walking dogs? Yes
Static caravans? Yes
Cost of static? From £230.00 per week
Mobile caravans? Yes
Cost of mobile? From £16.50 per night
Tents? No
Cost of tent pitch?
Electricity at the pitch? Yes
Showers? Yes
Onsite Entertainment? No
Opening times? 1st March - 14th November

Wild Rose Caravan Park

Address: Ormside, Appleby-In-Westmorland, Cumbria CA16 6EJ
Telephone: 017683 51077
Website: www.wildrose.co.uk
Extra charge for dogs? Yes
Any breed restrictions? Yes
Dog bins? Yes
Area for walking dogs? Yes
Static caravans? No
Cost of static?
Mobile caravans? Yes
Cost of mobile? From £17.00 per night with electric
Tents? Yes
Cost of tent pitch? From £17.00 per night with electric
Electricity at the pitch? Yes
Showers? Yes
Onsite Entertainment? Restaurant
Opening times? All Year
Comments: No Dangerous Breeds. They have a doggy shower.

Manor House Caravan Park

Address: Manor House, Edderside Rd, Allonby, Maryport, Cumbria CA15 6RA
Telephone: 01900 881236
Website: www.manorhousepark.co.uk
Extra charge for dogs? Yes (Statics only)
Any breed restrictions? No
Dog bins? No
Area for walking dogs? Off Site
Static caravans? Yes

Cost of static? ?
Mobile caravans? Yes
Cost of mobile? ?
Tents? Yes
Cost of tent pitch?
Electricity at the pitch? Yes
Showers? Yes
Onsite Entertainment? Sometimes
Opening times? 1st March - 3rd January
Comments: Building a Club House.

Rowanbank Caravan Park

Address: Beckfoot, Silloth, Cumbria CA7 4LA
Telephone: 0169 7331653
Website:www.rowanbankcaravanpark.co.uk
Extra charge for dogs? No
Any breed restrictions? No
Dog bins? No
Area for walking dogs? Yes
Static caravans? Yes
Cost of static? From £170.00 per week
Mobile caravans? Yes
Cost of mobile? From £14.50 per night
Tents? Yes
Cost of tent pitch? From £12.50 per night
Electricity at the pitch? Yes
Showers? Yes
Onsite Entertainment? No
Opening times? 1st March - 4th January (Statics) 1st April - 31st October (Touring)
Comments: Maximum 2 dogs.

Trafford Caravan Park

Address: Bassenthwaite, Keswick, Cumbria CA12 4QH
Telephone: 017687 76298
Website:
Extra charge for dogs? No
Any breed restrictions? No
Dog bins? No
Area for walking dogs? Yes
Static caravans? No
Cost of static?
Mobile caravans? Yes
Cost of mobile? From £12.00 per night
Tents? Yes
Cost of tent pitch? From £5.00 per night
Electricity at the pitch? Yes
Showers? Yes
Onsite Entertainment? No
Opening times?

Troutbeck Head Caravan Club Site

Address: Troutbeck, Penrith, Cumbria CA11 0SS
Telephone: 017684 83521
Website: www.thecaravanclub.co.uk
Extra charge for dogs? No
Any breed restrictions? No
Dog bins? Yes
Area for walking dogs? Yes
Static caravans? No
Cost of static?
Mobile caravans? Yes
Cost of mobile? From £14.90 for 2 people per night
Tents? No
Cost of tent pitch?
Electricity at the pitch? Yes
Showers? Yes
Onsite Entertainment? No
Opening times? February - January

Acres Down Farm

Address: Minstead, Lyndhurst, Hampshire SO43 7GE

Telephone: 02380 813693

Website:

Extra charge for dogs?

Any breed restrictions? Yes

Dog bins? No

Area for walking dogs? Off Site

Static caravans? No

Cost of static?

Mobile caravans? Yes

Cost of mobile? From £10.00 per night

Tents? Yes

Cost of tent pitch? From £7.50 per night

Electricity at the pitch? No

Showers? One Shower only

Onsite Entertainment? No

Opening times? All Year

Comments: Dog must be kept on a lead. No Dangerous Breeds

Adgestone Camping Park

Address: Lower Adgestone Road, Nr Sandown, Isle of Wight, Hampshire PO36 0HL

Telephone: 01983 403432

Website: www.campingandcaravanning club.co.uk

Extra charge for dogs? No

Any breed restrictions? No

Dog bins? No

Area for walking dogs? Yes

Static caravans? Yes

Cost of static? ?

Mobile caravans? Yes

Cost of mobile? From £6.05 per adult £2.25 per child

Tents? Yes

Cost of tent pitch? From £6.05 per adult £2.25 per child

Electricity at the pitch? Yes

Showers? Yes

Onsite Entertainment? No

Opening times? Mid March - October

Comments: Dog must be kept on a lead.

Aldridge Hill Caravan & Camping Site

Address: Brockenhurst, Hampshire SO42 7QD

Telephone: 0131 314 6505

Website: www.forestholidays.co.uk

Extra charge for dogs? Yes

Any breed restrictions? No

Dog bins? Yes

Area for walking dogs? Off Site

Static caravans? No

Cost of static?

Mobile caravans? Yes

Cost of mobile? From £8.50 per night

Tents? Yes

Cost of tent pitch? From £8.50 per night

Electricity at the pitch? No

Showers? No

Onsite Entertainment? No

Opening times? 22nd May - 3rd June & 19th June - 9th Sept

Comments: Maximum 3 dogs per pitch.

Appuldurcombe Gardens Holiday Park

Address: Wroxall, Ventnor, Isle of Wight, Hampshire PO38 3EP
Telephone: 01983 852597
Website: www.appuldurcombe.co.uk
Extra charge for dogs? Yes
Any breed restrictions? No
Dog bins? No
Area for walking dogs? No
Static caravans? Yes
Cost of static? From £195.00 per week
Mobile caravans? Yes
Cost of mobile? From £4.20 per night
Tents? Yes
Cost of tent pitch? From £4.20 per night
Electricity at the pitch? Yes
Showers? Yes
Onsite Entertainment? Some in Summer Months
Opening times? All Year

Beaper Farm Camping & Caravan Park

Address: Nr Ryde, Isle of Wight, Hampshire PO33 1QJ
Telephone: 01983 615210
Website: www.beaperfarm.com
Extra charge for dogs? Yes
Any breed restrictions? Yes
Dog bins? Yes
Area for walking dogs? Yes
Static caravans? No
Cost of static?
Mobile caravans? Yes
Cost of mobile? From £4.00 - £6.50 per person per night
Tents? Yes
Cost of tent pitch? From £4.00 - £6.50 per person per night
Electricity at the pitch? Yes
Showers? Yes
Onsite Entertainment? Yes
Opening times? May - End September
Comments: No dangerous breeds, dogs must be kept on a lead. There is a childrens playground on site.

Black Knowl Caravan Club Site

Address: Aldridge Hill, Brockenhurst, Hampshire SO42 7QD
Telephone: 01590 623600
Website: www.caravanclub.co.uk
Extra charge for dogs? No
Any breed restrictions? No
Dog bins? Yes
Area for walking dogs? Off Site
Static caravans? No
Cost of static?
Mobile caravans? Yes
Cost of mobile? From £15.60 - £19.60 per pitch per night for 2 people
Tents? No
Cost of tent pitch?
Electricity at the pitch? Yes
Showers? Yes
Onsite Entertainment? No
Opening times? March - November:

Compton Farm

Address: Brook, Newport, Isle of Wight Hampshire PO30 4HF
Telephone: 01983 740215
Website:
Extra charge for dogs? No
Any breed restrictions? No
Dog bins? Yes
Area for walking dogs? Off Site
Static caravans? Yes
Cost of static? From £200.00 - £420.00

per week

Mobile caravans? No

Cost of mobile?

Tents? Yes

Cost of tent pitch? From £6.50 - £7.50 per adult per night £3.00 - £3.50 per child per night

Electricity at the pitch? No

Showers? Yes

Onsite Entertainment? No

Opening times? May - September

Croft Cottage Camping

Address: Godshill (New Forest), Fordingbridge, Hampshire SP6 2LE

Telephone: 01425 657955

Website:

Extra charge for dogs? No

Any breed restrictions? No

Dog bins? No

Area for walking dogs? Yes

Static caravans? No

Cost of static?

Mobile caravans? Yes

Cost of mobile? From £5.00 per pitch per night + £5.00 per adult

Tents? Yes

Cost of tent pitch?

Electricity at the pitch? Yes

Showers? Yes

Onsite Entertainment? Sports Facilities

Opening times? Weekends in July, Bank Holidays & 2 weeks at End of July Only

Comments: Maximum 1 dog per pitch. Dogs must be kept on a lead at all times.

Drove Lea Farm Camping & Caravanning

Address: Mill Lane, Titchfield, Fareham, Hampshire PO15 5DX

Telephone: 01329 841864

Website: www.droveleacaravans.co.uk

Extra charge for dogs? No

Any breed restrictions? Yes

Dog bins? No

Area for walking dogs? Off Site

Static caravans? No

Cost of static?

Mobile caravans? Yes

Cost of mobile? From £7.50 per night

Tents? Yes

Cost of tent pitch? From £7.50 per night

Electricity at the pitch? Yes

Showers? No

Onsite Entertainment? No

Opening times? February - November

Comments: No Dangerous Breeds. There is a pub just down the road.

Ellerslie Touring Caravan & Camping Park

Address: Downend Rd, Fareham, Hampshire PO16 8TS

Telephone: 01329 822248

Website:

Extra charge for dogs? Yes

Any breed restrictions? No

Dog bins? No

Area for walking dogs? No

Static caravans? No

Cost of static?

Mobile caravans? Yes

Cost of mobile? From £12.50 per night

Tents? Yes

Cost of tent pitch? From £10.50 per night

Electricity at the pitch? Yes

Showers? Yes

Onsite Entertainment? No

Opening times? 1st April - End October

Fair View Farm

Address: London Road, Stockbridge, Hampshire SO20 6EN

Telephone: 01264 810033

Website:

Extra charge for dogs? No

Any breed restrictions? No

Dog bins? No

Area for walking dogs? Off Site

Static caravans? No

Cost of static?

Mobile caravans? Yes

Cost of mobile? From £8.00 per night

Tents? Yes

Cost of tent pitch? From £6.00 per night

Electricity at the pitch? Yes

Showers? No

Onsite Entertainment? No

Opening times? All Year

Comments: Dog must be kept on a lead at all times.

Fishery Creek Touring Park

Address: 100, Fishery Lane, Hayling Island, Hampshire PO11 9NR

Telephone: 02392 462164

Website: www.fisherycreek.co.uk

Extra charge for dogs? Yes

Any breed restrictions? No

Dog bins? Yes

Area for walking dogs? Yes

Static caravans? No

Cost of static?

Mobile caravans? Yes

Cost of mobile? From £12.00 per night

Tents? Yes

Cost of tent pitch? From £12.00 per night

Electricity at the pitch? Yes

Showers? Yes

Onsite Entertainment? No

Opening times? 1st March - 31st October

Comments: Maximum of 2 dogs

Fleet Farm Camping & Caravan Site

Address: Yew Tree Rd, Hayling Island, Hampshire PO11 0QE

Telephone: 02392 463684

Website:

Extra charge for dogs? Yes

Any breed restrictions? No

Dog bins? Yes

Area for walking dogs? Yes

Static caravans? No

Cost of static?

Mobile caravans? Yes

Cost of mobile? From £21.00 per night with electric

Tents? Yes

Cost of tent pitch? From £15.00 per night

Electricity at the pitch? Yes

Showers? Yes

Onsite Entertainment? No

Opening times? March - November

Comments: Dogs must be kept on a lead at all times.

Folly Farm Touring Caravan Park

Address: Crawley, Winchester, Hampshire SO21 2PH

Telephone: 01962 776486

Website:

Extra charge for dogs? No

Any breed restrictions? No

Dog bins? No

Area for walking dogs? Off Site
Static caravans? No
Cost of static?
Mobile caravans? Yes
Cost of mobile? From £14.00 including electric
Tents? Yes
Cost of tent pitch? From £14.00 including electric
Electricity at the pitch? Yes
Showers? Yes
Onsite Entertainment? No
Opening times? All Year

Forest Edge Holiday Park

Address: 229 Ringwood Road, St Leonards, Ringwood, Hampshire BH24 2SH
Telephone: 01202 872817/ 01590 648331
Website: www.shorefield.co.uk
Extra charge for dogs? Yes
Any breed restrictions? No
Dog bins? Yes
Area for walking dogs? Off Site
Static caravans? Yes
Cost of static? From £169.00 per week
Mobile caravans? Yes
Cost of mobile? From £8.50 - £25.50 per pitch per night
Tents? Yes
Cost of tent pitch? From £8.50 - £25.50 per pitch per night
Electricity at the pitch? Yes
Showers? Yes
Onsite Entertainment? No (But sister site down road does)
Opening times? February - End December

Gorse Farm Caravan Site

Address: Fordingbridge, Hampshire SP6 2JH
Telephone: 01425 653250
Website:
Extra charge for dogs? Yes
Any breed restrictions? No
Dog bins? Yes
Area for walking dogs? Off Site
Static caravans? No
Cost of static?
Mobile caravans? Yes
Cost of mobile? From £9.50 per night for 2 people with electric
Tents? Yes
Cost of tent pitch? From £7.50 for 2 people without electric
Electricity at the pitch? Yes
Showers? Yes
Onsite Entertainment? No
Opening times? All Year

Grange Farm Campsite

Address: Brightstone Bay, Isle of Wight PO30 4DA
Telephone: 01983 740296
Website: www.brighstonebay.fsnet.co.uk
Extra charge for dogs? Yes
Any breed restrictions? Yes
Dog bins? No
Area for walking dogs? Yes
Static caravans? Yes
Cost of static? From £270.00 - £645.00 per week
Mobile caravans? Yes
Cost of mobile? From £12.00 - £21.00 per night
Tents? Yes

Cost of tent pitch? From £12.00 - £14.00 per night

Electricity at the pitch? Yes

Showers? Yes

Onsite Entertainment? No

Opening times? 1st March - 1st November

Comments: Only Small dogs allowed in the Caravans. There are lots of Farm Animals on site. There is a shop on site. They can arrange Ferry deals. Dogs must be kept on a lead on the farm

Green Pastures Farm Touring Park

Address: Whitemoor Lane, Ower, Romsey, Hampshire SO51 6AJ

Telephone: 02380 814444

Website: www.greenpasturesfarm.com

Extra charge for dogs? No

Any breed restrictions? No

Dog bins? No

Area for walking dogs? Yes

Static caravans? No

Cost of static?

Mobile caravans? Yes

Cost of mobile? £15.00 per night

Tents? Yes

Cost of tent pitch? From £12.00 - £20.00 per night

Electricity at the pitch? Yes

Showers? Yes

Onsite Entertainment? No

Opening times? 15th March - 31st October

Comments: Dogs must be kept on a lead on the campsite. There is a Dog Kennelling service available at a cost of £6.00 for up to 4 hours.

Hayling Island Holiday Park

Address: Manor Rd, Hayling Island, Hampshire PO11 0QS

Telephone: 023 9246 5021

Website: www.parkdeanholidays.co.uk

Extra charge for dogs? Yes

Any breed restrictions? No

Dog bins? Yes

Area for walking dogs? Yes

Static caravans? Yes

Cost of static? From £139.00 per week

Mobile caravans? No

Cost of mobile?

Tents? No

Cost of tent pitch?

Electricity at the pitch? No

Showers? No

Onsite Entertainment? Yes

Opening times? 1st March - 31st December

Heathfield Farm Camping Site

Address: Heathfield Road, Freshwater, Isle of Wight, Hampshire PO40 9SH

Telephone: 01983 756756

Website: www.heathfieldcamping.co.uk

Extra charge for dogs? Yes

Any breed restrictions? No

Dog bins? No

Area for walking dogs? Yes

Static caravans? No

Cost of static?

Mobile caravans? Yes

Cost of mobile? From £10.00 -£15.00

Tents? Yes

Cost of tent pitch? From £8.75 - £13.50

Electricity at the pitch? Yes

Showers? Yes

Onsite Entertainment? No

Opening times? 1st May - End Sept

Hill Cottage Farm Camping & Caravan Park

Address: Sandleheath Road, Alderholt, Fordingbridge, Hampshire SP6 3EG

Telephone: 01425 650513

Website: www.hillcottagefarmcampingandcaravanpark.co.uk

Extra charge for dogs? Yes

Any breed restrictions? No

Dog bins? Yes

Area for walking dogs? Yes

Static caravans? No

Cost of static?

Mobile caravans? Yes

Cost of mobile? From £15.00 per night

Tents? Yes

Cost of tent pitch? From £12.00 per night

Electricity at the pitch? Yes

Showers? Yes

Onsite Entertainment? No

Opening times? 1st March - 31st October

Hill Farm Caravan Park

Address: Branches Lane, Sherfield English, Romsey, Hampshire SO51 6FH

Telephone: 01794 340402

Website: www.hillfarmpark.com

Extra charge for dogs? No

Any breed restrictions? No

Dog bins? Yes

Area for walking dogs? Yes

Static caravans? Yes

Cost of static? From £240.00 - £500.00 per week

Mobile caravans? Yes

Cost of mobile? From £14.00 - £36.00 per night

Tents? Yes

Cost of tent pitch? From £14.00 - £36.00 per night

Electricity at the pitch? Yes

Showers? Yes

Onsite Entertainment? No

Opening times? Touring/March - October Statics/February - December

Hoburne Bashley

Address: Sway Rd, New Milton, Hampshire BH25 5QS

Telephone: 01425 612340

Website: www.hoburne.com

Extra charge for dogs? Yes

Any breed restrictions? No

Dog bins? Yes

Area for walking dogs? Yes

Static caravans? No

Cost of static?

Mobile caravans? Yes

Cost of mobile? From £13.50 - £38.00 per night

Tents? No

Cost of tent pitch?

Electricity at the pitch? Yes

Showers? Yes

Onsite Entertainment? Yes

Opening times? All Year (November - March Weekends only)

Comments: Children and Adults entertainment during peak season.

Hollands Wood Caravan & Camping Site

Address: Brockenhurst, Hampshire SO42 7QH

Telephone: 01590 622967

Website: www.forestholidays.co.uk

Extra charge for dogs? Yes

Any breed restrictions? No

Dog bins? Yes
Area for walking dogs? Yes
Static caravans? No
Cost of static?
Mobile caravans? Yes
Cost of mobile? From £12.50 per night per pitch for 2 people
Tents? Yes
Cost of tent pitch? From £12.50 per night per pitch for 2 people
Electricity at the pitch? Yes
Showers? Yes
Onsite Entertainment? No
Opening times? 6th March - 28th September
Comments: There are Dog Showers on site. Camping and Caravanning Club Members & Forest Experience Cardholders will receive a £3.00 per night discount.

Holmsley Caravan & Camping Site

Address: Forest Road, Holmsley (New Forest), Christchurch, Hampshire BH23 7EQ
Telephone: 01425 674502
Website: www.forestholidays.co.uk
Extra charge for dogs? Yes
Any breed restrictions? No
Dog bins? No
Area for walking dogs? Off Site
Static caravans? No
Cost of static?
Mobile caravans? Yes
Cost of mobile? From £11.80 per pitch for 2 people with electric per night
Tents? Yes
Cost of tent pitch? From £11.80 per pitch for 2 people with electric per night
Electricity at the pitch? Yes
Showers? Yes
Onsite Entertainment? Yes
Opening times? 6th March - 2nd November
Comments: There is a childrens playground on site. Dogs must be kept on a lead at all times.

Hurst View Caravan Park

Address: Lower Pennington Lane, Pennington, Lymington, Hampshire SO41 8AL
Telephone: 01590 671648
Website: www.hurstviewleisure.co.uk
Extra charge for dogs? Yes
Any breed restrictions? Yes
Dog bins? Yes
Area for walking dogs? Yes
Static caravans? Yes
Cost of static? From £220.00 per week
Mobile caravans? Yes
Cost of mobile? From £12.00 per night
Tents? Yes
Cost of tent pitch? From £12.00 per night
Electricity at the pitch? Yes
Showers? Yes
Onsite Entertainment? No
Opening times? All Year
Comments: No Dangerous Breeds.

Kingfisher Caravan Park

Address: Browndown Rd, Lee-On-The-Solent, Hampshire PO13 9UG
Telephone: 02392 502611
Website: www.kingfisher-caravan-park.co.uk
Extra charge for dogs? Yes
Any breed restrictions? No
Dog bins? No
Area for walking dogs? Off Site

Static caravans? Yes

Cost of static? From £215.00 per week

Mobile caravans? Yes

Cost of mobile? From £16.00 for 2 people per night

Tents? Yes

Cost of tent pitch? From £11.00 per night

Electricity at the pitch? Yes

Showers? Yes

Onsite Entertainment? Yes

Opening times? 1st March - 3rd January

Comments: Restaurant and a Bar with disco and live singers at weekends.

Kite Hill Farm Caravan & Camping

Address: Wootton Bridge, Ryde Isle of Wight Hampshire PO33 4LE

Telephone: 01983 880147

Website:

Extra charge for dogs? No

Any breed restrictions? No

Dog bins? No

Area for walking dogs? Yes

Static caravans? No

Cost of static?

Mobile caravans? Yes

Cost of mobile? £4.50 - £5.00 per person per night

Tents? Yes

Cost of tent pitch? £4.50 - £5.00 per person per night

Electricity at the pitch? Yes

Showers? Yes

Onsite Entertainment? No

Opening times? All Year

Landguard Holidays

Address: Landguard Manor Road, Shanklin, Isle of Wight Hampshire PO37 7PJ

Telephone: 0871 6649810

Website: www.park-resorts.com

Extra charge for dogs? Yes

Any breed restrictions? Yes

Dog bins? No

Area for walking dogs? On Park

Static caravans? Yes

Cost of static? From £259.00 per week

Mobile caravans? Yes

Cost of mobile? From £49.00 per week

Tents? Yes

Cost of tent pitch? From £49.00 per week

Electricity at the pitch? Yes

Showers? Yes

Onsite Entertainment? Yes

Opening times? March - October

Comments: Some Dog breeds are restricted please check when booking

Little Paddock

Address: 218, Hurn Rd, Matchams, Ringwood, Hampshire BH24 2BT

Telephone: 01425 470889

Website: www.little-paddock.com

Extra charge for dogs? No

Any breed restrictions? No

Dog bins? No

Area for walking dogs? Off Site

Static caravans? No

Cost of static?

Mobile caravans? Yes

Cost of mobile? From £12.00 per night for 2 people & 2 children

Tents? No

Cost of tent pitch?

Electricity at the pitch? Yes

Showers? Yes

Onsite Entertainment? No

Opening times? All Year

Longbeach Caravan & Camping Site

Address: Lyndhurst, Hampshire SO43 7HH

Telephone: 0131 314 6505

Website: www.forestholidays.co.uk

Extra charge for dogs? Yes

Any breed restrictions? No

Dog bins? Yes

Area for walking dogs? No

Static caravans? No

Cost of static?

Mobile caravans? Yes

Cost of mobile? From £7.30 per night

Tents? Yes

Cost of tent pitch? From £7.30 per night

Electricity at the pitch? No

Showers? No

Onsite Entertainment? No

Opening times? 6th March - 28th September

Lower Hyde Holiday Park

Address: Shanklin, Isle of Wight, Hampshire PO37 7LL

Telephone: 0871 6649810

Website: www.park-resorts.com

Extra charge for dogs? Yes

Any breed restrictions? Yes

Dog bins? No

Area for walking dogs? On Park

Static caravans? Yes

Cost of static? From £129.00 per week

Mobile caravans? Yes

Cost of mobile? From £49.00 per week

Tents? Yes

Cost of tent pitch? From £49.00 per week

Electricity at the pitch? Yes

Showers? Yes

Onsite Entertainment? Yes

Opening times? March - October

Comments: Some Dog breeds are restricted please check when booking

Lytton Lawn Touring Park

Address: New Lane, Milford On Sea, Lymington, Hampshire SO41 0UQ

Telephone: 01590 648331

Website: www.shorefield.co.uk

Extra charge for dogs? Yes

Any breed restrictions? Yes

Dog bins? Yes

Area for walking dogs? Yes

Static caravans? Yes

Cost of static? From £193.00 per week

Mobile caravans? Yes

Cost of mobile? From £10.50 per night with electric

Tents? Yes

Cost of tent pitch? From £10.50 per night with electric

Electricity at the pitch? Yes

Showers? Yes

Onsite Entertainment? Yes (5 mins away at sister accomodation)

Opening times? February - End December

Martins Farm

Address: Shepherds Road, Bartley, Southampton, Hampshire SO40 2LH

Telephone: 023 80813431

Website: www.martins-farm.com

Extra charge for dogs? No

Any breed restrictions? No

Dog bins? No

Area for walking dogs? Off Site

Static caravans? No

Cost of static?

Mobile caravans? Yes

Cost of mobile? From £8.50 per night
Tents? No
Cost of tent pitch?
Electricity at the pitch? Yes
Showers? No
Onsite Entertainment? No
Opening times? All Year

Matley Wood Caravan & Camping Site

Address: Lymington, Hampshire SO43 7FZ
Telephone: 02380 293144
Website: www.forestholidays.co.uk
Extra charge for dogs? Yes
Any breed restrictions? No
Dog bins? Yes
Area for walking dogs? Off Site
Static caravans? No
Cost of static?
Mobile caravans? Yes
Cost of mobile? From £9.80 per night
Tents? Yes
Cost of tent pitch? From £9.80 per night
Electricity at the pitch? No
Showers? No
Onsite Entertainment? No
Opening times? 6th March - 28th September

Meon Springs Fly Fishery

Address: Whitewool Farm, Petersfield, Hampshire GU32 1HW
Telephone: 01730 823134
Website: www.meonsprings.com
Extra charge for dogs? No
Any breed restrictions? No
Dog bins? No
Area for walking dogs? Yes
Static caravans? No
Cost of static?
Mobile caravans? Yes
Cost of mobile? From £5.00 per person per night
Tents? Yes
Cost of tent pitch? From £5.00 per person per night
Electricity at the pitch? Yes
Showers? No
Onsite Entertainment? Fishery, Clay Pigeon Shooting
Opening times? All Year

Minstead Manor Farm

Address: Emery Down (New Forest), Lyndhurst, Hampshire SO43 7GA
Telephone: 02380 283706
Website: www.campingandcaravanning club.co.uk
Extra charge for dogs? No
Any breed restrictions? No
Dog bins? No
Area for walking dogs? Yes
Static caravans? No
Cost of static?
Mobile caravans? Yes
Cost of mobile? From £10.00 per pitch per night
Tents? Yes
Cost of tent pitch? From £10.00 per pitch per night
Electricity at the pitch? Yes
Showers? Yes
Onsite Entertainment? No
Opening times? Easter - End October

Morn Hill Caravan Club Site

Address: Morn Hill, Winchester, Hampshire SO21 1HL
Telephone: 01962 869877
Website:

Extra charge for dogs? No
Any breed restrictions? No
Dog bins? Yes
Area for walking dogs? Yes
Static caravans? No
Cost of static?
Mobile caravans? Yes
Cost of mobile? From £3.40 per person per night
Tents? Yes
Cost of tent pitch? From £3.00 per person per night
Electricity at the pitch? Yes
Showers? Yes
Onsite Entertainment? No
Opening times? March - November

Mount Pleasant Caravan & Camping Park

Address: Matchams Lane, Hurn, Christchurch, Hampshire BH23 6AW
Telephone: 01202 475474
Website: www.mount-pleasant-cc.co.uk
Extra charge for dogs? Yes
Any breed restrictions? No
Dog bins? Yes
Area for walking dogs? Yes
Static caravans? No
Cost of static?
Mobile caravans? Yes
Cost of mobile? From £12.00 - £16.00 per night
Tents? No
Cost of tent pitch?
Electricity at the pitch? Yes
Showers? Yes
Onsite Entertainment? No
Opening times? 1st March - 1st November

Nodes Point Holiday Park

Address: St Helens, Ryde, Isle of Wight, Hampshire PO33 1YA
Telephone: 0871 6649758
Website: www.park-resorts.com
Extra charge for dogs? Yes
Any breed restrictions? Yes
Dog bins? No
Area for walking dogs? On Park
Static caravans? Yes
Cost of static? From £259.00 per week
Mobile caravans? Yes
Cost of mobile? From £49.00 per week
Tents? Yes
Cost of tent pitch? From £49.00 per week
Electricity at the pitch? Yes
Showers? Yes
Onsite Entertainment? Yes
Opening times? March - October
Comments: Some Dog breeds are restricted please check when booking

Oakdene Forrest Park

Address: St. Leonards, Ringwood, Hampshire BH24 2RZ
Telephone: 01590 648331
Website: www.shorefield.co.uk
Extra charge for dogs? Yes
Any breed restrictions? Yes
Dog bins? Yes
Area for walking dogs? Yes
Static caravans? Yes
Cost of static? From £220.00 per week
Mobile caravans? No
Cost of mobile?
Tents? No
Cost of tent pitch?
Electricity at the pitch? No
Showers? No
Onsite Entertainment? Yes (Peak Holidays)

Opening times? All Year

Comments: No Dangerous Breeds. Dogs must be kept on a lead.

Ocknell Caravan & Camping Site

Address: Lyndhurst, Hampshire SO43 7HH

Telephone: 0131 314 6505

Website: www.forestholidays.co.uk

Extra charge for dogs? Yes

Any breed restrictions? No

Dog bins? Yes

Area for walking dogs? Yes

Static caravans? No

Cost of static?

Mobile caravans? Yes

Cost of mobile? From £7.30 per person per night

Tents? Yes

Cost of tent pitch? From £7.30 per person per night

Electricity at the pitch? No

Showers? No

Onsite Entertainment? No

Opening times? 6th March - 28th September

OrchardsHoliday Caravan & Camping Park

Address: Newbridge, Yarmouth, Isle of Wight Hampshire PO41 0TS

Telephone: 01983 531331

Website: www.orchards-holiday-park.co.uk

Extra charge for dogs? Yes

Any breed restrictions? No

Dog bins? No

Area for walking dogs? Yes

Static caravans? Yes

Cost of static? From £225.00 per week

Mobile caravans? Yes

Cost of mobile? From £15.00 per night for 2 Adults

Tents? Yes

Cost of tent pitch? From £15.00 per night for 2 Adults

Electricity at the pitch? Yes

Showers? Yes

Onsite Entertainment? No

Opening times? All Year

Oven Camp Site

Address: Manor Rd, Hayling Island, Hampshire PO11 0QX

Telephone: 023 9246 4695

Website: www.haylingcampsites.co.uk

Extra charge for dogs? Yes

Any breed restrictions? No

Dog bins? Yes

Area for walking dogs? Yes

Static caravans? No

Cost of static?

Mobile caravans? Yes

Cost of mobile? From £12.50 per night

Tents? Yes

Cost of tent pitch? From £12.50 per night

Electricity at the pitch? Yes

Showers? Yes

Onsite Entertainment? Yes

Opening times? 1st March - 31st October

Comments: There is a magic show and disco for the children once a week.

Red Shoot Camping Park

Address: Linwood, Ringwood, Hampshire BH24 3QT

Telephone: 023 8045 7462

Website: www.redshoot-campingpark.com

Extra charge for dogs? Yes

Any breed restrictions? No
Dog bins? Yes
Area for walking dogs? Off Site
Static caravans? No
Cost of static?
Mobile caravans? Yes
Cost of mobile? From £15.00 per night
Tents? Yes
Cost of tent pitch? From £15.00 per night
Electricity at the pitch? Yes
Showers? Yes
Onsite Entertainment? Yes
Opening times? 1st March - 31st October

Comments: There is a pub on site, 2 beer festivals a year and live music on some evenings. During some months there is a 20% discount. No dangerous breeds.

Riverside Holidays

Address: Satchell Lane, Hamble, Southampton, Hampshire SO31 4HR
Telephone: 023 9281 6413
Website: www.riversideholidays.co.uk
Extra charge for dogs? Yes
Any breed restrictions? No
Dog bins? No
Area for walking dogs? Yes
Static caravans? No
Cost of static?
Mobile caravans? Yes
Cost of mobile? From £14.00 per night
Tents? Yes
Cost of tent pitch? From £12.00 per night
Electricity at the pitch? Yes
Showers? Yes
Onsite Entertainment? No
Opening times? 1st March - End October

Rookesbury Park Caravan Club Site

Address: Hundred Acres Rd, Wickham, Fareham, Hampshire PO17 6JR
Telephone: 01329 834085
Website: www.thecaravanclub.co.uk
Extra charge for dogs? No
Any breed restrictions? No
Dog bins? Yes
Area for walking dogs? Yes
Static caravans? No
Cost of static?
Mobile caravans? Yes
Cost of mobile? From £12.20 - £18.10 per pitch for 2 people per night with electric
Tents? No
Cost of tent pitch?
Electricity at the pitch? Yes
Showers? Yes
Onsite Entertainment? No
Opening times? End March - End October

Rookley Country Park

Address: Rookley, Isle of Wight, Hampshire PO38 3LU
Telephone: 01983 721606
Website: www.islandviewholidays.co.uk
Extra charge for dogs? Yes
Any breed restrictions? No
Dog bins? No
Area for walking dogs? No
Static caravans? Yes
Cost of static? From £190.00 per week
Mobile caravans? No
Cost of mobile?
Tents? No
Cost of tent pitch?
Electricity at the pitch? Yes
Showers? No

Onsite Entertainment? Yes
Opening times? All Year

Roundhill Caravan & Camping Site

Address: Brockenhurst, Hampshire SO42 7QL

Telephone: 0131 314 6505

Website: www.forestholidays.co.uk

Extra charge for dogs? Yes
Any breed restrictions? No
Dog bins? No
Area for walking dogs? Off Site
Static caravans? No
Cost of static?
Mobile caravans? Yes
Cost of mobile? From £8.00 - £17.00
Tents? Yes
Cost of tent pitch? From £8.00 - £17.00
Electricity at the pitch? No
Showers? Yes
Onsite Entertainment? No
Opening times? 6th March - 28th September

Comments: Maximum of 3 dogs.

Rowlands Wait Touring Park

Address: Rye Hill, Bere Regis, Hampshire BH20 7LP

Telephone: 01929 472727

Website: www.rowlandswait.co.uk

Extra charge for dogs? Yes
Any breed restrictions? No
Dog bins? No
Area for walking dogs? Yes
Static caravans? No
Cost of static?
Mobile caravans? Yes
Cost of mobile? From £11.00 - £16.00 per night
Tents? Yes
Cost of tent pitch? From £11.00 - £16.00 per night
Electricity at the pitch? Yes
Showers? Yes
Onsite Entertainment? No
Opening times? 15th March - 31st October

Comments: Open in winter by arrangement

Rushcroft Farm Camping Park

Address: Station Approach, Sway, Lymington, Hampshire SO41 6EE

Telephone: 07850 258790

Website: www.certificatedsites.co.uk

Extra charge for dogs? No
Any breed restrictions? Yes
Dog bins? No
Area for walking dogs? Yes
Static caravans? No
Cost of static?
Mobile caravans? Yes
Cost of mobile? From £12.00 per night
Tents? Yes
Cost of tent pitch? From £10.00 per night
Electricity at the pitch? Yes
Showers? Yes
Onsite Entertainment? No
Opening times? All Year

Comments: No dangerous breeds

Sandy Balls Holiday Centre

Address: Godshill, Fordingbridge, Hampshire SP6 2JY

Telephone: 01425 653042

Website: www.sandy-balls.co.uk

Extra charge for dogs? Yes
Any breed restrictions? No
Dog bins? Yes
Area for walking dogs? Yes

Static caravans? Yes
Cost of static? From £75.00 for short break
Mobile caravans? Yes
Cost of mobile? From £10.00 per night
Tents? Yes
Cost of tent pitch? From £10.00 per night
Electricity at the pitch? Yes
Showers? Yes
Onsite Entertainment? Yes
Opening times? All Year

Setthorns Caravan & Camping Site

Address: New Milton, Hampshire BH25 5UA
Telephone: 0131 314 6505
Website: www.forestholidays.co.uk
Extra charge for dogs? Yes
Any breed restrictions? No
Dog bins? Yes
Area for walking dogs? Yes
Static caravans? No
Cost of static?
Mobile caravans? Yes
Cost of mobile? From £7.50 - £16.00 per night
Tents? Yes
Cost of tent pitch? From £7.50 - £16.00 per night
Electricity at the pitch? Yes
Showers? No
Onsite Entertainment? No
Opening times? All Year
Comments: Dogs must be kept on a lead

Shamba Holidays

Address: 230, Ringwood Rd, St. Leonards, Ringwood, Hampshire BH24 2SB
Telephone: 01202 873302
Website: www.shambaholidays.co.uk
Extra charge for dogs? Yes
Any breed restrictions? No
Dog bins? Yes
Area for walking dogs? Yes
Static caravans? No
Cost of static?
Mobile caravans? Yes
Cost of mobile? From £16.00 - £26.00 per night for 2 people
Tents? Yes
Cost of tent pitch? From £16.00 - £26.00 per night for 2 people
Electricity at the pitch? Yes
Showers? Yes
Onsite Entertainment? Yes
Opening times? March - October
Comments: Dogs must be kept on a lead. There is a swimming pool and a club house on site.

Shorefield Country Park

Address: Milford on Sea, Hampshire SO14 0LH
Telephone: 01590 642513
Website: www.shorefield.co.uk
Extra charge for dogs? Yes
Any breed restrictions? Yes
Dog bins? Yes
Area for walking dogs? Yes
Static caravans? Yes
Cost of static?
Mobile caravans?
Cost of mobile?
Tents?
Cost of tent pitch?
Electricity at the pitch?
Showers?
Onsite Entertainment? All Year

Opening times?

Comments: Maximum of 2 dogs No dangerous breeds.

Sir Walter Tyrrell Campsite

Address: Brook, Lyndhurst, Hampshire SO43 7HD

Telephone: 023 80813170

Website:

Extra charge for dogs? Yes

Any breed restrictions? No

Dog bins? No

Area for walking dogs? Yes

Static caravans? No

Cost of static?

Mobile caravans? Yes

Cost of mobile? From £13.00 per night with electric

Tents? Yes

Cost of tent pitch? From £15.00 per night

Electricity at the pitch? Yes

Showers? No

Onsite Entertainment? Yes

Opening times? All Year

Comments: There is a quiz every Friday evening.

Solent View Camping

Address: New Forest, Lower Pennington Lane, Lymington, Hampshire SO41 8AL

Telephone: 01590 671648

Website: www.hurstviewleisure.co.uk

Extra charge for dogs? No

Any breed restrictions? No

Dog bins? No

Area for walking dogs? Off Site

Static caravans? Yes

Cost of static? From £210.00 per week

Mobile caravans? Yes

Cost of mobile? From £15.00 per night

Tents? Yes

Cost of tent pitch? From £15.00 per night

Electricity at the pitch? Yes

Showers? Yes

Onsite Entertainment? Yes

Opening times? All Year

Comments: There is a children's playground on site. Dogs must be kept on a lead at all times. Maximum 2 dogs.

Southland Camping Park

Address: Newchurch, Nr. Sandown, Isle of Wight, Hampshire PO36 0LZ

Telephone: 01983 867663

Website: www.southland.co.uk

Extra charge for dogs? Yes

Any breed restrictions? Yes

Dog bins? No

Area for walking dogs? Yes

Static caravans? No

Cost of static?

Mobile caravans? Yes

Cost of mobile? From £5.60 - £8.50 per adult

Tents? Yes

Cost of tent pitch?

Electricity at the pitch? Yes

Showers? Yes

Onsite Entertainment? No

Opening times? 1st April - 30th Sept

Comments: Some Dog breeds are restricted so please check when booking

Southsea Leisure Park

Address: Melville Rd, Southsea, Hampshire PO4 9TB

Telephone: 0239273 5070

Website: www.southsealeisurepark.com
Extra charge for dogs? Yes
Any breed restrictions? No
Dog bins? Yes
Area for walking dogs? Off Site
Static caravans? Yes
Cost of static? From £290.00 per week
Mobile caravans? Yes
Cost of mobile? From £17.00 per night with electric
Tents? Yes
Cost of tent pitch? From £10.00 per night
Electricity at the pitch? Yes
Showers? Yes
Onsite Entertainment? Yes
Opening times? All Year

The Caravan Club Ltd

Address: Mornhill Caravan Park, Alresford Rd, Winchester, Hampshire SO21 1HJ
Telephone: 01962 869877
Website: www.thecaravanclub.co.uk
Extra charge for dogs? No
Any breed restrictions? No
Dog bins? Yes
Area for walking dogs? Yes
Static caravans? No
Cost of static?
Mobile caravans? Yes
Cost of mobile? From £18.40 per pitch per night for 2 people
Tents? Yes
Cost of tent pitch? From £18.40 per pitch per night for 2 people
Electricity at the pitch? Yes
Showers? Yes
Onsite Entertainment? No
Opening times? End March - End October

The Caravan Club Ltd

Address: New Forest Centenary Site, Forest Road, Bransgore, Christchurch, Hampshire BH23 8EB
Telephone: 01425 673638
Website: www.thecaravanclub.co.uk
Extra charge for dogs? No
Any breed restrictions? No
Dog bins? Yes
Area for walking dogs? Yes
Static caravans? No
Cost of static?
Mobile caravans? Yes
Cost of mobile? From £4.90 - £8.30 per pitch per night & £5.00 - £6.50 per adult per night
Tents? No
Cost of tent pitch?
Electricity at the pitch? Yes
Showers? Yes
Onsite Entertainment? No
Opening times? March - October

The Deers Hut Public House

Address: Griggs Green, Liphook, Hampshire GU30 7PD
Telephone: 01428 724406
Website: www.deers-hut.co.uk
Extra charge for dogs? No
Any breed restrictions? Yes
Dog bins? No
Area for walking dogs? Yes
Static caravans? No
Cost of static?
Mobile caravans? Yes
Cost of mobile? From £11.00 per night
Tents? Yes
Cost of tent pitch? From £8.50 - £10.50 per night
Electricity at the pitch? Yes
Showers? Yes

Onsite Entertainment? Yes

Opening times? All Year

Comments: No Dangerous Breeds. Dogs must be kept on a lead. They are a pub.

The White Horse Inn

Address: Petersfield, Hampshire GU32 1DA

Telephone: 01420 588387

Website: www.stewartinns.co.uk

Extra charge for dogs? No

Any breed restrictions? No

Dog bins? No

Area for walking dogs? Yes

Static caravans? No

Cost of static?

Mobile caravans? Yes

Cost of mobile? From £12.00 per pitch per night

Tents? Yes

Cost of tent pitch? From £12.00 per person per night

Electricity at the pitch? No

Showers? No

Onsite Entertainment? Pub & Restaurant

Opening times? All Year

Thorness Bay Holiday Park

Address: Thorness, Nr Cowes, Isle of Wight, Hampshire PO31 8NJ

Telephone: 0871 6649758

Website: www.park-resorts.com

Extra charge for dogs? Yes

Any breed restrictions? Yes

Dog bins? No

Area for walking dogs? On Park

Static caravans? Yes

Cost of static? From £169.00

Mobile caravans? Yes

Cost of mobile? From £49.00 per week

Tents? Yes

Cost of tent pitch? From £49.00 per week

Electricity at the pitch? Yes

Showers? Yes

Onsite Entertainment? Yes

Opening times? March - October

Comments: Some Dog breeds are restricted please check when booking

Tom's Field

Address: Godshill Pottery, The Ridge, Fordingbridge, Hampshire SP6 2LN

Telephone: 07759 474158

Website: www.tomsfield.com

Extra charge for dogs? No

Any breed restrictions? No

Dog bins? Yes

Area for walking dogs? Yes

Static caravans? No

Cost of static?

Mobile caravans? No

Cost of mobile?

Tents? Yes

Cost of tent pitch? From £5.00 per pitch & £5.00 per adult per night

Electricity at the pitch? No

Showers? No

Onsite Entertainment? No

Opening times? Weekends only from 1st July - End August and Bank Holidays from May

Village Way Caravan & Camping

Address: Newport Road, Sandown, Isle of Wight Hampshire PO36 0PJ

Telephone: 01983 863279

Website: www.isleofwight.com

Extra charge for dogs? Yes

Any breed restrictions? No

Dog bins? No

Area for walking dogs? Yes
Static caravans? Yes
Cost of static? From £170.00 per week
Mobile caravans? Yes
Cost of mobile? From £4.50 - £6.00 per person
Tents? Yes
Cost of tent pitch? From £4.50 - £6.00 per person
Electricity at the pitch? Yes (£3.00 per day)
Showers? Yes
Onsite Entertainment? Fishing on site
Opening times? All Year

Wareham Forest Tourist Park

Address: Bere Road, North Trigon, Wareham, Hampshire BH20 7NZ
Telephone: 01929 551393
Website: www.warehamforest.co.uk
Extra charge for dogs? Yes
Any breed restrictions? No
Dog bins? Yes
Area for walking dogs? Yes
Static caravans? No
Cost of static?
Mobile caravans? Yes
Cost of mobile? From £9.50 - £16.25 + Adults £2.75 - £4.50 per night
Tents? Yes
Cost of tent pitch? From £7.00 - £14.00 per night
Electricity at the pitch? Yes
Showers? Yes
Onsite Entertainment? No
Opening times? Caravan All Year/ Camping Closed Winter depending on Weather

Waverley Park

Address: Old Road, East Cowes, Isle of Wight Hampshire PO32 6AW
Telephone: 01983 293452
Website: www.waverley-park.co.uk
Extra charge for dogs? Yes
Any breed restrictions? Yes
Dog bins? No
Area for walking dogs? Yes
Static caravans? Yes
Cost of static? From £150.00 - £800.00 per week
Mobile caravans? Yes
Cost of mobile? From £5.00 per adult £2.50 per child per night
Tents? Yes
Cost of tent pitch? From £5.00 per adult £2.50 per child per night
Electricity at the pitch? Yes (£3.00 per day)
Showers? Yes
Onsite Entertainment? Yes
Opening times? March - October
Comments: Dogs must be kept on a lead. Dogs must not be left unattended in caravans.

White Cliff Bay Holiday Park

Address: Hillway Road, Bembridge, Isle of Wight Hampshire PO35 5PL
Telephone: 01983 872671
Website: www.whitecliff-bay.com
Extra charge for dogs? Yes
Any breed restrictions? No
Dog bins? No
Area for walking dogs? Yes
Static caravans? No
Cost of static?
Mobile caravans? Yes
Cost of mobile? From £10.50 - £14.00 for 2 adults
Tents? Yes

Cost of tent pitch? From £10.50 - £14.00 for 2 adults
Electricity at the pitch? Yes
Showers? Yes
Onsite Entertainment? No
Opening times? Mid March - Early November
Comments: Dogs must be kept on a lead.

Woolsbridge Manor Farm Caravan Park

Address: Ringwood, Hampshire BH21 6RA
Telephone: 01202 826369
Website: www.woolsbridgemanorcaravanpark.co.uk
Extra charge for dogs? Yes
Any breed restrictions? No
Dog bins? No
Area for walking dogs? Yes
Static caravans? No
Cost of static?
Mobile caravans? Yes
Cost of mobile? From £15.50 - £22.50 per night
Tents? Yes
Cost of tent pitch? From £15.50 - £22.50 per night
Electricity at the pitch? Yes
Showers? Yes
Onsite Entertainment? No
Opening times? 1st March - End October
Comments: Dogs must be kept on a lead.

Wyke Down Touring Caravan & Camping Park

Address: Picket Piece, Andover, Hampshire SP11 6LX
Telephone: 01264 352048
Website: www.wykedown.co.uk
Extra charge for dogs? Yes
Any breed restrictions? No
Dog bins? Yes
Area for walking dogs? Off Site
Static caravans? No
Cost of static?
Mobile caravans? Yes
Cost of mobile? From £16.00 per night with electric and water for 2 people
Tents? Yes
Cost of tent pitch? From £12.00 per night for 2 people
Electricity at the pitch? Yes
Showers? Yes
Onsite Entertainment? Pub & Restaurant
Opening times? January - December
Comments: No dangerous breeds

Sunnydale Farm Campsite

Address: Sunnydale Farm, Grange Rd, Netley, Southampton, Hampshire SO31 8GD
Telephone: 02380 457462
Website: www.sunnydalefarm.co.uk
Extra charge for dogs? Yes
Any breed restrictions? No
Dog bins? Yes
Area for walking dogs? Yes
Static caravans? No
Cost of static?
Mobile caravans? Yes
Cost of mobile? From £13.00 per night
Tents? Yes
Cost of tent pitch? From £13.00 per night
Electricity at the pitch? Yes
Showers? Yes
Onsite Entertainment? No

Opening times? All Year

Comments: Dogs must be kept on a lead.

The Camping & Caravanning Club

Address: Chichester Site, Main Rd, Southbourne, Emsworth, Hampshire PO10 8JH

Telephone: 01243 373202

Website: www.thecampingandcaravanningclub.co.uk

Extra charge for dogs? No

Any breed restrictions? No

Dog bins? Off Site

Area for walking dogs? Off Site

Static caravans? No

Cost of static?

Mobile caravans? Yes

Cost of mobile? Prices vary between members & non members

Tents? Yes

Cost of tent pitch? Prices vary between members & non members

Brampton Holidays Adults Only

Address: Little Brampton, Madley, Herefordshire HR2 9LX

Telephone: 01981 251308

Website: www.bramptonhols.co.uk

Extra charge for dogs? No

Any breed restrictions? No

Dog bins? Yes

Area for walking dogs? Yes. Also on golf course on lead

Static caravans? No

Cost of static?

Mobile caravans? Yes

Cost of mobile? £12.50

Tents? No

Cost of tent pitch?

Electricity at the pitch? Yes

Showers? Yes

Onsite Entertainment? 9 hole golf coarse. Fishing and café on site

Opening times? All Year

Comments: Also have holiday homes that allow dogs and children

Broadmeadow Caravan Park

Address: Broadmeadows. Ross on Wye. Herefordshire. HR9 7BW

Telephone: 01989 768076

Website: www.broadmeadow.info.com

Extra charge for dogs? £1.50

Any breed restrictions? No

Dog bins? Yes

Area for walking dogs? Yes

Static caravans? No

Cost of static?

Mobile caravans? Yes

Cost of mobile? £12.50

Tents? Yes

Cost of tent pitch? £9.00

Electricity at the pitch? Yes

Showers? Yes

Onsite Entertainment? No

Opening times? Easter - End September

Millpond

Address: Little Tarrington. Hereford. HR1 4JA

Telephone: 01432 890243

Website: www.campingandcaravaning club.co.uk

Extra charge for dogs? No

Any breed restrictions? No

Dog bins? Yes

Area for walking dogs? Yes. Have to be on lead

Static caravans? No

Cost of static?

Mobile caravans? Yes

Cost of mobile? From £16.10 - £24.10

Tents? Yes

Cost of tent pitch? From £6.60 - £7.60

Electricity at the pitch? Yes. Extra £2.90

Showers? Yes

Onsite Entertainment? No

Opening times? 1st March - End October

Comments: Fishing lake.

Cuckoos Corner Camp Site

Address: Moreton-on-Lugg, Hereford, Herefordshire HR4 8AH

Telephone: 01432 760234
Website:
Extra charge for dogs? No
Any breed restrictions? No
Dog bins? No
Area for walking dogs? Public foot path leading to fields
Static caravans? No
Cost of static?
Mobile caravans? Yes
Cost of mobile? From £10.00 inc elec
Tents? Yes
Cost of tent pitch? From £8.00 inc elec
Electricity at the pitch? Yes
Showers? Yes
Onsite Entertainment? Pool table and broadband.
Opening times? All year except January

Doward Park Camp Site

Address: Gt Doward. Simmons Yat West, Ross on Wye Herefordshire, HR9 6BP
Telephone: 01600 890438
Website: www.dowardpark.co.uk
Extra charge for dogs? Yes
Any breed restrictions? No
Dog bins? No
Area for walking dogs? Not on site, but on top of woods
Static caravans? No
Cost of static?
Mobile caravans? No
Cost of mobile?
Tents? Yes
Cost of tent pitch? £12.50-£16.50
Electricity at the pitch? Yes
Showers? Yes
Onsite Entertainment? No
Opening times? Easter - October

Great Hall Camping

Address: Welsh Newton Common, Monmouth, Herefordshire NP25 5RR
Telephone: 01989 770473
Website:
Extra charge for dogs? No
Any breed restrictions? No
Dog bins? No
Area for walking dogs? Yes. Up lane foot path to the meadow
Static caravans? No
Cost of static?
Mobile caravans? Yes
Cost of mobile? £7.00 + £2.00 hook up
Tents? Yes
Cost of tent pitch? £5.00 + £2.00 Hook up
Electricity at the pitch? Yes
Showers? Yes
Onsite Entertainment? No
Opening times? Easter - End September

Haywood Farm Camping & Caravanning Park

Address: Gorsley, Ross-on-Wye, Herefordshire HR9 7EB
Telephone: 01989 720453
Website: http://www.btinternet.com/~yeatesprint/ross/haywood.html
Extra charge for dogs? Yes
Any breed restrictions? No
Dog bins? No
Area for walking dogs? Woodlands.
Static caravans? No
Cost of static?
Mobile caravans? Yes
Cost of mobile? £14.50

Tents? Yes

Cost of tent pitch? From £8.50 - £120.50

Electricity at the pitch? Yes

Showers? Yes

Onsite Entertainment? No

Opening times? March - End November

Home Farm

Address: Bircher, Leominster, Herefordshire HR6 0AX

Telephone: 01568 780525

Website: www.homefarmaccomadation.co.uk

Extra charge for dogs? Yes

Any breed restrictions? No

Dog bins? No

Area for walking dogs? Yes. 3 acres

Static caravans? No

Cost of static?

Mobile caravans? Yes

Cost of mobile? £13.00 inc elec

Tents? Yes

Cost of tent pitch? From £8.00

Electricity at the pitch? Yes

Showers? Yes

Onsite Entertainment? No

Opening times? All year round

Comments: Contact Mrs Dawn Brazier

Hollybush camp site

Address: Ols Brecon Road. Hay on Wye. Herefordshire, HR3 5PS

Telephone: 01497 847371

Website: www.hollybushcamping.co.uk

Extra charge for dogs? No

Any breed restrictions? No

Dog bins? No

Area for walking dogs? On leads. Yes

Static caravans? Yes

Cost of static? Weekly £55.00

Mobile caravans? Yes

Cost of mobile? From £6.00 Children £3.00

Tents? Yes

Cost of tent pitch? From £6.00 Children £3.00

Electricity at the pitch? Hook up £2.00 per night

Showers? Yes

Onsite Entertainment? Yes. In the pub adjoining the camp site

Opening times? All year round

Comments: Pub is dog friendly

Old Mill Camp Site

Address: Old Mill, Craswell, Hereford, Herefordshire HR2 0PN

Telephone: 01981 510226

Website:

Extra charge for dogs? No

Any breed restrictions? N

Dog bins? No

Area for walking dogs? Yes on the farm on a lead

Static caravans? No

Cost of static?

Mobile caravans? Yes

Cost of mobile? £5.00 per night

Tents? Yes

Cost of tent pitch? £5.00 per night

Electricity at the pitch? No

Showers? No

Onsite Entertainment? No

Opening times? Easter - October

Penlan Caravan Park

Address: Penlan, Brilley, Hay-on-Wye, Herefordshire HR3 6JW

Telephone: 01497 831485

Website: www.penlancaravanpark.co.uk

Extra charge for dogs? Yes

Any breed restrictions? No

Dog bins? No

Area for walking dogs? Yes. On the farm

Static caravans? No

Cost of static?

Mobile caravans? Yes

Cost of mobile? £13.00

Tents? Yes

Cost of tent pitch? £6.00 adult £4.00 under 12. Free under 5

Electricity at the pitch? Yes. £2.50 per night

Showers? Yes

Onsite Entertainment? No

Opening times? Easter - End October

Pearl Lake

Address: Shobdon. Leominster. Herefordshire. HR6 9NQ

Telephone: 01568 708326

Website: www.bestparks.co.uk

Extra charge for dogs? Yes

Any breed restrictions? No

Dog bins? Yes

Area for walking dogs? Yes.

Static caravans? No

Cost of static?

Mobile caravans? Yes

Cost of mobile? From £15.00 - £20.00 inc elec

Tents? Yes

Cost of tent pitch? From £15.00 - £20.00 inc elec

Electricity at the pitch? Yes

Showers? Yes

Onsite Entertainment? Yes. Bar & restaurant

Opening times? 1st March - End November

Comments: Fishing, 9 hole golf course & crown bowls.

Poston Mill Park

Address: Peterchurch. Goldern Valley. Hereford. Herefordshire. HR2 0SF

Telephone: 01981 550225

Website: www.bestparks.co.uk

Extra charge for dogs? Yes

Any breed restrictions? No

Dog bins? Yes

Area for walking dogs? 10 acre Dog Walk. Doggy shower

Static caravans? No

Cost of static?

Mobile caravans? Yes

Cost of mobile? From £15.00 - £20.00 inc elec

Tents? Yes

Cost of tent pitch? From £15.00 - £20.00 inc elec

Electricity at the pitch? Yes

Showers? Yes

Onsite Entertainment? Children's Play Area. Snooker table. hole 'Pitch 'n putt'

Opening times? All year

Comments: Riverside walk and nature trails. Local Farm Shop offering home produced meats & eggs

Pixley End Caravan & Camp Site

Address: Trumpet, Ledbury, Herefordshire HR8 2RA

Telephone: 07968 160168

Website: www.pixleyend.com

Extra charge for dogs? No

Any breed restrictions? No

Dog bins? Yes

Area for walking dogs? Yes

Static caravans? No
Cost of static?
Mobile caravans? Yes
Cost of mobile? From £12.00 - £19.00
Tents? Yes
Cost of tent pitch? From £7.50 - £12.00
Electricity at the pitch? Yes
Showers? Yes
Onsite Entertainment? No
Opening times? March - End October

Pound Camping

Address: The Pound, Whitney On Wye, Hay-on-Wye, Herefordshire HR3 6EH
Telephone: 01497 831391
Website: www.thepoundbandb.co.uk
Extra charge for dogs? No
Any breed restrictions? No
Dog bins? No
Area for walking dogs? Yes
Static caravans? No
Cost of static?
Mobile caravans? Yes
Cost of mobile? £5.00 per person per night
Tents? Yes
Cost of tent pitch? £5.00 per person per night
Electricity at the pitch? No
Showers? Yes
Onsite Entertainment? Pub on site, plus further development.
Opening times? All year
Comments: £5.00 English breakfast or vegetarian

Rowley Farm

Address: Rowley Farm, Leominster, Herefordshire HR6 0EX
Telephone: 01568 616123
Website: www.rowleyholidaypark.co.uk
Extra charge for dogs? No
Any breed restrictions? No
Dog bins? NO
Area for walking dogs? Yes. Fields and lots of walks
Static caravans? No
Cost of static?
Mobile caravans? Yes
Cost of mobile? £9.00
Tents? Yes
Cost of tent pitch? £4.00
Electricity at the pitch? Yes
Showers? Yes
Onsite Entertainment? No
Opening times? All Year

Shobdon Airfield Caravan Site

Address: Shobdon, Leominster, Herefordshire HR6 9NR
Telephone: 01568 708326
Website: www.bestparks.co.uk
Extra charge for dogs? Yes
Any breed restrictions? No
Dog bins? Yes
Area for walking dogs? Yes. 20 acres of woodland etc
Static caravans? No
Cost of static?
Mobile caravans? Yes
Cost of mobile? From £17.00 for 2 adults inc elc
Tents? Yes
Cost of tent pitch? From £8.00 per night
Electricity at the pitch? Yes
Showers? Yes
Onsite Entertainment? Restaurant and bar.
Opening times? 1st March - 1st November

Tan House Farm

Address: Long Town, Hereford, Herefordshire HR2 0LT

Telephone: 01873 860221

Website: www.camping4us.co.uk

Extra charge for dogs? yes

Any breed restrictions? No

Dog bins? No

Area for walking dogs? Yes must be on lead

Static caravans? No

Cost of static?

Mobile caravans? No

Cost of mobile?

Tents? Yes

Cost of tent pitch? £4.00 per person inc toilets and showers

Electricity at the pitch? No

Showers? Yes

Onsite Entertainment? No

Opening times? May - September

Yew Tree Inn Caravan Site

Address: Peteretow, Ross-on-Wye, Herefordshire HR9 6JZ

Telephone: 01989 562815

Website:

Extra charge for dogs? No

Any breed restrictions? No

Dog bins? Yes

Area for walking dogs? Yes on leads

Static caravans? No

Cost of static?

Mobile caravans? Yes

Cost of mobile? From 10.00 - £12.00

Tents? Yes

Cost of tent pitch? From £8.00

Electricity at the pitch? Yes

Showers? Yes

Onsite Entertainment? Pub with food.

Opening times? 1st March - End September

Eaton Farm

Address: Stoke Prior Lane, Leominster, Herefordshire, HR6 0NA

Telephone: 01568 612095

Website:

Extra charge for dogs? No

Any breed restrictions? Yes. Pitt Balls and Rockweilers

Dog bins? No

Area for walking dogs? Yes. Riverside walk, and up on Eaton Hill

Static caravans?

Cost of static?

Mobile caravans? Yes

Cost of mobile? From £10.00

Tents? Yes

Cost of tent pitch? From £5.00 - £8.00

Electricity at the pitch? Yes

Showers? Yes

Onsite Entertainment? No

Opening times? April - October

Hertford Camping and Caravanning Site

Address: Mangrove Road, Hertford, Hertfordshire, SG13 8AJ

Telephone: 01992 586696

Website: www.campingandcaravaning club.co.uk

Extra charge for dogs? No

Any breed restrictions? No

Dog bins? Yes

Area for walking dogs? Dog walking area

Static caravans? No

Cost of static?

Mobile caravans? Yes

Cost of mobile? From £11.00

Tents? Yes

Cost of tent pitch? From £11.00

Electricity at the pitch? Yes

Showers? Yes

Onsite Entertainment? No

Opening times? All year

Breakspear Way Caravan Club Site

Address: Buncefield Lane, Breakspar way, Hemel Hempstead, Hertfordshire, HP2 4TZ

Telephone: 01442 268286

Website:

Extra charge for dogs? No

Any breed restrictions? No

Dog bins? No

Area for walking dogs? Yes on lead

Static caravans? No

Cost of static?

Mobile caravans? Yes

Cost of mobile? From £10.00 - £10.00

Tents? Yes

Cost of tent pitch? From £10.00 - £10.00

Electricity at the pitch? Yes

Showers? Yes

Onsite Entertainment? No

Opening times? All year

Loves Lane Camping & Caravanning

Address: Loves Lane, Ashwell, Hertfordshire, SG7 5HZ

Telephone: 01462 742382

Website: www.loveslane.co.uk

Extra charge for dogs? No

Any breed restrictions? No

Dog bins? No

Area for walking dogs? Lots of foot paths

Static caravans? No

Cost of static?

Mobile caravans? Yes

Cost of mobile? £10.00

Tents? Yes

Cost of tent pitch? £10.00

Electricity at the pitch? Yes

Showers? Yes

Onsite Entertainment? No

Opening times? All year

Ashridge Farm Caravan Club Site

Address: 1 Ashwell St, Ashwell, Baldock, Hertfordshire, SG7 5QF

Telephone: 01462 742527

Website:

Extra charge for dogs? No

Any breed restrictions?

Dog bins?

Area for walking dogs? Yes

Static caravans?

Cost of static?

Mobile caravans? Yes

Cost of mobile? From £10.00 - £15.00

Tents? Yes

Cost of tent pitch? From £10.00 - £15.00

Electricity at the pitch? Yes

Showers? Yes

Onsite Entertainment? No

Opening times? All year

Radwell Mill Lake

Address: Radwell Mill, Baldock, Hertfordshire, SG7 5ET

Telephone: 01462 730253

Website:

Extra charge for dogs? No

Any breed restrictions? No

Dog bins? No

Area for walking dogs? Lots of foot paths

Static caravans? No

Cost of static?

Mobile caravans? Yes

Cost of mobile? £2.50 - £3.00 + £1.00 per child

Tents? Yes

Cost of tent pitch? £2.50 - £3.00 + £1.00 per child

Electricity at the pitch? No

Showers? No

Onsite Entertainment? No

Opening times? April - End October

Lee Valley Caravan Park Dobbs Weir

Address: Essex Rd, Dobbs Weir, Hoddesdon, Hertfordshire, EN11 0AS

Telephone: 01992 462090

Website: www.leevalleypark.org.uk

Extra charge for dogs? Yes

Any breed restrictions? No

Dog bins? Yes

Area for walking dogs? Yes

Static caravans? No

Cost of static?

Mobile caravans? Yes

Cost of mobile? £17.10 2 adults with electric

Tents? Yes

Cost of tent pitch? £17.10 2 adults with electric

Electricity at the pitch? Yes

Showers? Yes

Onsite Entertainment? No

Opening times? 1st March - 30th November

Allhallows Place Touring Park

Address: Stoke Road, Allhallows, Rochester, Kent, ME3 9PD

Telephone: 01634 270106

Website: www.allhallowsplacetouringpark.co.uk

Extra charge for dogs? Yes

Any breed restrictions? Yes

Dog bins? Yes

Area for walking dogs? Yes

Static caravans? No

Cost of static?

Mobile caravans? Yes

Cost of mobile? From £15.50 per night

Tents? Yes

Cost of tent pitch? From £15.50 per night

Electricity at the pitch? Yes

Showers? Yes

Onsite Entertainment? Yes

Opening times? All Year

Comments: There is a licensed bar. They don't allow Pitbulls or Bull Mastifs on site. Dogs must be kept on a lead.

Apple Acres

Address: Mabledon Farm, London Road, Southborough, Tonbridge, Kent, TN4 0UQ

Telephone: 01732 352080

Website: www.mabledonfarm.co.uk

Extra charge for dogs? No

Any breed restrictions? No

Dog bins? No

Area for walking dogs? Yes

Static caravans? No

Cost of static?

Mobile caravans? Yes

Cost of mobile? From £11.50 per night for 2 people including electric

Tents? Yes

Cost of tent pitch? From £5.00 per tent + £2.00 per person

Electricity at the pitch? Yes

Showers? Yes

Onsite Entertainment? No

Opening times? 1st March - 15th January

Ashcroft Coast Holiday Park

Address: Plough Road, Minster On Sea, Kent, ME12 4JH

Telephone: 0871 664 9701

Website: www.park-resorts.com

Extra charge for dogs? Yes

Any breed restrictions? Yes

Dog bins? Yes

Area for walking dogs? Yes

Static caravans? Yes

Cost of static? From £120.00 per week

Mobile caravans? No

Cost of mobile?

Tents? No

Cost of tent pitch?

Electricity at the pitch?

Showers?

Onsite Entertainment? Yes

Opening times? March - November

Comments: No Dangerous Breeds.

Ashfield Farm

Address: Waddenhall, Petham, Canterbury, Kent, CT4 5PX

Telephone: 01227 700624
Website:
Extra charge for dogs? No
Any breed restrictions? No
Dog bins? No
Area for walking dogs? Yes
Static caravans? Yes
Cost of static? From £200.00 - £250.00 per week
Mobile caravans? Yes
Cost of mobile? From £13.00 per night with electric
Tents? Yes
Cost of tent pitch? From £11.00 per night for up to 4 people
Electricity at the pitch? Yes
Showers? Yes
Onsite Entertainment? No
Opening times? April - October
Comments: They have disabled toilets on site.

Bartons Point Coastal Park

Address: Marine Parade, Sheerness, Kent, ME12 2BX
Telephone: 07809 422787
Website: www.bartonspoint.co.uk
Extra charge for dogs? No
Any breed restrictions? No
Dog bins? Yes
Area for walking dogs? Yes
Static caravans? No
Cost of static?
Mobile caravans? Yes
Cost of mobile? From £10.00 per night
Tents? Yes
Cost of tent pitch? From £10.00 per night
Electricity at the pitch? No
Showers? Yes
Onsite Entertainment? Sometimes
Opening times? Easter - End September
Comments: Dogs must be kept on a lead. They have disabled facilities on site.

Bearsted Caravan Club Site

Address: Ashford Road, Hollingbourne, Maidstone, Kent, ME17 1XH
Telephone: 01622 730018
Website: www.thecaravanclub.co.uk
Extra charge for dogs? No
Any breed restrictions? No
Dog bins? Yes
Area for walking dogs? No
Static caravans? No
Cost of static?
Mobile caravans? Yes
Cost of mobile? From £4.30 per pitch + £3.95 per adult per night
Tents? No
Cost of tent pitch?
Electricity at the pitch? Yes
Showers? Yes
Onsite Entertainment? No
Opening times? All Year
Comments: Closed for refurbishment opening on 1st July 2008

Beckenham Park.

Address: 2 Beckenham Park, Otterham Quay Lane, Rainham, Kent, ME8 7XF
Telephone: 01634 231426
Website:
Extra charge for dogs?
Any breed restrictions?
Dog bins?
Area for walking dogs?
Static caravans?
Cost of static?
Mobile caravans?
Cost of mobile?

Tents?
Cost of tent pitch?
Electricity at the pitch?
Showers?
Onsite Entertainment?
Opening times?

Black Horse Farm Caravan Club Site

Address: 385 Canterbury Road, Densole, Folkestone, Kent, CT18 7BG
Telephone: 01303 892665
Website: www.caravanclub.co.uk
Extra charge for dogs? No
Any breed restrictions? No
Dog bins? Yes
Area for walking dogs? Yes
Static caravans? No
Cost of static?
Mobile caravans? Yes
Cost of mobile? From £12.20 per pitch per night for 2 adults (non member additional £7.00)
Tents? Yes
Cost of tent pitch? From £12.20 per pitch per night for 2 adults (non member additional £7.00)
Electricity at the pitch? Yes
Showers? Yes
Onsite Entertainment? No
Opening times? All Year

Blossoms Caravan Park

Address: Church Hill, Charing Heath, Ashford, Kent, TN27 0BU
Telephone: 01233 712886
Website: www.blossomscaravanpark.co.uk
Extra charge for dogs? No
Any breed restrictions? No
Dog bins? No
Area for walking dogs? Yes
Static caravans? No
Cost of static?
Mobile caravans? Yes
Cost of mobile? From £15.00 per night with electric
Tents? Yes
Cost of tent pitch? From £15.00 per night with electric
Electricity at the pitch? Yes
Showers? Yes
Onsite Entertainment? No
Opening times? All Year
Comments: Pub and restaurant within walking distance

Broadhembury Holiday Park

Address: Steeds Lane, Kingsnorth, Ashford, Kent, TN26 1NQ
Telephone: 01233 620859
Website: www.broadhembury.co.uk
Extra charge for dogs? No
Any breed restrictions? No
Dog bins? Yes
Area for walking dogs? Yes
Static caravans? No
Cost of static?
Mobile caravans? Yes
Cost of mobile? From £24.00 - £26.00 per service pitch per night
Tents? Yes
Cost of tent pitch? From £14.00 - £18.00 per night
Electricity at the pitch? Yes
Showers? Yes
Onsite Entertainment? No
Opening times? All Year

Canterbury Camping And Caravanning Club Site

Address: Bekesbourne Lane, Canterbury, Kent, CT3 4AB

Telephone: 01227 463216

Website: www.thecampingand caravanningclub.co.uk

Extra charge for dogs? No

Any breed restrictions? No

Dog bins? Yes

Area for walking dogs? Yes

Static caravans? No

Cost of static?

Mobile caravans? Yes

Cost of mobile? From £5.90 per adult per night

Tents? Yes

Cost of tent pitch? From £5.90 per adult per night

Electricity at the pitch? Yes

Showers? Yes

Onsite Entertainment? Yes

Opening times? All Year

Comments: Dangerous dogs have to wear a muzzle on site. There is a playground on site and there is a chip van on a Friday.

Cobbs Meadow

Address: Bekesbourne Lane, Bekesbourne, Canterbury, Kent, CT4 5DY

Telephone: 01227 830214

Website: www.cobbsmeadow.co.uk

Extra charge for dogs? No

Any breed restrictions? No

Dog bins? No

Area for walking dogs? Off Site

Static caravans? No

Cost of static?

Mobile caravans? Yes

Cost of mobile? From £10.50 per night

Tents? Yes

Cost of tent pitch? From £10.50 per night

Electricity at the pitch? Yes

Showers? No

Onsite Entertainment? No

Opening times? All Year

Cottington Lakes

Address: Sandwich Road, Sholden, Deal, Kent, CT14 0AR

Telephone: 01304 371898

Website:

Extra charge for dogs? No

Any breed restrictions? No

Dog bins? No

Area for walking dogs? Yes

Static caravans? No

Cost of static?

Mobile caravans? Yes

Cost of mobile? From £9.00 without electric £11.00 with electric for 2 people

Tents? Yes

Cost of tent pitch?

Electricity at the pitch? Yes

Showers? Yes

Onsite Entertainment? No

Opening times? March - December

Comments: Dogs must be kept on a lead at all times.

Counter Farmhouse Cl

Address: Brook Street, Woodchurch, Ashford, Kent, TN26 3SP

Telephone: 01233 860448

Website:

Extra charge for dogs? No

Any breed restrictions? No

Dog bins? No

Area for walking dogs? Off Site
Static caravans? No
Cost of static?
Mobile caravans? Yes
Cost of mobile? From £8.00 per night
Tents? No
Cost of tent pitch?
Electricity at the pitch? Yes
Showers? No
Onsite Entertainment? Fishing
Opening times? March - October

Daleacres Caravan Club Site

Address: Lower Wall Road, West Hythe, Hythe, Kent, CT21 4NW
Telephone: 01303 267679
Website: www.thecaravanclub.co.uk
Extra charge for dogs? No
Any breed restrictions? No
Dog bins? Yes
Area for walking dogs? Yes
Static caravans? No
Cost of static?
Mobile caravans? Yes
Cost of mobile? From £12.20 - £18.10 per night for 2 adults
Tents? No
Cost of tent pitch?
Electricity at the pitch? Yes
Showers? Yes
Onsite Entertainment? No
Opening times? March - Beg November
Comments: Have to be members of the Caravan Club.

Dunn Street Farm

Address: Westwell, Ashford, Kent, TN25 4NJ
Telephone: 01233 712537
Website:
Extra charge for dogs? No
Any breed restrictions? No
Dog bins? No
Area for walking dogs? Off Site
Static caravans? No
Cost of static?
Mobile caravans? Yes
Cost of mobile? From £5.00 per person per night
Tents? Yes
Cost of tent pitch? From £5.00 per person per night
Electricity at the pitch? Yes
Showers? Yes
Onsite Entertainment? No
Opening times? End March - End October

Fairdean

Address: Palmers Farm, Fordcombe, Tunbridge Wells, TN3 0RN
Telephone: 01892 740209
Website:
Extra charge for dogs? No
Any breed restrictions? No
Dog bins? No
Area for walking dogs? Yes
Static caravans? No
Cost of static?
Mobile caravans? Yes
Cost of mobile? From £4.00 per person per night
Tents? Yes
Cost of tent pitch? From £4.00 per person per night
Electricity at the pitch? No
Showers? No
Onsite Entertainment? No
Opening times? April - 1st October
Comments: Dogs must be kept on a lead.

Fir Tree Farm Camp Site

Address: Fir Tree Farm, Chapel Lane, Rhodes Minnis, Canterbury, Kent, CT4 6XR
Telephone: 01303 862155
Website:
Extra charge for dogs? No
Any breed restrictions? No
Dog bins? Yes
Area for walking dogs? Off Site
Static caravans? No
Cost of static?
Mobile caravans? Yes
Cost of mobile? From £4.50 per van per night
Tents? Yes
Cost of tent pitch? From £4.50 per tent per night
Electricity at the pitch? Yes
Showers? No
Onsite Entertainment? No
Opening times? All Year
Comments: Dogs must be kept on a lead and well behaved.

Hart Holiday Village

Address: Leysdown Rd, Leysdown-on-Sea, ME12 4QT
Telephone: 01795 510225
Website: www.parkholidaysuk.com
Extra charge for dogs? Yes
Any breed restrictions? Yes
Dog bins? Yes
Area for walking dogs? Yes
Static caravans? Yes
Cost of static? From £130.00 per week
Mobile caravans?
Cost of mobile?
Tents?
Cost of tent pitch?
Electricity at the pitch?
Showers?
Onsite Entertainment? Yes
Opening times? March - October
Comments: No Dangerous Dogs. There is a clubhouse with weekly entertainment.

Hawthorn Road Caravan Park

Address: Martin Mill, Dover, Kent, CT15 5LA
Telephone: 01304 852658
Website: www.keatfarm.co.uk
Extra charge for dogs? Yes
Any breed restrictions? ?
Dog bins? Yes
Area for walking dogs? No
Static caravans? No
Cost of static?
Mobile caravans? Yes
Cost of mobile? From £12.00 per night
Tents? Yes
Cost of tent pitch? From £12.00 per night
Electricity at the pitch? Yes
Showers? Yes
Onsite Entertainment? No
Opening times? March - October
Comments: One dog per unit

Homing Leisure Park

Address: Church Lane, Seasalter, Whitstable, Kent, CT5 4BU
Telephone: 01227 771777
Website: www.homingpark.co.uk
Extra charge for dogs? No
Any breed restrictions? No
Dog bins? Yes
Area for walking dogs? No
Static caravans? No
Cost of static?

Mobile caravans? Yes
Cost of mobile? From £9.50 - £20.00 per night
Tents? Yes
Cost of tent pitch? From £9.50 - £20.00 per night
Electricity at the pitch? Yes
Showers? Yes
Onsite Entertainment? Yes
Opening times? Beg March - End October

Little Satmar Holiday Park

Address: Winehouse Lane, Capel le Ferne, Folkestone, Kent, CT18 7JF
Telephone: 01303 251188
Website: www.keatfarm.co.uk
Extra charge for dogs? Yes
Any breed restrictions? ?
Dog bins? Yes
Area for walking dogs? No
Static caravans? No
Cost of static?
Mobile caravans? Yes
Cost of mobile? From £12.00 per night
Tents? Yes
Cost of tent pitch? From £12.00 per night
Electricity at the pitch? Yes
Showers? Yes
Onsite Entertainment? No
Opening times? March - October
Comments: One dog per unit

Little Switzerland Caravan Site

Address: Wear Bay Road, Folkestone, Kent, CT19 6PS
Telephone: 01303 252168
Website: www.caravanandcampingsite.co.uk
Extra charge for dogs? No
Any breed restrictions? No
Dog bins? No
Area for walking dogs? Yes
Static caravans? No
Cost of static?
Mobile caravans? Yes
Cost of mobile? From £10.00 per night
Tents? Yes
Cost of tent pitch? From £7.00 per person per night
Electricity at the pitch? Yes
Showers? Yes
Onsite Entertainment? No
Opening times? March - October

Manor Court Farm

Address: Ashurst, Tunbridge Wells, Kent, TN3 9TB
Telephone: 01892 740279
Website: www.manorcourtfarm.co.uk
Extra charge for dogs? No
Any breed restrictions? Flexible
Dog bins? No
Area for walking dogs? Yes
Static caravans? No
Cost of static?
Mobile caravans? Yes
Cost of mobile? From £7.00 per adult per night
Tents? Yes
Cost of tent pitch?
Electricity at the pitch? Yes
Showers? Yes
Onsite Entertainment? No
Opening times? All Year
Comments: Dogs must be kept on a lead.

Manston Caravan & Camping Park

Address: Manston Court Road, Manston, Ramsgate, Kent, CT12 5AU
Telephone: 01843 823442
Website: www.manston-park.co.uk
Extra charge for dogs? Yes
Any breed restrictions? Yes
Dog bins? Yes
Area for walking dogs? Yes
Static caravans? No
Cost of static?
Mobile caravans? Yes
Cost of mobile? From £15.00 per night for 2 people
Tents? Yes
Cost of tent pitch? From £11.00 per night for 2 people
Electricity at the pitch? Yes
Showers? Yes
Onsite Entertainment? No
Opening times? April - End October
Comments: No Dangerous Breeds and Dogs must be kept on a lead.

Marlie Farm Holiday Park

Address: Dymchurch Road, New Romney, Kent, TN28 8UE
Telephone: 0845 815 9750
Website: www.parkholidaysuk.com
Extra charge for dogs? Yes
Any breed restrictions? Yes
Dog bins? Yes
Area for walking dogs? Yes
Static caravans? No
Cost of static?
Mobile caravans? Yes
Cost of mobile? From £15.00 - £20.00 per pitch per night
Tents? Yes
Cost of tent pitch? From £15.00 - £20.00 per pitch per night
Electricity at the pitch? Yes (Not Tents)
Showers? Yes
Onsite Entertainment? Yes
Opening times? March - End October
Comments: No Dangerous Breeds and only 2 Dogs per pitch.

Monks Cottage Caravan Park

Address: Leaveland, Faversham, Kent, ME13 0NP
Telephone: 01233 740419
Website: www.caravansitesinkent.com
Extra charge for dogs? No
Any breed restrictions? No
Dog bins? No
Area for walking dogs? Yes
Static caravans? No
Cost of static?
Mobile caravans? Yes
Cost of mobile? From £12.00 per night
Tents? No
Cost of tent pitch?
Electricity at the pitch? Yes
Showers? Yes
Onsite Entertainment? No
Opening times? All Year

Neals Place Farm

Address: Neals Place Road, Canterbury, Kent, CT2 8HX
Telephone: 01227 765632
Website: www.ukcampsite.co.uk
Extra charge for dogs? Yes
Any breed restrictions? No
Dog bins? No
Area for walking dogs? Yes

Static caravans? No
Cost of static?
Mobile caravans? Yes
Cost of mobile? From £15.00 per pitch per night with electric and water
Tents? Yes
Cost of tent pitch? From £10.00 per night with water
Electricity at the pitch? Yes
Showers? No
Onsite Entertainment? No
Opening times? April - End September

Nethercourt Touring Park

Address: Nethercourt Hill, Ramsgate, Kent, CT11 0RX
Telephone: 01843 595485
Website: www.barrowcliffe.net
Extra charge for dogs? Yes
Any breed restrictions? No
Dog bins? No
Area for walking dogs? Off Site
Static caravans? No
Cost of static?
Mobile caravans? Yes
Cost of mobile? From £12.50 per night
Tents? Yes
Cost of tent pitch? From £9.50 per night
Electricity at the pitch? Yes
Showers? Yes
Onsite Entertainment? No
Opening times? April - End October
Comments: There is a park next door where dogs can be exercised.

New Beach Holiday Park

Address: Hythe Road, Dymchurch, Kent, TN29 0JX
Telephone: 0845 815 9720
Website: www.parkholidays.co.uk
Extra charge for dogs? Yes
Any breed restrictions? No
Dog bins? Yes
Area for walking dogs? No
Static caravans? Yes
Cost of static? From £120.00 per week
Mobile caravans? Yes
Cost of mobile? From £19.00 per night
Tents? No
Cost of tent pitch? From £19.00 per night
Electricity at the pitch? Yes
Showers? Yes
Onsite Entertainment? Yes
Opening times? March - End October
Comments: There is a Clubhouse on site.

Norwood Farm Caravan & Camping Park

Address: Newchurch, Romney Marsh, Kent, TN29 0DU
Telephone: 01303 873659
Website: www.norwoodfarmuchurch.co.uk
Extra charge for dogs? Yes
Any breed restrictions? Yes
Dog bins? Yes
Area for walking dogs? Yes
Static caravans? No
Cost of static?
Mobile caravans? Yes
Cost of mobile? From £4.50 per adult per night
Tents? Yes
Cost of tent pitch?
Electricity at the pitch? Yes
Showers? Yes
Onsite Entertainment? No
Opening times? 1st April - 30th September

Comments: Dogs must be kept on a lead. This is a working a sheep farm. Must check with owners about breeds.

Painters Farm Caravan Camping Site

Address: Painters Farm, Forstal, Faversham, Kent, ME13 0EG
Telephone: 01795 532995
Website:
Extra charge for dogs? No
Any breed restrictions? Yes
Dog bins? No
Area for walking dogs? Off Site
Static caravans? No
Cost of static?
Mobile caravans? Yes
Cost of mobile? From £4.50 - £4.90 per pitch with Electric + £3.60 - £4.70 per adult
Tents? Yes
Cost of tent pitch? From £2.50 - £3.00 per pitch + £3.60 - £4.70 per adult
Electricity at the pitch? Yes
Showers? Yes
Onsite Entertainment? No
Opening times? Mid March - End October
Comments: No dangerous breeds. Dogs must be kept on a lead. There is a pub a few minutes walk away.

Palace Farm Camp Site

Address: Down Court Road, Dodding, Sittingbourne, Kent, ME9 0AU
Telephone: 01795 886200
Website: www.palacefarm.com
Extra charge for dogs? No
Any breed restrictions? No
Dog bins? No
Area for walking dogs? Off Site
Static caravans? No
Cost of static?
Mobile caravans? No
Cost of mobile?
Tents? Yes
Cost of tent pitch? From £6.00 - £10.00 per person per night
Electricity at the pitch? No
Showers? Yes
Onsite Entertainment? No
Opening times? April - October
Comments: Dogs must be kept on a lead.

Plough Leisure Caravan Park

Address: Plough Road, Minster On Sea, Kent, ME12 4JF
Telephone: 01795 872895
Website: www.ploughleisurecaravanpark.com
Extra charge for dogs? No
Any breed restrictions? No
Dog bins? No
Area for walking dogs? Yes
Static caravans? No
Cost of static?
Mobile caravans? Yes
Cost of mobile? From £15.00 per night
Tents? Yes
Cost of tent pitch? From £12.00 per night
Electricity at the pitch? Yes
Showers? Yes
Onsite Entertainment? No
Opening times? 1st April - End October
Comments: Dogs must be kept on a lead. There is a swimming pool, laundry room and children's playground on site.

Primrose Cottage Caravan Park

Address: Golden Hill, Whitstable, Kent, CT5 3AR

Telephone: 01227 273694

Website:

Extra charge for dogs? No
Any breed restrictions? No
Dog bins? No
Area for walking dogs? Off Site
Static caravans? Yes
Cost of static? From £190.00 per week
Mobile caravans? Yes
Cost of mobile? From £14.00 per night for 2 people
Tents? Yes
Cost of tent pitch? From £12.00 per night for 2 people
Electricity at the pitch? Yes
Showers? Yes
Onsite Entertainment? No
Opening times? March - October

Comments: Dogs must be kept on a lead.

Priory Hill Holiday Parks

Address: Wing Road, Leysdown, Kent, ME12 4QT

Telephone: 01795 510 267

Website: www.prioryhill.co.uk

Extra charge for dogs? No
Any breed restrictions? No
Dog bins? No
Area for walking dogs? Off Site
Static caravans? No
Cost of static?
Mobile caravans? Yes
Cost of mobile? From £14.00 per night
Tents? Yes
Cost of tent pitch? From £14.00 per night
Electricity at the pitch? Yes
Showers? Yes
Onsite Entertainment? Yes
Opening times? March - October

Quex Caravan Park

Address: Park Road, Birchington, Kent, CT7 0BL

Telephone: 01843 841273

Website: www.keatfarm.co.uk

Extra charge for dogs? Yes
Any breed restrictions? ?
Dog bins? Yes
Area for walking dogs? No
Static caravans? No
Cost of static?
Mobile caravans? Yes
Cost of mobile? From £12.00 per night
Tents? Yes
Cost of tent pitch? From £12.00 per night
Electricity at the pitch? Yes
Showers? Yes
Onsite Entertainment? No
Opening times? March - October

Comments: One dog per unit

Red Lion Caravan Park

Address: Old London Road, Dunkirk, Kent, ME13 9LL

Telephone: 01227 750661

Website: www.redlionparkhomes.co.uk

Extra charge for dogs? No
Any breed restrictions? Yes
Dog bins? Yes
Area for walking dogs? Off Site
Static caravans? No
Cost of static?
Mobile caravans? Yes
Cost of mobile? From £15.00 per night for 2 people with electric

Tents? Yes
Cost of tent pitch? From £10.00 per night
Electricity at the pitch? Yes
Showers? Yes
Onsite Entertainment? No
Opening times? All Year
Comments: No dangerous breeds. Dogs must be kept on a lead. There is a pub nearby.

Romney Farm

Address: Romney Road, Lydd, Kent, TN29 9LS
Telephone: 01797 361499
Website: www.romneyfarm.com
Extra charge for dogs? Yes
Any breed restrictions? No
Dog bins? No
Area for walking dogs? Yes
Static caravans? No
Cost of static?
Mobile caravans? Yes
Cost of mobile? From £11.00 per night for 2 people
Tents? Yes
Cost of tent pitch? From £11.00 per night for 2 people
Electricity at the pitch? Yes
Showers? Yes
Onsite Entertainment? No
Opening times? April - October
Comments: Maximum of 2 dogs per unit.

Romney Sands Holiday Village

Address: The Parade, Greatstone On Sea, New Romney, Kent, TN28 8RN
Telephone: 0871 664 9761
Website: www.parkresorts.com
Extra charge for dogs? Yes
Any breed restrictions? Yes
Dog bins? Yes
Area for walking dogs? No
Static caravans? Yes
Cost of static? From £156.00 - £759.00 per week
Mobile caravans? No
Cost of mobile?
Tents? No
Cost of tent pitch?
Electricity at the pitch? No
Showers? No
Onsite Entertainment? Yes
Opening times? March - October
Comments: No Dangerous Breeds. There is a Clubhouse on site.

Rose & Crown Camping Park

Address: Stelling Minnis, Canterbury, Kent, CT4 6AS
Telephone: 01227 709265
Website:
Extra charge for dogs? No
Any breed restrictions? No
Dog bins? No
Area for walking dogs? Off Site
Static caravans? No
Cost of static?
Mobile caravans? Yes
Cost of mobile? From £5.00 per night
Tents? Yes
Cost of tent pitch? From £5.00 per night
Electricity at the pitch? No
Showers? No
Onsite Entertainment? Pub
Opening times? March - October
Comments: Dogs must be kept on a lead.

Royal Oak Camping

Address: 114 Sweech Gate, Broad Oak, Canterbury, Kent, CT5 0QP

Telephone: 01227 710448

Website:

Extra charge for dogs? No

Any breed restrictions? No

Dog bins? No

Area for walking dogs? Off Site

Static caravans? Yes

Cost of static? From £60.00 per week

Mobile caravans? Yes

Cost of mobile? From £15.00 per night

Tents? Yes

Cost of tent pitch? From £8.00 small tent/ £10.00 for large tent

Electricity at the pitch? Yes

Showers? Yes

Onsite Entertainment? Yes

Opening times? March - October

Comments: Pub they have singers on a Saturday night.

Sandwich Leisure Park

Address: Woodnesborough Rd, sandwich, Kent, CT13 0AA

Telephone: 01304 612681

Website: www.sandwichleisure.co.uk

Extra charge for dogs? Yes

Any breed restrictions? No

Dog bins? Yes

Area for walking dogs? Off Site

Static caravans? Yes

Cost of static? From £250.00 - £550.00 per week

Mobile caravans? Yes

Cost of mobile? From £18.00 - £29.00 per night

Tents? Yes

Cost of tent pitch? From £18.00 - £29.00 per night

Electricity at the pitch? Yes

Showers? Yes

Onsite Entertainment? No

Opening times? March - End October

Sea View Holiday Park

Address: St Johns Rd, Swalecliffe, Whitstable, CT5 2RY

Telephone: 01227 792246

Website: www.parkholidaysuk.com

Extra charge for dogs? Yes

Any breed restrictions? Yes

Dog bins? Yes

Area for walking dogs? Yes

Static caravans? No

Cost of static?

Mobile caravans? No

Cost of mobile?

Tents? Yes

Cost of tent pitch? From £16.00 - £19.00 per pitch per night

Electricity at the pitch? Yes

Showers? Yes

Onsite Entertainment? Yes

Opening times? 1st March - 31st October

Comments: No Dangerous Breeds. There is a Clubhouse on site with entertainment for adults and children. There is a Shop and a Café on site as well.

Sheerness Holiday Park

Address: Halfway Road, Minster-on-Sea, Sheerness, Kent, ME12 3AA

Telephone: 0845 815 9760

Website: www.parkholidaysuk.com

Extra charge for dogs? Yes

Any breed restrictions? Yes

Dog bins? Yes

Area for walking dogs? Yes

Static caravans? No

Cost of static?

Mobile caravans? Yes
Cost of mobile? From £9.00 per night
Tents? Yes
Cost of tent pitch? From £9.00 per night
Electricity at the pitch? Yes
Showers? Yes
Onsite Entertainment? Yes
Opening times? April - September
Comments: No Dangerous Breeds.

Shurland Dale Holiday Park

Address: Warden Road, Eastchurch, Kent, ME12 4EN
Telephone: 0871 664 9770
Website: www.park-resorts.com
Extra charge for dogs? Yes
Any breed restrictions? Yes
Dog bins? Yes
Area for walking dogs? Yes
Static caravans? Yes
Cost of static? From £150.00 per week
Mobile caravans?
Cost of mobile?
Tents?
Cost of tent pitch?
Electricity at the pitch?
Showers?
Onsite Entertainment? Yes
Opening times? 1st March - 31st October
Comments: No Dangerous Breeds.

St Margaret's Holiday Park

Address: Reach Road, St Margarets-at-Cliffe, Dover, Kent, CT15 6AG
Telephone: 0871 664 9773
Website: www.park-resorts.com
Extra charge for dogs? Yes
Any breed restrictions? Yes
Dog bins? Yes
Area for walking dogs? Yes
Static caravans? Yes
Cost of static? From £201.00 per week
Mobile caravans? No
Cost of mobile?
Tents? No
Cost of tent pitch?
Electricity at the pitch? No
Showers? No
Onsite Entertainment? Yes
Opening times? 1st March - 7th January
Comments: No Dangerous Breeds

St Nicholas Camping Site

Address: Court Road, St Nicholas at Wade, Birchington, Kent, CT7 0NA
Telephone: 01843 847245
Website:
Extra charge for dogs? Yes
Any breed restrictions? No
Dog bins? No
Area for walking dogs? Off Site
Static caravans? No
Cost of static?
Mobile caravans? Yes
Cost of mobile? From £14.50 per night with electric
Tents? Yes
Cost of tent pitch? From £7.50 without electric + £2.00 per adult per night
Electricity at the pitch? Yes
Showers? Yes
Onsite Entertainment? No
Opening times? Easter - End October

Sutton Vale Country Club & Holiday Park

Address: Vale Road, Sutton By Dover, Kent, CT15 5DH
Telephone: 01304 374155
Website: www.suttonvale.co.uk

Extra charge for dogs? Yes
Any breed restrictions? No
Dog bins? No
Area for walking dogs? Yes
Static caravans? No
Cost of static?
Mobile caravans? Yes
Cost of mobile? From £16.00 - £21.00 per night
Tents? Yes
Cost of tent pitch? From £16.00 - £21.00 per night
Electricity at the pitch? Yes
Showers? Yes
Onsite Entertainment? Yes
Opening times? March - January

Tanner Farm Touring Caravan & Camping Park

Address: Tanner Farm, Goudhurst Road, Marden, Kent, TN12 9ND
Telephone: 01622 832399
Website: www.tannerfarmpark.co.uk
Extra charge for dogs? No
Any breed restrictions? No
Dog bins? Yes
Area for walking dogs? Yes
Static caravans? No
Cost of static?
Mobile caravans? Yes
Cost of mobile? From £13.20 - £19.20 per night for 2 people & Electric
Tents? Yes
Cost of tent pitch? From £12.40 -£16.50 per night for 2 people
Electricity at the pitch? Yes
Showers? Yes
Onsite Entertainment? No
Opening times? All Year

The Crown Inn

Address: The Street, Finglesham, Deal, Kent, CT14 0NA
Telephone: 01304 612555
Website: www.thecrownatfinglesham.co.uk
Extra charge for dogs? No
Any breed restrictions? No
Dog bins? No
Area for walking dogs? Yes
Static caravans? No
Cost of static?
Mobile caravans? Yes
Cost of mobile? From £4.00 per night without electric £8.00 per night with electric
Tents? Yes
Cost of tent pitch? From £4.00 per night without electric £8.00 per night with electric
Electricity at the pitch? Yes
Showers? No
Onsite Entertainment? Pub
Opening times? All Year

The Foxhunter Park

Address: Monkton, Ramsgate, CT12 4JG
Telephone: 01843 821311
Website: www.thefoxhunterpark.co.uk
Extra charge for dogs? Yes
Any breed restrictions? Yes
Dog bins? Yes
Area for walking dogs? No
Static caravans? Yes
Cost of static? From £275.00 per week
Mobile caravans? No
Cost of mobile?
Tents? No
Cost of tent pitch?
Electricity at the pitch? No
Showers? No
Onsite Entertainment? Yes

Opening times? March - October
Comments: No Dangerous Breeds.

Thriftwood Caravan Park

Address: Plaxdale Green Road, Wrotham Hill, Kent, TN15 7PB
Telephone: 01732 822261
Website:
Extra charge for dogs? Yes
Any breed restrictions? No
Dog bins? Yes
Area for walking dogs? Yes
Static caravans? No
Cost of static?
Mobile caravans? Yes
Cost of mobile? From £12.00 - £16.00 per pitch per night
Tents? Yes
Cost of tent pitch? From £12.00 - £16.00 per pitch per night
Electricity at the pitch? Yes
Showers? Yes
Onsite Entertainment? Sometimes
Opening times? March - January
Comments: Dogs must be kept on a lead at all times.

To The Woods

Address: Botsom Lane, West Kingsdown, Sevenoaks, Kent, TN15 6BN
Telephone: 01322 863751
Website:
Extra charge for dogs? No
Any breed restrictions? Yes
Dog bins? No
Area for walking dogs? Off Site
Static caravans? No
Cost of static?
Mobile caravans? Yes
Cost of mobile? From £10.00 per night with electric for 2 people
Tents? Yes
Cost of tent pitch? From £7.00 per night for 2 people
Electricity at the pitch? Yes
Showers? Yes
Onsite Entertainment? No
Opening times? All Year
Comments: No Dangerous Breeds.

Varne Ridge Caravan Park

Address: 145 Old Dover Rd, Capel Le Ferne, Folkestone, Kent, CT18 7HX
Telephone: 01303 251765
Website: www.varne-ridge.co.uk
Extra charge for dogs? Yes
Any breed restrictions? No
Dog bins? No
Area for walking dogs? Yes
Static caravans? Yes
Cost of static? From £235.00 per week
Mobile caravans? Yes
Cost of mobile? From £14.00 per night with electric for 2 people
Tents? No
Cost of tent pitch?
Electricity at the pitch? Yes
Showers? Yes
Onsite Entertainment? No
Opening times? End April - End October

Warden Springs Holiday Park

Address: Warden Point, Eastchurch, Isle of Sheppy, Kent, ME12 4HF
Telephone: 0871 664 9791
Website: www.park-resorts.com
Extra charge for dogs? Yes
Any breed restrictions? Yes
Dog bins? Yes
Area for walking dogs? Yes
Static caravans? Yes

Cost of static? ?
Mobile caravans? Yes
Cost of mobile? ?
Tents? Yes
Cost of tent pitch? ?
Electricity at the pitch? Yes
Showers? Yes
Onsite Entertainment? Yes
Opening times? March - End October
Comments: No Dangerous Breeds.

Welsummer Camping

Address: Chalk House, LenhamRoad, Platt's Heath, Harrietsham, Kent, ME17 1NQ
Telephone: 01622 844 048
Website:
Extra charge for dogs? No
Any breed restrictions? No
Dog bins? No
Area for walking dogs? Yes
Static caravans? No
Cost of static?
Mobile caravans? No
Cost of mobile?
Tents? Yes
Cost of tent pitch? From £9.60 per night
Electricity at the pitch? No
Showers? No
Onsite Entertainment? Yes
Opening times? April - October
Comments: Dogs must be kept on a lead. There is a communal fire.

Woodlands Park Camping Park

Address: Tenterden Road, Biddenden, Kent, TN27 8BT
Telephone: 01580 291216
Website: www.campingsite.co.uk
Extra charge for dogs? No
Any breed restrictions? No
Dog bins? No
Area for walking dogs? Yes
Static caravans? No
Cost of static?
Mobile caravans? Yes
Cost of mobile? From £12.00 - £14.00 for 2 people per night
Tents? Yes
Cost of tent pitch? From £2.50 - £3.00 per adult per night
Electricity at the pitch? Yes
Showers? Yes
Onsite Entertainment? No
Opening times? Begin March - End October (Weather Permitting)
Comments: Dogs must be kept on a lead

Woolmans Wood Camping Site

Address: Bridgewood, Rochester, Chatham, Kent, ME5 9SB
Telephone: 01634 867685
Website:
Extra charge for dogs? No
Any breed restrictions? Yes
Dog bins? No
Area for walking dogs? No
Static caravans? No
Cost of static?
Mobile caravans? Yes
Cost of mobile? From £15.00 per night
Tents? No
Cost of tent pitch?
Electricity at the pitch? Yes
Showers? Yes
Onsite Entertainment? No
Opening times? All Year

Comments: Adult only park. Small and Medium dogs only.

Palmers Farm Camp Site

Address: Fairdene, Palmers Farm, Fordcombe, Tunbridge Wells, Kent, TN3 0RN

Telephone: 01892 740209

Website:

Extra charge for dogs? No

Any breed restrictions? No

Dog bins? No

Area for walking dogs? Yes

Static caravans? No

Cost of static?

Mobile caravans? Yes

Cost of mobile? From £4.00 per night per person

Tents? Yes

Cost of tent pitch? From £4.00 per night per person

Electricity at the pitch? No

Showers? No

Onsite Entertainment? No

Opening times? April - October

Lancashire

A & J Knowles

Address: Edisford Camp Site, Edisford Bridge, Edisford Rd, Clitheroe, Lancashire BB7 3LJ

Telephone: 01200 427868

Website: www.thecampingandcaravanningclub.co.uk

Extra charge for dogs? No

Any breed restrictions? No

Dog bins? Yes

Area for walking dogs? Off Site

Static caravans? No

Cost of static?

Mobile caravans? Yes

Cost of mobile? From £10.00 per night

Tents? Yes

Cost of tent pitch? From £7.00 per night

Electricity at the pitch? Yes

Showers? Yes

Onsite Entertainment? No

Opening times? March - January

Abbey Farm Caravan Park

Address: Dark Lane Farm, Dark Lane, Lathom, Ormskirk, Lancashire L40 5TR

Telephone: 01695 572686

Website: www.abbeyfarmcaravanpark.co.uk

Extra charge for dogs? No

Any breed restrictions? No

Dog bins? Yes

Area for walking dogs? Yes

Static caravans? No

Cost of static?

Mobile caravans? Yes

Cost of mobile? From £15.20 per night

Tents? Yes

Cost of tent pitch? From £11.00 per night

Electricity at the pitch? Yes

Showers? Yes

Onsite Entertainment? No

Opening times? All Year

Beacon Fell View Holiday Park

Address: 110, Higher Rd, Longridge, Preston, Lancashire PR3 2TF

Telephone: 01772 785434

Website: www.hagansleisure.co.uk

Extra charge for dogs? Yes

Any breed restrictions? Yes

Dog bins? Yes

Area for walking dogs? Yes

Static caravans? Yes

Cost of static? From £153.00 per week

Mobile caravans? Yes

Cost of mobile? From £5.50 per night

Tents? Yes

Cost of tent pitch? From £5.50 per night

Electricity at the pitch? Yes

Showers? Yes

Onsite Entertainment? Yes

Opening times? 1st March - 11th November

Blackpool South Caravan Club Site

Address: Cropper Road, Marton, Blackpool, Lancashire FY4 5LB

Telephone: 01253 762051

Website: www.thecaravanclub.co.uk

Extra charge for dogs? No

Any breed restrictions? No
Dog bins? Yes
Area for walking dogs? Off Site
Static caravans? No
Cost of static?
Mobile caravans? Yes
Cost of mobile? From £4.60 per adult & £4.80 per pitch
Tents? No
Cost of tent pitch?
Electricity at the pitch? Yes
Showers? Yes
Onsite Entertainment? No
Opening times? 7th March - 5th January

Comments: Dogs must be kept on a lead at all times. This is a members club only.

Bolton Holmes & Detrongate Holiday Park

Address: Bolton Holmes Farm, Bolton Le Sands, Carnforth, Lancashire LA5 8ES
Telephone: 01524 732854
Website: www.holgates.co.uk
Extra charge for dogs? Yes
Any breed restrictions? No
Dog bins? No
Area for walking dogs? Yes
Static caravans? No
Cost of static?
Mobile caravans? Yes
Cost of mobile? From £8.00 per night
Tents? Yes
Cost of tent pitch? From £8.00 per night
Electricity at the pitch? Yes
Showers? Yes
Onsite Entertainment? No
Opening times? 1st March - 31st October

Bridge Heywood Caravan Park

Address: Dunkirk Farm, Whalley Rd, Read, Burnley, Lancashire BB12 7RR
Telephone: 01254 886103
Website:
Extra charge for dogs? No
Any breed restrictions? No
Dog bins? No
Area for walking dogs? Yes
Static caravans? No
Cost of static?
Mobile caravans? Yes
Cost of mobile? From £10.00 per night
Tents? No
Cost of tent pitch?
Electricity at the pitch? Yes
Showers? Yes
Onsite Entertainment? No
Opening times? March - January

Bridge House Marina

Address: Nateby Crossings Lane, Nateby, Preston, Lancashire PR3 0JJ
Telephone: 01995 603207
Website: www.bridgehousemarina.co.uk
Extra charge for dogs? No
Any breed restrictions? No
Dog bins? No
Area for walking dogs? Off Site
Static caravans? No
Cost of static?
Mobile caravans? Yes
Cost of mobile? From £17.50 per caravan with electric and awning
Tents? No
Cost of tent pitch?
Electricity at the pitch? Yes
Showers? Yes
Onsite Entertainment? No
Opening times? 1st March - 4th January

Comments: Dogs must be kept on a lead.

Brocklehead Farm

Address: Roman Road, Blacksnape, Darwen, Lancashire BB3 3PJ

Telephone: 01254 703742

Website: www.brockleheadpark.co.uk

Extra charge for dogs? No

Any breed restrictions? Yes

Dog bins? Yes

Area for walking dogs? Off Site

Static caravans? No

Cost of static?

Mobile caravans? Yes

Cost of mobile? From £10.00 for 2 people per night

Tents? Yes

Cost of tent pitch? From £10.00 for 2 people per night

Electricity at the pitch? Yes

Showers? Yes

Onsite Entertainment? No

Opening times? March - October

Comments: No Rottweilers.

Bryning Caravan Park

Address: C/O Westwinds, Bryning Lane, Warton, Preston, Lancashire PR4 1TN

Telephone: 01772 632259

Website: www.bryningcaravanpark.co.uk

Extra charge for dogs? No

Any breed restrictions? No

Dog bins? No

Area for walking dogs? Off Site

Static caravans? No

Cost of static?

Mobile caravans? Yes

Cost of mobile? From £9.50 per night

Tents? No

Cost of tent pitch?

Electricity at the pitch? Yes

Showers? No

Onsite Entertainment? No

Opening times? All Year

Burrs Country Park Club Site

Address: Woodhill Road, Bury, Lancashire BL8 1BN

Telephone: 0161 761 0489

Website: www.caravanclub.co.uk

Extra charge for dogs? No

Any breed restrictions? No

Dog bins? Yes

Area for walking dogs? Off Site

Static caravans? No

Cost of static?

Mobile caravans? Yes

Cost of mobile? From £14.00 per pitch for 2 people including electric for members £21.00 for non members

Tents? No

Cost of tent pitch?

Electricity at the pitch? Yes

Showers? Yes

Onsite Entertainment? No

Opening times? All Year

Comments: Dogs must be kept on a lead.

Cala Gran Holiday Park

Address: Fleetwood Road, Fleetwood, Lancashire FY7 8JY

Telephone: 01253 872555

Website: www.havenholidays.co.uk

Extra charge for dogs? Yes

Any breed restrictions? Yes

Dog bins? Yes

Area for walking dogs? No

Static caravans? Yes
Cost of static? From £199.00 per week
Mobile caravans? No
Cost of mobile?
Tents? No
Cost of tent pitch?
Electricity at the pitch? No
Showers? No
Onsite Entertainment? Yes
Opening times? March - October
Comments: No Dangerous Breeds.

Charity Farm Caravan Park

Address: Chorley, Lancashire WN6 9PP
Telephone: 01257 451326
Website: www.charityfarmonline.co.uk
Extra charge for dogs? No
Any breed restrictions? Yes
Dog bins? Yes
Area for walking dogs? Yes
Static caravans? No
Cost of static?
Mobile caravans? Yes
Cost of mobile? From £14.50 per night
Tents? Yes
Cost of tent pitch? From £10.00 per night
Electricity at the pitch? Yes
Showers? Yes
Onsite Entertainment? No
Opening times? All Year
Comments: No Dangerous Breeds, Dogs must be kept on a lead.

Claylands Caravan Park

Address: Cabus, Garstang, Lancashire PR3 1AJ
Telephone: 01524 791242
Website: www.claylands.com
Extra charge for dogs? Yes
Any breed restrictions? No
Dog bins? Yes
Area for walking dogs? Yes
Static caravans? No
Cost of static?
Mobile caravans? Yes
Cost of mobile? From £12.00 per night
Tents? Yes
Cost of tent pitch? From £9.00 per night
Electricity at the pitch? Yes
Showers? Yes
Onsite Entertainment? Yes
Opening times? March - November
Comments: Dogs must be kept on a lead.

Clifton Fields Caravan Park

Address: Peel Road, Blackpool, Lancashire FY4 5JU
Telephone: 01253 761676
Website: www.clifton-fields.co.uk
Extra charge for dogs? No
Any breed restrictions? No
Dog bins? Yes
Area for walking dogs? Yes
Static caravans? No
Cost of static?
Mobile caravans? Yes
Cost of mobile? From £16.00 per night with electric for 2 adults
Tents? No
Cost of tent pitch?
Electricity at the pitch? Yes
Showers? Yes
Onsite Entertainment? No
Opening times? 1st March - 31st October
Comments: There have a sister park next door where there is a clubhouse.

Clitheroe Camping & Caravanning Club Site

Address: Edisford Road, Clitheroe, Lancashire BB7 3LA

Telephone: 01200 425294

Website: www.thecampingandcaravanningclub.co.uk

Extra charge for dogs? No
Any breed restrictions? No
Dog bins? Yes
Area for walking dogs? Off Site
Static caravans? No
Cost of static?
Mobile caravans? Yes
Cost of mobile? From £5.15 per adult per night + £6.00 site fee
Tents? Yes
Cost of tent pitch? From £5.15 per adult per night + £6.00 site fee
Electricity at the pitch? Yes
Showers? Yes
Onsite Entertainment? No
Opening times? March - End October

Cockerham Sands Country Park

Address: Cockerham, Lancaster, Lancashire LA2 0BB

Telephone: 01524 751387

Website: www.cockerhamsandscountrypark.co.uk

Extra charge for dogs? Yes
Any breed restrictions? No
Dog bins? Yes
Area for walking dogs? Yes
Static caravans? Yes
Cost of static? From £190.00 per week
Mobile caravans? No
Cost of mobile?
Tents? No
Cost of tent pitch?
Electricity at the pitch? No
Showers? No
Onsite Entertainment? Yes
Opening times? March - End November

Crawford Camping & Caravan Park

Address: Crawford, Lancashire ML12 6TW

Telephone: 07799 306821

Website:

Extra charge for dogs? No
Any breed restrictions? No
Dog bins? Yes
Area for walking dogs? Yes
Static caravans? No
Cost of static?
Mobile caravans? Yes
Cost of mobile? From £15.00 per night
Tents? No
Cost of tent pitch? From £10.00 per night
Electricity at the pitch? Yes
Showers? Yes
Onsite Entertainment? No
Opening times? March - November

Comments: There is a children's playground on site and a pub across the road.

Dalesbridge The Outdooor Centre

Address: Austwick, Lancaster, Lancashire LA2 8AZ

Telephone: 015242 51021

Website: www.dalesbridge.co.uk

Extra charge for dogs? Yes
Any breed restrictions? No
Dog bins? Yes
Area for walking dogs? Yes
Static caravans? No
Cost of static?
Mobile caravans? Yes
Cost of mobile? From £10.00 per night for 2 people
Tents? Yes

Cost of tent pitch? From £4.00 per person & £2.00 per tent per night

Electricity at the pitch? Yes

Showers? Yes

Onsite Entertainment? Yes

Opening times? All Year

Comments: Bar open on Fridays, Saturdays and sometimes Sundays.

Flying Horseshoe Campsite

Address: Clapham, Lancaster, Lancashire LA2 8ES

Telephone: 015242 51532

Website: www.laughing-gravy.co.uk

Extra charge for dogs? Yes

Any breed restrictions? No

Dog bins? No

Area for walking dogs? Yes

Static caravans? No

Cost of static?

Mobile caravans? Yes

Cost of mobile? From £12.00 per night

Tents? Yes

Cost of tent pitch? From £4.50 per person per night

Electricity at the pitch? Yes

Showers? Yes

Onsite Entertainment? No

Opening times? April - October

Gatelands Caravan Park

Address: Gatelands, Carnforth, Lancashire LA6 1JH

Telephone: 01524 781133

Website:

Extra charge for dogs? No

Any breed restrictions? No

Dog bins? No

Area for walking dogs? Off Site

Static caravans? No

Cost of static?

Mobile caravans? Yes

Cost of mobile? From £9.00 per night with electric

Tents? Yes

Cost of tent pitch? From £5.00 per night

Electricity at the pitch? Yes

Showers? Yes

Onsite Entertainment? No

Opening times? 1st March - 31st October

Comments: Dogs must be kept on a lead.

Gelder Clough Park

Address: Ashworth Road, Heywood, Lancashire OL10 4BD

Telephone: 01706 364858

Website: www.ukparks.co.uk/gelderwood

Extra charge for dogs? No

Any breed restrictions? No

Dog bins? No

Area for walking dogs? Off Site

Static caravans? No

Cost of static?

Mobile caravans? Yes

Cost of mobile? From £15.00 per night

Tents? No

Cost of tent pitch?

Electricity at the pitch? Yes

Showers? Yes

Onsite Entertainment? No

Opening times? All Year

Gibraltar Farm Camp Site

Address: Gibraltar Farm, Silverdale, Carnforth, Lancashire LA5 0UA

Telephone: 01524 701736

Website: www.gibraltarfarm.co.uk

Extra charge for dogs? No

Any breed restrictions? Yes
Dog bins? No
Area for walking dogs? Off Site
Static caravans? No
Cost of static?
Mobile caravans? Yes
Cost of mobile? From £14.00 per night
Tents? Yes
Cost of tent pitch? From £8.00 per night for 2 man tent
Electricity at the pitch? Yes
Showers? Yes
Onsite Entertainment? No
Opening times? April - October
Comments: There are some breed restrictions so have to check first.

Glenfield Caravan Park

Address: Smallwood Hey, Pilling, Preston, Lancashire PR3 6HE
Telephone: 01253 790782
Website: www.luxuryparks.co.uk
Extra charge for dogs? No
Any breed restrictions? No
Dog bins? Yes
Area for walking dogs? Yes
Static caravans? No
Cost of static?
Mobile caravans? Yes
Cost of mobile? From
Tents? No
Cost of tent pitch?
Electricity at the pitch? Yes
Showers? Yes
Onsite Entertainment? No
Opening times? March - January

Greenacres Camping & Caravan Site

Address: Blackpool, Lancashire FY4 5QQ
Telephone: 01253 696266
Website:
Extra charge for dogs? No
Any breed restrictions? No
Dog bins? No
Area for walking dogs? Off Site
Static caravans? No
Cost of static?
Mobile caravans? Yes
Cost of mobile? From £8.00 per night
Tents? Yes
Cost of tent pitch? From £6.00 per night
Electricity at the pitch? No
Showers? No
Onsite Entertainment? No
Opening times? All Year (Weather Permitting)
Comments: Dogs must be kept on a lead and kept under control.

Greenbank Farm

Address: Wigan Road, Leyland, Lancashire PR25 5SB
Telephone: 01772 433123
Website:
Extra charge for dogs? No
Any breed restrictions? No
Dog bins? No
Area for walking dogs? Off Site
Static caravans? No
Cost of static?
Mobile caravans? Yes
Cost of mobile? From £6.00 per night with electric
Tents? No
Cost of tent pitch?
Electricity at the pitch? Yes
Showers? No
Onsite Entertainment? No
Opening times? All Year

Grisedale Farm

Address: Leighton, Carnforth, Lancashire LA5 9ST

Telephone: 01524 734360

Website: www.grisedalefarm.co.uk

Extra charge for dogs? No

Any breed restrictions? No

Dog bins? No

Area for walking dogs? Off Site

Static caravans? No

Cost of static?

Mobile caravans? Yes

Cost of mobile? From £12.00 per night

Tents? No

Cost of tent pitch?

Electricity at the pitch? Yes

Showers? No

Onsite Entertainment? No

Opening times? All Year

Comments: Maximum of 2 Dogs per pitch.

H E & M Hird

Address: Wood End Farm, Austwick, Lancaster, Lancashire LA2 8DH

Telephone: 015242 51296

Website: www.woodendcampsite.co.uk

Extra charge for dogs? No

Any breed restrictions? No

Dog bins? No

Area for walking dogs? Off Site

Static caravans? No

Cost of static?

Mobile caravans? Yes

Cost of mobile? From £14.00 per night for 2 people

Tents? Yes

Cost of tent pitch? From £12.00 per night for 2 people

Electricity at the pitch? Yes (Caravans only)

Showers? Yes

Onsite Entertainment? No

Opening times? January - December

Hampton Road Caravan Park

Address: Hampton Rd, Blackpool, Lancashire FY4 1JB

Telephone: 01253 341020

Website: www.hamptonroadsc.co.uk

Extra charge for dogs? No

Any breed restrictions? No

Dog bins? Yes

Area for walking dogs? No

Static caravans? No

Cost of static?

Mobile caravans? Yes

Cost of mobile? From £14.00 - £22.00 per night

Tents? No

Cost of tent pitch?

Electricity at the pitch? Yes

Showers? Yes

Onsite Entertainment? Yes

Opening times? All Year

Comments: There is a Clubhouse on site.

Haven Holidays

Address: Marton Mere Holiday Village, Mythop Rd, Blackpool, Lancashire FY4 4XN

Telephone: 0871 2301900

Website: www.haven.com

Extra charge for dogs? Yes

Any breed restrictions? Yes

Dog bins? Yes

Area for walking dogs? No

Static caravans? Yes

Cost of static? Prices vary as discounts may apply

Mobile caravans? Yes

Cost of mobile? Prices vary as discounts may apply
Tents? Yes
Cost of tent pitch? Prices vary as discounts may apply
Electricity at the pitch? Yes
Showers? Yes
Onsite Entertainment? Yes
Opening times? March - October
Comments: No Dangerous Breeds. Dogs must be kept on a lead at all times.

Highgate Barn

Address: Highgate Lane, Stalmine, Poulton Le Fylde, Lancashire FY6 0JF
Telephone: 01253 702510
Website:
Extra charge for dogs? No
Any breed restrictions? No
Dog bins? Yes
Area for walking dogs? Yes
Static caravans? No
Cost of static?
Mobile caravans? Yes
Cost of mobile? From £15.00 per night
Tents? Yes
Cost of tent pitch? From £15.00 per night
Electricity at the pitch? Yes
Showers? Yes
Onsite Entertainment? Fishing
Opening times? All Year

Hillcrest Caravan Park

Address: Kirkham, Lancashire PR4 3NB
Telephone: 01253 836614
Website:
Extra charge for dogs? No
Any breed restrictions? No
Dog bins? No
Area for walking dogs? Yes
Static caravans? No
Cost of static?
Mobile caravans? Yes
Cost of mobile? From £12.00 per night
Tents? No
Cost of tent pitch?
Electricity at the pitch? Yes
Showers? Yes
Onsite Entertainment? No
Opening times? 1st March - 31st October
Comments: Dogs must be kept under control.

Holgates Caravan Parks Ltd

Address: Middlebrow Plain, Cove Rd, Silverdale, Carnforth, Lancashire LA5 0SH
Telephone: 01524 701508
Website: www.holgates.co.uk
Extra charge for dogs? No
Any breed restrictions? ?
Dog bins? Yes
Area for walking dogs? Yes
Static caravans? Yes
Cost of static? From £285.00 per week
Mobile caravans? Yes
Cost of mobile? From £33.00 per night
Tents? Yes
Cost of tent pitch? From £30.00 per night
Electricity at the pitch? Yes
Showers? Yes
Onsite Entertainment? Yes
Opening times? 22nd December - Early November

Holme Head Caravan Park

Address: Holme Lea, Ingleton, Carnforth, Lancashire LA6 3ET
Telephone: 01524 241874
Website:
Extra charge for dogs? No

Any breed restrictions? No
Dog bins? Yes
Area for walking dogs? Off Site
Static caravans? Yes
Cost of static? From £80.00 per week
Mobile caravans? Yes
Cost of mobile? From £8.00 per night
Tents? No
Cost of tent pitch?
Electricity at the pitch? Yes
Showers? Yes
Onsite Entertainment? No
Opening times? All Year

John S Brown

Address: Ireby Green Caravan Park, Ireby, Carnforth, Lancashire LA6 2JH
Telephone: 015242 41203
Website:
Extra charge for dogs? No
Any breed restrictions? Yes
Dog bins? No
Area for walking dogs? Off Site
Static caravans? No
Cost of static?
Mobile caravans? Yes
Cost of mobile? From £14.00 per night
Tents? No
Cost of tent pitch?
Electricity at the pitch? Yes
Showers? Yes
Onsite Entertainment? No
Opening times? Begin March - End October

Kneps Farm Enterprises

Address: Caravan Park, River Rd, Thornton-Cleveleys, Lancashire FY5 5LR
Telephone: 01253 823632
Website: www.knepsfarm.co.uk
Extra charge for dogs? Yes
Any breed restrictions? Yes
Dog bins? No
Area for walking dogs? Off Site
Static caravans? No
Cost of static?
Mobile caravans? Yes
Cost of mobile? From £17.50 per night for 2 people
Tents? No
Cost of tent pitch?
Electricity at the pitch? Yes
Showers? Yes
Onsite Entertainment? No
Opening times? March - Mid November
Comments: Maximum of 2 dogs. No Dangerous Breeds.

Laundsfield Caravan Site

Address: Stoney Lane, Galgate, Nr Lancaster, Lancashire LA2 0JZ
Telephone: 01524 751763
Website:
Extra charge for dogs? No
Any breed restrictions? No
Dog bins? No
Area for walking dogs? Yes
Static caravans? No
Cost of static?
Mobile caravans? Yes
Cost of mobile? From £10.00 per night for 2 people
Tents? Yes
Cost of tent pitch? From £10.00 per night for 2 people
Electricity at the pitch? No
Showers? Yes
Onsite Entertainment? No
Opening times? 1st March - End October

Comments: Dogs must be kept on a lead.

Leisure Lakes Caravan Park

Address: The Gravel, Mere Brow, Preston, Lancashire PR4 6JX
Telephone: 01772 813446
Website: www.leisurelakes.co.uk
Extra charge for dogs? No
Any breed restrictions? No
Dog bins? No
Area for walking dogs? Yes
Static caravans? No
Cost of static?
Mobile caravans? Yes
Cost of mobile? From £15.00 per night with electric
Tents? Yes
Cost of tent pitch? From £12.00 per night
Electricity at the pitch? Yes
Showers? Yes
Onsite Entertainment? Yes
Opening times? All Year
Comments: Dogs must be kept on a lead. There is a pub on site which has entertainment at weekends.

Little Orchard Caravan Site

Address: Kirkham, Lancashire PR4 3HN
Telephone: 01253 836658
Website: www.littleorchardcaravanpark.com
Extra charge for dogs? No
Any breed restrictions? Yes
Dog bins? Yes
Area for walking dogs? Yes
Static caravans? No
Cost of static?
Mobile caravans? Yes
Cost of mobile? From £15.50 with electric for 2 people per night
Tents? Yes
Cost of tent pitch? From £12.50 per night for 2 people
Electricity at the pitch? Yes
Showers? Yes
Onsite Entertainment? No
Opening times? 14th February - 1st January
Comments: No Dangerous Breeds. Maximum of 2 Dogs.

Little Stubbins

Address: Claughton-on-brock, Garstang, Lancashire PR3 0PL
Telephone: 01995 640376
Website: www.littlestubbins.co.uk
Extra charge for dogs? No
Any breed restrictions? No
Dog bins? Yes
Area for walking dogs? Yes
Static caravans? No
Cost of static?
Mobile caravans? Yes
Cost of mobile? From £10.00 per night
Tents? No
Cost of tent pitch?
Electricity at the pitch? Yes
Showers? Yes
Onsite Entertainment? No
Opening times? All Year

Lower Greenhill Caravan Site

Address: Kelbrook Rd, Salterforth, Barnoldswick, Lancashire BB18 5TG
Telephone: 01282 813067
Website:
Extra charge for dogs? No
Any breed restrictions? No

Dog bins? Yes
Area for walking dogs? Yes
Static caravans? No
Cost of static?
Mobile caravans? Yes
Cost of mobile? From £10.00 - £11.50 per night including electric
Tents? Yes
Cost of tent pitch? From £6.00 per night
Electricity at the pitch? Yes
Showers? Yes
Onsite Entertainment? No
Opening times? All Year

Manor House Park

Address: Kitty Lane, Blackpool, Lancashire FY4 5EG
Telephone: 01253 764723
Website: www.manorhousecaravanpark.co.uk
Extra charge for dogs? No
Any breed restrictions? Yes
Dog bins? Yes
Area for walking dogs? Off Site
Static caravans? No
Cost of static?
Mobile caravans? Yes
Cost of mobile? From £13.00 per night
Tents? No
Cost of tent pitch?
Electricity at the pitch? Yes
Showers? Yes
Onsite Entertainment? No
Opening times? All Year
Comments: No Dangerous Breeds

Marton Mere Holiday Village

Address: Mythop Road, Blackpool, Lancashire FY4 4XN
Telephone: 01253 767544
Website: www.haven.com
Extra charge for dogs? Yes
Any breed restrictions? Yes
Dog bins? Yes
Area for walking dogs? Yes
Static caravans? Yes
Cost of static? From £246.50 per week
Mobile caravans? Yes
Cost of mobile? ?
Tents? No
Cost of tent pitch?
Electricity at the pitch? Yes
Showers? Yes
Onsite Entertainment? Yes
Opening times? March - November
Comments: No Dangerous Breeds and no Rottweilers or Staffordshire Bull Terriers.

Morecambe Lodge Caravan Park

Address: Shore Lane, Carnforth, Lancashire LA5 8JP
Telephone: 01524 824361
Website: www.morecambe-lodge.co.uk
Extra charge for dogs? No
Any breed restrictions? No
Dog bins? No
Area for walking dogs? Yes
Static caravans? No
Cost of static?
Mobile caravans? Yes
Cost of mobile? From £16.50 per night
Tents? No
Cost of tent pitch?
Electricity at the pitch? Yes
Showers? Yes
Onsite Entertainment? No
Opening times? 1st March - 31st October

Mosswood Caravan Park

Address: Crimbles Lane, Cockerham, Lancashire LA2 0ES
Telephone: 01524 791041
Website: www.mosswood.co.uk
Extra charge for dogs? No
Any breed restrictions? No
Dog bins? Yes
Area for walking dogs? Yes
Static caravans? No
Cost of static?
Mobile caravans? Yes
Cost of mobile? From £18.00 - £22.00 per night
Tents? No
Cost of tent pitch?
Electricity at the pitch? Yes
Showers? Yes
Onsite Entertainment? No
Opening times? 1st March - 31st October

Mowbreck Holiday & Residential Park

Address: Mowbreck Lane, Wesham, Preston, Lancashire PR4 3HA
Telephone: 01772 682494
Website: www.mowbreckpark.co.uk
Extra charge for dogs? Yes
Any breed restrictions? Yes
Dog bins? Yes
Area for walking dogs? Yes
Static caravans? Yes
Cost of static? From £265.00 per week
Mobile caravans? No
Cost of mobile?
Tents? No
Cost of tent pitch?
Electricity at the pitch? No
Showers? No
Onsite Entertainment? No
Opening times? 1st March - 16th January
Comments: Only allow small dogs.

Near Moss Farm Leisure Ltd

Address: Gulf Lane, Cockerham, Lancaster, Lancashire LA2 0ER
Telephone: 01253 790504
Website: www.nearmossfarm.co.uk
Extra charge for dogs? Yes
Any breed restrictions? No
Dog bins? No
Area for walking dogs? Yes
Static caravans? No
Cost of static?
Mobile caravans? Yes
Cost of mobile? From £10.00 per pitch + £1.00 per person per night
Tents? No
Cost of tent pitch?
Electricity at the pitch? Yes
Showers? Yes
Onsite Entertainment? Yes
Opening times? All Year
Comments: There is a games room and fishing lake on site. Maximum of 2 dogs per pitch.

Netherbeck Holiday Home Park

Address: North Rd, Carnforth, Lancashire LA5 9NG
Telephone: 01524 735101
Website: www.holgates.co.uk
Extra charge for dogs? Yes (Statics only)
Any breed restrictions? No
Dog bins? Yes
Area for walking dogs? Yes
Static caravans? Yes
Cost of static? From £285.00 per week
Mobile caravans? Yes
Cost of mobile? From £33.00 per night
Tents? Yes

Cost of tent pitch? From £30.00 per night
Electricity at the pitch? Yes
Showers? Yes
Onsite Entertainment? Yes
Opening times? 23rd December - 5th November

Oaklands Caravan Park Ltd

Address: Lytham Rd, Warton, Preston, Lancashire PR4 1AH
Telephone: 01772 634459
Website: www.oaklandscaravanpark.com
Extra charge for dogs? Yes
Any breed restrictions? No
Dog bins? Yes
Area for walking dogs? Yes
Static caravans? No
Cost of static?
Mobile caravans? Yes
Cost of mobile? From £10.00 per night
Tents? Yes
Cost of tent pitch? From £10.00 per night
Electricity at the pitch? Yes
Showers? Yes
Onsite Entertainment? No
Opening times? All Year

Ocean Edge Leisure Park

Address: Moneyclose Lane, Heysham, Morecambe, Lancashire LA3 2XA
Telephone: 01524 855657
Website: www.southlakelandparks.co.uk
Extra charge for dogs? Yes
Any breed restrictions? Yes
Dog bins? Yes
Area for walking dogs? Yes
Static caravans? Yes
Cost of static? From £149.00 - £497.00 per week
Mobile caravans? Yes
Cost of mobile? From £15.00 - £19.00 per night
Tents? Yes
Cost of tent pitch? From £15.00 - £19.00 per night
Electricity at the pitch? Yes
Showers? Yes
Onsite Entertainment? Sometimes
Opening times? March - October
Comments: No Dangerous Breeds.

Old Hall Caravan Park

Address: Capernwray, Carnforth, Lancashire LA6 1AD
Telephone: 01524 733276
Website: www.oldhallcaravanpark.co.uk
Extra charge for dogs? No
Any breed restrictions? No
Dog bins? No
Area for walking dogs? Yes
Static caravans? No
Cost of static?
Mobile caravans? Yes
Cost of mobile? From £16.50 per night
Tents? No
Cost of tent pitch?
Electricity at the pitch? Yes
Showers? Yes
Onsite Entertainment? No
Opening times? 1st March - 31st October
Comments: Dogs must be kept on a lead.

Oysterber Farm Caravan Club

Address: Low Bentham, Lancaster, Lancashire LA2 7ET
Telephone: 01524 261567
Website: www.oysterberfarm.co.uk

Extra charge for dogs? Yes
Any breed restrictions? No
Dog bins? No
Area for walking dogs? Off Site
Static caravans? No
Cost of static?
Mobile caravans? Yes
Cost of mobile? From £8.00 per night for 2 people
Tents? No
Cost of tent pitch?
Electricity at the pitch? Yes
Showers? Yes
Onsite Entertainment? No
Opening times? All Year

Parker

Address: Marsh House Farm, Crag Bank Road, Carnforth, Lancashire LA5 9JA
Telephone: 01524 732897
Website:
Extra charge for dogs? No
Any breed restrictions? No
Dog bins? No
Area for walking dogs? Off Site
Static caravans? No
Cost of static?
Mobile caravans? Yes
Cost of mobile? From £6.00 per night
Tents? Yes
Cost of tent pitch? From £6.00 per night
Electricity at the pitch? No
Showers? Yes
Onsite Entertainment? No
Opening times? March - October

Poulton Plaiz Holiday Park

Address: Garstang Road West, Poulton-Le-Fylde, Lancashire FY6 8AR
Telephone: 01253 888930
Website: www.poultonpiaz.co.uk
Extra charge for dogs? No
Any breed restrictions? No
Dog bins? No
Area for walking dogs? Yes
Static caravans? Yes
Cost of static? From £227.20 per week
Mobile caravans? No
Cost of mobile?
Tents? No
Cost of tent pitch?
Electricity at the pitch? No
Showers? No
Onsite Entertainment? Fishing
Opening times? March - End October

Primrose Bank Caravan Park Ltd

Address: High Moor Farm, Singleton Rd, Weeton, Preston, Lancashire PR4 3JJ
Telephone: 01253 836273
Website: www.primrosecaravanpark.co.uk
Extra charge for dogs? No
Any breed restrictions? Yes
Dog bins? No
Area for walking dogs? No
Static caravans? No
Cost of static?
Mobile caravans? Yes
Cost of mobile? From £14.50 per night
Tents? No
Cost of tent pitch?
Electricity at the pitch? Yes
Showers? Yes
Onsite Entertainment? No
Opening times? March - Mid January
Comments: No Dangerous Breeds and no Bull Mastifs or Staffordshire Bull Terriers.

Redwell Fisheries Caravan Park

Address: Kirkby Lonsdale Road, Arkholme, Lancashire LA6 1BQ

Telephone: 015242 21979

Website: www.redwellfisheries.co.uk

Extra charge for dogs? Yes

Any breed restrictions? Yes

Dog bins? No

Area for walking dogs? Yes

Static caravans? No

Cost of static?

Mobile caravans? Yes

Cost of mobile? From £12.00 - £14.00 for 2 people per night

Tents? Yes

Cost of tent pitch? From £6.00 per person per night

Electricity at the pitch? Yes

Showers? Yes

Onsite Entertainment? Fishing

Opening times? March - October

Comments: No Dangerous Breeds. Must bring your own dustbins and take rubbish away with you.

Regent Leisure Park

Address: Westgate, Morecambe, Lancashire LA3 3DF

Telephone: 01524 413940

Website: www.southlakelandparks.co.uk

Extra charge for dogs? Yes

Any breed restrictions? No

Dog bins? Yes

Area for walking dogs? Yes

Static caravans? Yes

Cost of static? From £178.00 per week

Mobile caravans? No

Cost of mobile?

Tents? No

Cost of tent pitch?

Electricity at the pitch? No

Showers? No

Onsite Entertainment? Yes

Opening times? March - November

Rimington Caravan Park

Address: Hardacre Lane, Rimington, Gisburn, Lancashire BB7 4EE

Telephone: 01200 445355

Website: www.rimingtoncaravanpark.co.uk

Extra charge for dogs? No

Any breed restrictions? Yes

Dog bins? Yes

Area for walking dogs? Yes

Static caravans? No

Cost of static?

Mobile caravans? Yes

Cost of mobile? From £16.00 per night with electric

Tents? No

Cost of tent pitch?

Electricity at the pitch? Yes

Showers? Yes

Onsite Entertainment? Yes

Opening times? 1st March - 31st October

Comments: No Dangerous Breeds including Alsatians and Rottweilers. .There is a Clubhouse on site.

Riverside Caravan Park

Address: Bentham, Lancaster, Lancashire LA2 7LW

Telephone: 01524 261272

Website: www.riversidecaravanpark.co.uk

Extra charge for dogs? Yes

Any breed restrictions? No

Dog bins? No

Area for walking dogs? Yes
Static caravans? No
Cost of static?
Mobile caravans? Yes
Cost of mobile? From £15.90 for 2 adults per night
Tents? No
Cost of tent pitch?
Electricity at the pitch? Yes
Showers? Yes
Onsite Entertainment? No
Opening times? March - January

Rose Acre Cottage

Address: Roseacre, Kirkham, Preston, Lancashire PR4 3UE
Telephone: 01772 690375
Website:
Extra charge for dogs? No
Any breed restrictions? No
Dog bins? No
Area for walking dogs? Off Site
Static caravans? No
Cost of static?
Mobile caravans? Yes
Cost of mobile? From £9.50 - £10.00 per night
Tents? No
Cost of tent pitch?
Electricity at the pitch? Yes
Showers? No
Onsite Entertainment? No
Opening times? All Year

Shaw Hall Caravan Park

Address: Smithy Lane, Scarisbrick, Ormskirk, Lancashire L40 8HJ
Telephone: 01704 840298
Website: www.shawhall.co.uk
Extra charge for dogs? No
Any breed restrictions? No
Dog bins? Yes
Area for walking dogs? Yes
Static caravans? No
Cost of static?
Mobile caravans? Yes
Cost of mobile? From £21.00 per night all inclusive
Tents? No
Cost of tent pitch?
Electricity at the pitch? Yes
Showers? Yes
Onsite Entertainment? Yes
Opening times? 1st March - 7th January

Six Arches Caravan Park

Address: Six Arches, Scorton, Preston, Lancashire PR3 1AL
Telephone: 01524 791683
Website: www.sixarchescaravanpark.co.uk
Extra charge for dogs? Yes
Any breed restrictions? No
Dog bins? Yes
Area for walking dogs? Yes
Static caravans? Yes
Cost of static? From £150.00 - £360.00 per week
Mobile caravans? Yes
Cost of mobile? From £13.00 - £14.50 per night
Tents? No
Cost of tent pitch?
Electricity at the pitch? Yes
Showers? Yes
Onsite Entertainment? Yes
Opening times? 1st March - End October
Comments: Maximum 2 dogs.

Stackstead Farm

Address: Ingleton, Carnforth, Lancashire LA6 3HS

Telephone: 01524 241386

Website: www.stacksteadfarm.co.uk

Extra charge for dogs? No

Any breed restrictions? No

Dog bins? No

Area for walking dogs? Off Site

Static caravans? No

Cost of static?

Mobile caravans? Yes

Cost of mobile? From £10.00 per night

Tents? No

Cost of tent pitch?

Electricity at the pitch? Yes

Showers? Yes

Onsite Entertainment? No

Opening times? All Year

Comments: Dogs must be kept on a lead.

Stanah House Caravan Park

Address: River Rd, Thornton-Cleveleys, Lancashire FY5 5LR

Telephone: 01253 824000

Website: www.touristsnetuk.com

Extra charge for dogs? No

Any breed restrictions? No

Dog bins? No

Area for walking dogs? Off Site

Static caravans? No

Cost of static?

Mobile caravans? Yes

Cost of mobile? From £16.00 per night with electric

Tents? Yes

Cost of tent pitch? From £12.00 per night for 2 people

Electricity at the pitch? Yes

Showers? Yes

Onsite Entertainment? No

Opening times? 1st March - 31st October

Comments: Dogs must be kept on a lead.

Stoneycroft Caravan Site

Address: 28 Chain House Lane, Whitestake, Preston, Lancashire PR4 4LE

Telephone: 01772 335879

Website:

Extra charge for dogs? No

Any breed restrictions? No

Dog bins? No

Area for walking dogs? Off Site

Static caravans? No

Cost of static?

Mobile caravans? Yes

Cost of mobile? From £12.00 per night

Tents? Yes

Cost of tent pitch? From £8.00 per pitch + £1.00 per person per night

Electricity at the pitch? Yes

Showers? Yes

Onsite Entertainment? No

Opening times? All Year

Tatham Bridge Inn Caravan & Camping

Address: Lower Tatham, Wennington, Lancashire LA2 8NL

Telephone: 015242 21326

Website:

Extra charge for dogs? No

Any breed restrictions? No

Dog bins? No

Area for walking dogs? No

Static caravans? No

Cost of static?

Mobile caravans? Yes

Cost of mobile? From £9.00 per night

Tents? No
Cost of tent pitch?
Electricity at the pitch? Yes
Showers? No
Onsite Entertainment? No
Opening times? All Year

The Camping & Caravanning Club

Address: Edisford Camp Site, Edisford Bridge, Edisford Rd, Clitheroe, Lancashire BB7 3LA
Telephone: 01200 425294
Website: www.thecampingandcaravanningclub.co.uk
Extra charge for dogs? No
Any breed restrictions? No
Dog bins? Yes
Area for walking dogs? Off Site
Static caravans? No
Cost of static?
Mobile caravans? Yes
Cost of mobile? From £5.15 per adult + £6.00 non members fee per night
Tents? Yes
Cost of tent pitch? From £5.15 per adult + £6.00 non members fee per night
Electricity at the pitch? Yes
Showers? Yes
Onsite Entertainment? No
Opening times? March - Early November

The Sands

Address: Carr Lane, Middleton, Morecambe, Lancashire LA3 3LH
Telephone: 01524 855064
Website:
Extra charge for dogs? No
Any breed restrictions? No
Dog bins? No
Area for walking dogs? Off Site
Static caravans? No
Cost of static?
Mobile caravans? Yes
Cost of mobile? From £10.00 per night
Tents? No
Cost of tent pitch?
Electricity at the pitch? Yes
Showers? No
Onsite Entertainment? Yes
Opening times? March - October

Three Rivers Woodlands Park

Address: Eaves Hall Lane, West Bradford, Clitheroe, Lancashire BB7 3JG
Telephone: 01200 423523
Website: www.threeriverspark.co.uk
Extra charge for dogs? Yes
Any breed restrictions? No
Dog bins? Yes
Area for walking dogs? Yes
Static caravans? Yes
Cost of static? From £241.00 per week
Mobile caravans? Yes
Cost of mobile? From £19.00 per night
Tents? Yes
Cost of tent pitch? From £18.00 per night
Electricity at the pitch? Yes
Showers? Yes
Onsite Entertainment? Yes (Weekends)
Opening times? All Year (Touring) February - November (Statics)

Venture Caravan Park

Address: Langridge Way, Westgate, Morecambe, Lancashire LA4 4TQ
Telephone: 01524 412986
Website: www.venturecaravanpark.co.uk

Extra charge for dogs? Yes
Any breed restrictions? No
Dog bins? Yes
Area for walking dogs? No
Static caravans? Yes
Cost of static? From £195.00 per week
Mobile caravans? Yes
Cost of mobile? From £18.00 per night with electric
Tents? No
Cost of tent pitch?
Electricity at the pitch? Yes
Showers? Yes
Onsite Entertainment? Yes
Opening times? All Year (Touring)

Westgate Caravan Park

Address: Westgate, Morecambe, Lancashire LA3 3DE
Telephone: 01524 411448
Website: www.westgatecaravanpark.co.uk
Extra charge for dogs? Yes
Any breed restrictions? No
Dog bins? No
Area for walking dogs? No
Static caravans? Yes
Cost of static? From £190.00 - £280.00 per week
Mobile caravans? Yes
Cost of mobile? From £13.50 per night
Tents? No
Cost of tent pitch?
Electricity at the pitch? Yes
Showers? Yes
Onsite Entertainment? No
Opening times? March - October

Willowbank Holiday Park

Address: Coastal Road, Ainsdale, Southport, Lancashire PR8 3ST
Telephone: 01704 571566
Website: www.willowbankcp.co.uk
Extra charge for dogs? Yes
Any breed restrictions? Yes
Dog bins? Yes
Area for walking dogs? Yes
Static caravans? No
Cost of static?
Mobile caravans? Yes
Cost of mobile? From £13.50 per night
Tents? No
Cost of tent pitch?
Electricity at the pitch? Yes
Showers? Yes
Onsite Entertainment? No
Opening times? 1st March - 10th January
Comments: No Dangerous Breeds. Only small and medium breeds. Dogs must be kept on a lead at all times. Maximum of 2 dogs.

Windy Harbour Holiday Centre

Address: Windy Harbour Road, Singleton, Poulton-Le-Fylde, Lancashire FY6 8NB
Telephone: 01253 883064
Website: www.partingtons.com
Extra charge for dogs? Yes
Any breed restrictions? Yes
Dog bins? Yes
Area for walking dogs? Yes
Static caravans? No
Cost of static?
Mobile caravans? Yes
Cost of mobile? From £14.50 per night
Tents? No
Cost of tent pitch?
Electricity at the pitch? Yes
Showers? Yes
Onsite Entertainment? Yes
Opening times? 1st March - 15th November

Comments: No Dangerous Breeds. Maxiumum 1 dog.

Wyreside Lakes Fishery

Address: Bayhorse, Lancashire LA2 9DG
Telephone: 01524 792093
Website: www.wyresidelake.co.uk
Extra charge for dogs? Yes
Any breed restrictions? No
Dog bins? Yes
Area for walking dogs? Yes
Static caravans? No
Cost of static?
Mobile caravans? Yes
Cost of mobile? From £5.00 per pitch + £3.50 per adult
Tents? No
Cost of tent pitch? From £5.00 per pitch + £3.50 per adult
Electricity at the pitch? No
Showers? Yes
Onsite Entertainment? Yes
Opening times? All Year

C W & W E Thompson

Address: Turnover Hall Farm, Rawcliffe Rd, St. Michaels, Preston, Lancashire PR3 0UE
Telephone: 01995 679275
Website:
Extra charge for dogs? No
Any breed restrictions? No
Dog bins? Yes
Area for walking dogs? Yes
Static caravans? No
Cost of static?
Mobile caravans? Yes
Cost of mobile? From £8.00 - £14.00 per night
Tents? No
Cost of tent pitch?
Electricity at the pitch? Yes
Showers? Yes
Onsite Entertainment? No
Opening times? March - October

Crawshaw Farm Caravan & Campsite

Address: Newton in Bowland, Clitheroe, Lancashire BB7 3EE
Telephone: 01200 446638
Website:
Extra charge for dogs? No
Any breed restrictions? Yes
Dog bins? No
Area for walking dogs? No
Static caravans? No
Cost of static?
Mobile caravans? Yes
Cost of mobile? From £5.00 per night
Tents? Yes
Cost of tent pitch? From £5.00 per night
Electricity at the pitch? No
Showers? No
Onsite Entertainment? No
Opening times? All Year
Comments: No Dangerous Breeds.

Glen Caravan Site

Address: Westgate, Morecambe, Lancashire LA3 3NR
Telephone: 01524 423896
Website:
Extra charge for dogs? No
Any breed restrictions? No
Dog bins? No
Area for walking dogs? Off Site
Static caravans? No
Cost of static?
Mobile caravans? Yes
Cost of mobile? From £8.50 per night
Tents? No

Cost of tent pitch?
Electricity at the pitch? Yes
Showers? Yes
Onsite Entertainment? No
Opening times? March - End October

Hollins Farm

Address: Far Arnside, Carnforth, Lancashire LA5 0SL
Telephone: 01524 701767
Website:
Extra charge for dogs? No
Any breed restrictions? Yes
Dog bins? Yes
Area for walking dogs? Yes
Static caravans? No
Cost of static?
Mobile caravans? Yes
Cost of mobile? From £10.00 per night
Tents? Yes
Cost of tent pitch? From £10.00 per night
Electricity at the pitch? No
Showers? Yes
Onsite Entertainment? No
Opening times? Easter - End October
Comments: No Dangerous Breeds. Maximum of 2 Dogs. Electricity is being put in for 2009.

Melbreak Caravan Park

Address: Carr lane, Middleton, Morecambe, Lancashire LA3 3LH
Telephone: 01524 852430
Website:
Extra charge for dogs? No
Any breed restrictions? No
Dog bins? No
Area for walking dogs? Off Site
Static caravans? No
Cost of static?
Mobile caravans? Yes
Cost of mobile? From £12.00 per night
Tents? Yes
Cost of tent pitch? From £10.00 per night
Electricity at the pitch? Yes
Showers? Yes
Onsite Entertainment? No
Opening times? March - October

Moorlands Caravan Park

Address: Ripponden Road, Denshaw, Oldham, Lancashire OL3 5UN
Telephone: 01457 874348
Website:
Extra charge for dogs? Yes
Any breed restrictions? Yes
Dog bins? No
Area for walking dogs? Yes
Static caravans? No
Cost of static?
Mobile caravans? Yes
Cost of mobile? From £14.00 per night for 2 people
Tents? Yes
Cost of tent pitch? From £4.00 per tent + £4.00 per person per night
Electricity at the pitch? Yes
Showers? Yes
Onsite Entertainment? No
Opening times? All Year
Comments: No Dangerous Breeds. Dogs must be kept on a lead.

North View Caravan Club

Address: Skitham Lane, Nateby, Garstang, Lancashire PR3 6BD
Telephone: 07961 228785
Website: www.garstang.net

Extra charge for dogs? No
Any breed restrictions? No
Dog bins? No
Area for walking dogs? Yes
Static caravans? No
Cost of static?
Mobile caravans? Yes
Cost of mobile? From £9.50 per night
Tents? No
Cost of tent pitch?
Electricity at the pitch? Yes
Showers? Yes
Onsite Entertainment? No
Opening times? All Year

Plex Moss Lane Caravan Park

Address: Plex Moss Lane, Off Moor Lane, Woodvale, Southport, Lancashire PR8 3NZ
Telephone: 01704 573259
Website:
Extra charge for dogs? No
Any breed restrictions? Yes
Dog bins? No
Area for walking dogs? Off Site
Static caravans? No
Cost of static?
Mobile caravans? Yes
Cost of mobile? From £12.00 per night for 2 people
Tents? No
Cost of tent pitch?
Electricity at the pitch? Yes
Showers? Yes
Onsite Entertainment? No
Opening times? April - End October
Comments: No Dangerous Breeds. Dogs must be kept on a lead. Adults only.

Royal Umpire Caravan Park

Address: Southport Road, Croston, Leyland, Lancashire PR5 7JB
Telephone: 01772 600257
Website: www.harrisonleisure.co.uk
Extra charge for dogs? No
Any breed restrictions? Yes
Dog bins? Yes
Area for walking dogs? Yes
Static caravans? No
Cost of static?
Mobile caravans? Yes
Cost of mobile? From £14.00 not including weekends
Tents? Yes
Cost of tent pitch? From £13.00 per night
Electricity at the pitch? No
Showers? Yes
Onsite Entertainment? No
Opening times? 24th December - 6th November
Comments: No Dangerous Breeds.

Sandside Caravan Park

Address: The Shore, Bolton Le Sands, Carnforth, Lancashire LA5 8JS
Telephone: 01524 822311
Website:
Extra charge for dogs? No
Any breed restrictions? No
Dog bins? No
Area for walking dogs? Off Site
Static caravans? No
Cost of static?
Mobile caravans? Yes
Cost of mobile? From £15.50 per night
Tents? Yes
Cost of tent pitch? From £13.50 per night
Electricity at the pitch? Yes
Showers? Yes

Onsite Entertainment? No
Opening times? March - October

Sunnyside Camp Site

Address: 250, Oxcliffe Rd, Morecambe, Lancashire LA3 3EH
Telephone: 01524 418373
Website:
Extra charge for dogs? No
Any breed restrictions? No
Dog bins? No
Area for walking dogs? Yes
Static caravans? No
Cost of static?
Mobile caravans? Yes
Cost of mobile? From £8.00 per night
Tents? Yes
Cost of tent pitch? From £8.00 per night
Electricity at the pitch? Yes
Showers? Yes
Onsite Entertainment? No
Opening times? March - October

Tristams Farm Caravan Park

Address: Ormskirk, Lancashire L39 8RJ
Telephone: 01704 840323
Website: www.thecaravanclub.co.uk
Extra charge for dogs? No
Any breed restrictions? No
Dog bins? No
Area for walking dogs? Yes
Static caravans? No
Cost of static?
Mobile caravans? Yes
Cost of mobile? From £10.00 per night with electric
Tents? No
Cost of tent pitch?
Electricity at the pitch? Yes
Showers? No
Onsite Entertainment? No
Opening times? All Year
Comments: Maximum 2 dogs. Dogs must be kept on a lead.

Redleigh Orchard Touring Caravan Park

Address: Cropper Rd, Blackpool, Lancashire FY4 5LB
Telephone: 01253 691459
Website: www.redleighorchard.co.uk
Extra charge for dogs? No
Any breed restrictions? No
Dog bins? Yes
Area for walking dogs? Yes
Static caravans?
Cost of static?
Mobile caravans? Yes
Cost of mobile? From £15.00 per night with electric
Tents? No
Cost of tent pitch?
Electricity at the pitch? Yes
Showers? Yes
Onsite Entertainment? No
Opening times? April - End October
Comments: Dogs must be kept on a lead.

Woodclose Caravan Park

Address: Kirkby Lonsdale, Lancashire LA6 2SE
Telephone: 01524 271597
Website: www.woodclosepark.com
Extra charge for dogs? Yes
Any breed restrictions? Yes
Dog bins? Yes
Area for walking dogs? Off Site
Static caravans? No
Cost of static?

Mobile caravans? Yes
Cost of mobile? From £10.00 per night
Tents? Yes
Cost of tent pitch? From £12.50 per night for 2 man tent
Electricity at the pitch? Yes
Showers? Yes
Onsite Entertainment? No
Opening times? 1st March - End October
Comments: No Dangerous Breeds.

Leicestershire

Billesdon - Grange Farm

Address: Tilton On The Hill, Leicester, Leicestershire LE7 9PD
Telephone: 0116 259 7220
Website:
Extra charge for dogs? No
Any breed restrictions? No
Dog bins? No
Area for walking dogs? Yes
Static caravans? No
Cost of static?
Mobile caravans? Yes
Cost of mobile? From £6.00 per night
Tents? Yes
Cost of tent pitch? From £5.00 per night
Electricity at the pitch? Yes
Showers? No
Onsite Entertainment? No
Opening times? All Year

Bosworth Caravan Park

Address: Market Bosworth, Leicestershire CV13 0BA
Telephone: 01455 292259
Website: www.bosworthcaravanpark.co.uk
Extra charge for dogs? No
Any breed restrictions? Yes
Dog bins? Yes
Area for walking dogs? Yes
Static caravans? No
Cost of static?
Mobile caravans? Yes
Cost of mobile? From £10.00 per night
Tents? No
Cost of tent pitch?
Electricity at the pitch? Yes
Showers? No
Onsite Entertainment? Off Site
Opening times? All Year
Comments: No Rottweilers.

Donington Park Farmhouse Hotel

Address: Castle Donington, Leicestershire DE74 2RN
Telephone: 01332 862409
Website: www.parkfarmhouse.co.uk
Extra charge for dogs? No
Any breed restrictions? Yes
Dog bins? No
Area for walking dogs? Yes
Static caravans? No
Cost of static?
Mobile caravans? Yes
Cost of mobile? From £20.00 per night
Tents? Yes
Cost of tent pitch? From £20.00 per night for framed tent + 2 people
Electricity at the pitch? Yes
Showers? Yes
Onsite Entertainment? No
Opening times? All Year
Comments: Dogs must be kept on a lead.

Five Ways Lakes Fishery

Address: Coventry Road, Wolvey, Hinkley, Leicestershire LE10 3LD
Telephone: 01455 882961
Website:

Extra charge for dogs? No
Any breed restrictions? No
Dog bins? Yes
Area for walking dogs? Yes
Static caravans? No
Cost of static?
Mobile caravans? Yes
Cost of mobile? From £10.00 per night
Tents? Yes
Cost of tent pitch? From £10.00 per night
Electricity at the pitch? Yes
Showers? Yes
Onsite Entertainment? Fishing
Opening times? All Year

Greendale Farm Caravan & Camping Park

Address: Oakham, Leicestershire LE15 7LB
Telephone: 01664 474516
Website: www.rutlandgreendale.co.uk
Extra charge for dogs? Yes
Any breed restrictions? Yes
Dog bins? No
Area for walking dogs? Off Site
Static caravans? No
Cost of static?
Mobile caravans? Yes
Cost of mobile? From £16.00 per night
Tents? Yes
Cost of tent pitch? From £16.00 per night
Electricity at the pitch? Yes
Showers? Yes
Onsite Entertainment? No
Opening times? May - October
Comments: No Dangerous Breeds. No aggressive breeds.

Hallaton Caravan Club

Address: 38 Medbourne Road, Hallaton, Leicestershire LE16 8UH
Telephone: 01858 555639
Website: www.thecaravanclub.co.uk
Extra charge for dogs? No
Any breed restrictions? No
Dog bins? Yes
Area for walking dogs? Off Site
Static caravans?
Cost of static?
Mobile caravans? Yes
Cost of mobile? From £7.00 per night
Tents? No
Cost of tent pitch?
Electricity at the pitch? Yes
Showers? No
Onsite Entertainment? No
Opening times? All Year
Comments: Members of The Caravan Club only. Dogs must be kept on a lead.

Ingles Hill Farm

Address: Ashby de la Zouch, Leicestershire LE65 2TE
Telephone: 01530 412224
Website: www.ingleshillcaravansite.co.uk
Extra charge for dogs? No
Any breed restrictions? No
Dog bins? No
Area for walking dogs? Yes
Static caravans? No
Cost of static?
Mobile caravans? Yes
Cost of mobile? From £7.00 per night
Tents? Yes
Cost of tent pitch? From £5.00 per person per night
Electricity at the pitch? Yes

Showers? Yes
Onsite Entertainment? No
Opening times? All Year
Comments: Dogs must be kept on a lead.

Inmarla Caravan & Camping Park

Address: Hallaton Rd, Medbourne, Market Harborough, Leicestershire LE16 8DR
Telephone: 01858 565478
Website:
Extra charge for dogs? No
Any breed restrictions? No
Dog bins? No
Area for walking dogs? Yes
Static caravans? No
Cost of static?
Mobile caravans? Yes
Cost of mobile? From £15.00 per night with electric
Tents? Yes
Cost of tent pitch? From £10.00 per night for 2 people
Electricity at the pitch? Yes
Showers? Yes
Onsite Entertainment? No
Opening times? All Year

Leicester Hill Wood Caravan Club

Address: Ulverscroft Lane, Newtown Linford, Leicestershire LE6 0AJ
Telephone: 01530 244784
Website: www.thecaravanclub.co.uk
Extra charge for dogs? No
Any breed restrictions? No
Dog bins? No
Area for walking dogs? Off Site
Static caravans? No
Cost of static?
Mobile caravans? Yes
Cost of mobile? From £10.00 per night
Tents? No
Cost of tent pitch?
Electricity at the pitch? Yes
Showers? No
Onsite Entertainment? No
Opening times? All Year
Comments: Members of The Caravan Club only. Dogs must be kept on a lead.

Lower Grange Farm

Address: Grange Road, Hugglescote, Leicestershire LE67 2BT
Telephone: 01530 838074
Website: www.thecampingandcaravanningclub.co.uk
Extra charge for dogs? Yes
Any breed restrictions? No
Dog bins? No
Area for walking dogs? Yes
Static caravans? No
Cost of static?
Mobile caravans? Yes
Cost of mobile? From £10.00 per night
Tents? Yes
Cost of tent pitch? From £5.00 for 1st person, £4.00 per person after that per night
Electricity at the pitch? Yes
Showers? Yes
Onsite Entertainment? No
Opening times? All Year
Comments: Dogs must be kept on a lead. Children under 5 are free.

Mill Farm

Address: Chaveney Road, Quorn, Loughborough, Leicestershire LE12 8AD
Telephone: 01509 413760
Website:

Extra charge for dogs? No
Any breed restrictions? No
Dog bins? Yes
Area for walking dogs? Yes
Static caravans? No
Cost of static?
Mobile caravans? Yes
Cost of mobile? From £10.00 per night
Tents? Yes
Cost of tent pitch? From £6.00 per night
Electricity at the pitch? Yes
Showers? No
Onsite Entertainment? No
Opening times? All Year

Pinewood Lodge

Address: Overton Road, Ibstock, Leicestershire LE67 6PD
Telephone: 01530 264477
Website:
Extra charge for dogs? No
Any breed restrictions? No
Dog bins? No
Area for walking dogs? Yes
Static caravans? No
Cost of static?
Mobile caravans? Yes
Cost of mobile? From £15.00 per night
Tents? Yes
Cost of tent pitch? From £10.00 per night
Electricity at the pitch? Yes
Showers? Yes
Onsite Entertainment? Yes
Opening times? All Year
Comments: Dogs must be kept under control. There is a bar on site where they have a pool table and karaoke.

Proctors Pleasure Park

Address: Proctors Park Rd, Barrow Upon Soar, Loughborough, Leicestershire LE12 8QF
Telephone: 01509 412434
Website:
Extra charge for dogs? No
Any breed restrictions? No
Dog bins? No
Area for walking dogs? Yes
Static caravans? No
Cost of static?
Mobile caravans? Yes
Cost of mobile? From £12.00 per night for 2 adults
Tents? Yes
Cost of tent pitch? From £12.00 per night for 2 adults
Electricity at the pitch? Yes
Showers? Yes
Onsite Entertainment? Yes
Opening times? All Year
Comments: There is a Clubhouse on site.

Ranksborough Hall

Address: Oakham, Rutland, Leicestershire LE15 7SR
Telephone: 01572 722984
Website: www.ranksboroughhall.com
Extra charge for dogs? Yes
Any breed restrictions? No
Dog bins? No
Area for walking dogs? Off Site
Static caravans? No
Cost of static?
Mobile caravans? Yes
Cost of mobile? From £15.74 per night
Tents? Yes
Cost of tent pitch? From £11.75 per night

Electricity at the pitch? Yes
Showers? Yes
Onsite Entertainment? No
Opening times? All Year
Comments: Adults only. Dogs must be kept on a lead. Café/Shop on site

Rutland Caravan & Camping

Address: 3, Shepherds Lane, Greetham, Oakham, Leicestershire LE15 7NX
Telephone: 01572 813520
Website: www.rutlandcaravanandcamping.co.uk
Extra charge for dogs? No
Any breed restrictions? No
Dog bins? Yes
Area for walking dogs? Yes
Static caravans? No
Cost of static?
Mobile caravans? Yes
Cost of mobile? From £12.50 - £17.00 per night for 2 adults
Tents? Yes
Cost of tent pitch? From £12.50 - £17.00 per night for 2 adults
Electricity at the pitch? Yes (Not Tents)
Showers? Yes
Onsite Entertainment? No
Opening times? All Year
Comments: Dogs must be kept on a lead.

Trouts Ponds Farm Caravan Site

Address: Sheepy Magna, Atherstone, Leicestershire CV9 3RT
Telephone: 01827 880498
Website:
Extra charge for dogs? No
Any breed restrictions? No
Dog bins? No
Area for walking dogs? Yes
Static caravans? No
Cost of static?
Mobile caravans? Yes
Cost of mobile? From £5.00 per night
Tents? Yes
Cost of tent pitch? From £5.00 per night
Electricity at the pitch? No
Showers? No
Onsite Entertainment? No
Opening times? All Year
Comments: Dogs must be kept on a lead.

Ullesthorpe Garden Centre

Address: Lutterworth Road, Ullesthorpe, Leicestershire LE17 5DR
Telephone: 01455 202144
Website: www.ullesthorpegardencentre.co.uk
Extra charge for dogs? No
Any breed restrictions? No
Dog bins? No
Area for walking dogs? Yes
Static caravans? No
Cost of static?
Mobile caravans? Yes
Cost of mobile? From £6.00 per night
Tents? No
Cost of tent pitch?
Electricity at the pitch? No
Showers? No
Onsite Entertainment? No
Opening times? All Year (Weather Permitting)

Victoria Farm Caravan Club

Address: High Cross Road, Claybrooke Magna, Lutterworth, Leicestershire LE17 5AU

Telephone: 01455 208270

Website: www.victoria-farm.org

Extra charge for dogs? No

Any breed restrictions? No

Dog bins? No

Area for walking dogs? Yes

Static caravans? No

Cost of static?

Mobile caravans? Yes

Cost of mobile? From £7.00 per night

Tents? Yes

Cost of tent pitch? From £7.00 per night

Electricity at the pitch? Yes

Showers? Yes

Onsite Entertainment? No

Opening times? All Year

Whatoff Lodge Farm

Address: Woodhouse Road, Quorn, Loughborough, Leicestershire LE12 8AL

Telephone: 01509 412127

Website:

Extra charge for dogs? No

Any breed restrictions? No

Dog bins? No

Area for walking dogs? Off Site

Static caravans? No

Cost of static?

Mobile caravans? Yes

Cost of mobile? From £12.50 per night with electric

Tents? Yes

Cost of tent pitch? From £10.50 per night

Electricity at the pitch? Yes

Showers? Yes

Onsite Entertainment? No

Opening times? All Year

Comments: Dogs must be kept under control it is a working farm.

Wing Caravan & Camping

Address: Wing Hall, Station Rd, Wing, Oakham, Leicestershire LE15 8RY

Telephone: 01572 737709

Website: www.winghall.co.uk

Extra charge for dogs? No

Any breed restrictions? No

Dog bins? No

Area for walking dogs? Yes

Static caravans? No

Cost of static?

Mobile caravans? Yes

Cost of mobile? From £14.50 per night with electric

Tents? Yes

Cost of tent pitch? From £6.00 per adult £3.00 per child per night

Electricity at the pitch? Yes

Showers? Yes

Onsite Entertainment? No

Opening times? All Year

Comments: Dogs must be kept on a lead.

Wolvey Caravan & Camping Park

Address: Wolvey Villa Farm, Coventry Rd, Wolvey, Hinckley, Leicestershire LE10 3HF

Telephone: 01455 220630

Website: www.wolveycaravanpark.itgo.com

Extra charge for dogs? Yes

Any breed restrictions? No

Dog bins? No

Area for walking dogs? Yes

Static caravans? No

Cost of static?

Mobile caravans? Yes

Cost of mobile? From £12.00 per night

Tents? Yes

Cost of tent pitch? From £12.00 per night

Electricity at the pitch? Yes
Showers? Yes
Onsite Entertainment? Yes
Opening times? All Year

Hill Top Caravan & Leisure Park

Address: 67 Old Gate Road, Thrussington, Leicestershire LE7 4TL
Telephone: 01664 424357
Website:
Extra charge for dogs? Yes
Any breed restrictions? No
Dog bins? No
Area for walking dogs? No
Static caravans? No
Cost of static?
Mobile caravans? Yes
Cost of mobile? From £10.00 per night
Tents? No
Cost of tent pitch?
Electricity at the pitch? Yes
Showers? No
Onsite Entertainment? No
Opening times? All Year

Holly Farm Caravan Park & Fishery

Address: Willoughby Road, Ashby Magna, Leicestershire LE17 5NP
Telephone: 01455 202391
Website: www.hollyfarmfishery.com
Extra charge for dogs? No
Any breed restrictions? No
Dog bins? No
Area for walking dogs? Yes
Static caravans? No
Cost of static?
Mobile caravans? Yes
Cost of mobile? From £8.00 per night
Tents? No
Cost of tent pitch?
Electricity at the pitch? Yes
Showers? Yes
Onsite Entertainment? No
Opening times? All Year
Comments: There is fishing on site.

Anglia Motel

Address: A17 Washway Road, Fleet Hargate, Holbeach Lincolnshire PE12 8LT
Telephone: 01406 422766
Website: www.angliamotel.co.uk
Extra charge for dogs? No
Any breed restrictions? No
Dog bins? No
Area for walking dogs? Yes
Static caravans? No
Cost of static?
Mobile caravans? Yes
Cost of mobile? From £6.00 per night
Tents? Yes
Cost of tent pitch? From £5.00 per night
Electricity at the pitch? Yes
Showers? Yes
Onsite Entertainment? Yes
Opening times? All Year
Comments: Bar and Restaurant on site

Arklow House Farm

Address: Rotten Row, Theddlesthorpe St Helen, Mablethorpe, Lincolnshire LN12 1NX
Telephone: 01507 473761
Website:
Extra charge for dogs? No
Any breed restrictions? No
Dog bins? No
Area for walking dogs? Yes
Static caravans? No
Cost of static?
Mobile caravans? Yes
Cost of mobile? From £10.00 per night
Tents? Yes
Cost of tent pitch? From £10.00 per night
Electricity at the pitch? Yes
Showers? Yes
Onsite Entertainment? Yes
Opening times? All Year
Comments: Fishing and Pitch and Putt Golf

Ashby Park

Address: Ashby Park, Furze Hills, West Ashby, Horncastle, Lincolnshire LN9 5PP
Telephone: 01507 527966
Website:
Extra charge for dogs? No
Any breed restrictions? No
Dog bins? Yes
Area for walking dogs? Yes
Static caravans? No
Cost of static?
Mobile caravans? Yes
Cost of mobile? From £16.00 per night with electric
Tents? Yes
Cost of tent pitch? From £16.00 per night with electric
Electricity at the pitch? Yes
Showers? Yes
Onsite Entertainment? No
Opening times? March - End November
Comments: Dogs must be kept on a lead on site except in the exercise area.

Ashes Farm Camping and Caravan Park

Address: Marsh Lane, Orby, Lincolnshire PE24 5JA

Telephone: 01754 810953

Website:

Extra charge for dogs? Yes

Any breed restrictions? No

Dog bins? Yes

Area for walking dogs? Off Site

Static caravans? No

Cost of static?

Mobile caravans? Yes

Cost of mobile? From £8.00 - £10.00 per night

Tents? Yes

Cost of tent pitch? From £5.00 - £8.00 per night

Electricity at the pitch? Yes

Showers? Yes

Onsite Entertainment? No

Opening times? March - End October

Bainland Country Park Ltd

Address: Horncastle Rd, Roughton Moor, Woodhall Spa, Lincolnshire LN10 6UX

Telephone: 01526 352903

Website: www.bainland.co.uk

Extra charge for dogs? Yes

Any breed restrictions? No

Dog bins? Yes

Area for walking dogs? Yes

Static caravans? No

Cost of static?

Mobile caravans? Yes

Cost of mobile? From £16.00 - £18.00 per night

Tents? Yes

Cost of tent pitch? From £14.00 per night

Electricity at the pitch? Yes

Showers? Yes

Onsite Entertainment? Yes (peak times)

Opening times? All Year

Bardney Dairies

Address: Wragby, Lincoln, Lincolnshire LN8 5JW

Telephone: 01526 398236

Website:

Extra charge for dogs? No

Any breed restrictions? No

Dog bins? No

Area for walking dogs? Yes

Static caravans? No

Cost of static?

Mobile caravans? Yes

Cost of mobile? From £8.00 per night with electric

Tents? Yes

Cost of tent pitch? From £8.00 per night

Electricity at the pitch? Yes

Showers? No

Onsite Entertainment? No

Opening times? All Year

Comments: Dogs must be kept on a lead.

Barff Farm Fenside

Address: Fen Lane, Metheringham, Lincolnshire LN4 3AQ

Telephone: 01526 323319

Website: www.metheringhammusic factory.co.uk

Extra charge for dogs? No

Any breed restrictions? No

Dog bins? No

Area for walking dogs? Off Site

Static caravans? No

Cost of static?

Mobile caravans? Yes

Cost of mobile? From £10.00 per night with electric

Tents? Yes

Cost of tent pitch? From £8.00 per night

Electricity at the pitch? Yes

Showers? No

Onsite Entertainment? No

Opening times? All Year

Comments: Dogs must be kept on a lead.

Bleakhouse Farm

Address: North End, Mablethorpe, Lincolnshire LN12 1QG

Telephone: 01507 472325/473516

Website:

Extra charge for dogs? No

Any breed restrictions? No

Dog bins? No

Area for walking dogs? Yes

Static caravans? No

Cost of static?

Mobile caravans? Yes

Cost of mobile? From £5.00 per night

Tents? No

Cost of tent pitch?

Electricity at the pitch? No

Showers? No

Onsite Entertainment? No

Opening times? Beg March - End October

Brandy Wharf Leisure Park

Address: Brandywharf, Waddingham, Gainsborough, Lincolnshire DN21 4RT

Telephone: 01673 818010

Website: www.brandywharfleisure park.co.uk

Extra charge for dogs? No

Any breed restrictions? No

Dog bins? No

Area for walking dogs? Yes

Static caravans? No

Cost of static?

Mobile caravans? Yes

Cost of mobile? From £12.00 per night including electric for 2 people

Tents? Yes

Cost of tent pitch? From £5.50 per person per night children under 10 Free

Electricity at the pitch? Yes

Showers? Yes

Onsite Entertainment? No

Opening times? All Year (Tents - Easter - End October)

Comments: No single sex groups and No teenage groups.

Brickyard Fishery Caravan Site

Address: Louth, Lincolnshire LN11 7PY

Telephone: 01507 358331

Website: www.brickfish.clara.co.uk

Extra charge for dogs? No

Any breed restrictions? No

Dog bins? Yes

Area for walking dogs? Yes

Static caravans? Yes

Cost of static? From £210.00 per week

Mobile caravans? Yes

Cost of mobile? From £15.00 per night including fishing

Tents? Yes

Cost of tent pitch? From £15.00 per night including fishing

Electricity at the pitch? Yes

Showers? Yes

Onsite Entertainment? No

Opening times? April - October

Comments: Adults only. There is a fishing lake on site.

Bridgend Touring Site

Address: Bridge End, Boltons Lane, Ingoldmells, Skegness, Lincolnshire PE25 1JJ

Telephone: 01754 872456

Website: www.bridgendtouringsite.co.uk

Extra charge for dogs? No

Any breed restrictions? Yes

Dog bins? No

Area for walking dogs? Off Site

Static caravans? No

Cost of static?

Mobile caravans? Yes

Cost of mobile? From £16.50 per night with electric

Tents? No

Cost of tent pitch?

Electricity at the pitch? Yes

Showers? Yes

Onsite Entertainment? No

Opening times? Easter - October

Comments: No Dangerous Breeds, No Rottweilers, No Dobermans and No Staffordshire Bull Terriers

Brookside Caravan Park

Address: Stather Road, Burton Upon Stather, Scunthorpe, Lincolnshire DN15 9DH

Telephone: 01724 721369

Website: www.brooksidecaravanpark.co.uk

Extra charge for dogs? No

Any breed restrictions? No

Dog bins? No

Area for walking dogs? Yes

Static caravans? No

Cost of static?

Mobile caravans? Yes

Cost of mobile? From £14.00 per night

Tents? Yes

Cost of tent pitch? From £12.00 per night

Electricity at the pitch? Yes

Showers? Yes

Onsite Entertainment? No

Opening times? All Year

Cherry Tree Site

Address: Huttoft Rd, Sutton-on-Sea, Mablethorpe, Lincolnshire LN12 2RU

Telephone: 01507 441626

Website: www.cherrytreesite.co.uk

Extra charge for dogs? Yes

Any breed restrictions? No

Dog bins? Yes

Area for walking dogs? Yes

Static caravans? No

Cost of static?

Mobile caravans? Yes

Cost of mobile? From £14.00 per night

Tents? No

Cost of tent pitch?

Electricity at the pitch? Yes

Showers? Yes

Onsite Entertainment? No

Opening times? March - October

Comments: Adults only. Maximum 3 dogs per pitch.

Claxby Grange Farm

Address: Claxby, Market Rasen, Lincolnshire LN8 3YR

Telephone: 01673 828272

Website:

Extra charge for dogs? No

Any breed restrictions? No

Dog bins? No

Area for walking dogs? Yes

Static caravans? No

Cost of static?

Mobile caravans? Yes
Cost of mobile? From £5.00 per night
Tents? Yes
Cost of tent pitch? From £5.00 per night
Electricity at the pitch? No
Showers? No
Onsite Entertainment? No
Opening times? February - October
Comments: Dogs must be on a lead.

Coastfield Holiday Village

Address: Roman Bank, Vickers Point, Ingoldmells, Skegness, Lincolnshire PE25 1JU
Telephone: 01754 872592
Website: www.coastfieldleisure.com
Extra charge for dogs? Yes
Any breed restrictions? Yes
Dog bins? No
Area for walking dogs? Yes
Static caravans? Yes
Cost of static? From £129.00 per week
Mobile caravans? No
Cost of mobile?
Tents? No
Cost of tent pitch?
Electricity at the pitch? No
Showers? No
Onsite Entertainment? Yes
Opening times? March - October
Comments: No Dangerous Breeds. There is a swimming pool on site.

Coral Beach Leisure

Address: Skegness Rd, Ingoldmells, Skegness, Lincolnshire PE25 1JW
Telephone: 01754 872402
Website: www.coral-beach.co.uk
Extra charge for dogs? Yes
Any breed restrictions? No
Dog bins? No
Area for walking dogs? Yes
Static caravans? Yes
Cost of static? From £100.00 per week
Mobile caravans? No
Cost of mobile?
Tents? No
Cost of tent pitch?
Electricity at the pitch? No
Showers? No
Onsite Entertainment? Yes
Opening times? March - End October

Corner House

Address: Spilsby Road, Wainfleet, Nr Skegness, Lincolnshire PE24 4LP
Telephone: 01754 881287
Website:
Extra charge for dogs? No
Any breed restrictions? No
Dog bins? No
Area for walking dogs? Off Site
Static caravans? No
Cost of static?
Mobile caravans? Yes
Cost of mobile? From £6.00 per night
Tents? Yes
Cost of tent pitch? From £5.00 per night
Electricity at the pitch? Yes
Showers? No
Onsite Entertainment? No
Opening times? 1st March - End October
Comments: Camping and Caravan Club members only.

Country Meadows Holiday Park

Address: Outgang Road, Towngate East, Market Deeping, Lincolnshire PE6 8LQ
Telephone: 01754 874455

Website: www.countrymeadows.co.uk
Extra charge for dogs? No
Any breed restrictions? No
Dog bins? Yes
Area for walking dogs? Yes
Static caravans? No
Cost of static?
Mobile caravans? Yes
Cost of mobile? From £15.00 per night with electric for 2 adults and 2 children
Tents? Yes
Cost of tent pitch? From £16.00 per night for 2 adults and 2 children
Electricity at the pitch? Yes
Showers? Yes
Onsite Entertainment? Yes
Opening times? 14th March - 26th October
Comments: Maximum 2 dogs. Dogs must be kept on a lead. There is a small playground and a fishing lake.

Countryman Inn (The)

Address: Chapel Road, Ingoldmells, Skegness, Lincolnshire PE25 1ND
Telephone: 01754 872268
Website:
Extra charge for dogs? No
Any breed restrictions? No
Dog bins? No
Area for walking dogs? Off Site
Static caravans? No
Cost of static?
Mobile caravans? Yes
Cost of mobile? From £15.00 per night
Tents? No
Cost of tent pitch?
Electricity at the pitch? Yes
Showers? Yes
Onsite Entertainment? Yes
Opening times? March - October
Comments: There is a pub on site.

Cross Guest House and Touring Site

Address: Alford Rd, Mablethorpe, Lincolnshire LN12 1PX
Telephone: 01507 477708
Website: www.thecrossguesthouse.co.uk
Extra charge for dogs? Yes
Any breed restrictions? No
Dog bins? No
Area for walking dogs? Off Site
Static caravans? No
Cost of static?
Mobile caravans? Yes
Cost of mobile? From £16.00 per night
Tents? No
Cost of tent pitch?
Electricity at the pitch? Yes
Showers? Yes
Onsite Entertainment? No
Opening times? Easter - End October
Comments: They serve breakfast in the mornings.

Deepings Caravan Park (The)

Address: Outgang Road, Towngate East, Market Deeping, Lincolnshire PE6 8LQ
Telephone: 01778 344335
Website: www.thedeepings.com
Extra charge for dogs? No
Any breed restrictions? No
Dog bins? No
Area for walking dogs? Off Site
Static caravans? Yes
Cost of static? From £200.00 - £250.00 per week
Mobile caravans? Yes
Cost of mobile? From £15.00 per night

with electric
Tents? Yes
Cost of tent pitch? From £15.00 per night with electric
Electricity at the pitch? Yes
Showers? Yes
Onsite Entertainment? Yes
Opening times? February - December
Comments: There is a Clubhouse on site.

Delph Bank Touring Caravan and Camping Park

Address: Old Main Road, Fleet Hargate, Lincolnshire PE12 8LL
Telephone: 01406 422910
Website: www.delphbank.co.uk
Extra charge for dogs? Yes
Any breed restrictions? No
Dog bins? Yes
Area for walking dogs? Yes
Static caravans? No
Cost of static?
Mobile caravans? Yes
Cost of mobile? From £11.50 per night
Tents? Yes
Cost of tent pitch? From £11.50 per night
Electricity at the pitch? Yes
Showers? Yes
Onsite Entertainment? No
Opening times? All Year
Comments: Adults only.

Denehurst Caravan Site

Address: Alford Road, Mablethorpe, Lincolnshire LN12 1PX
Telephone: 01507 472951
Website:
Extra charge for dogs? Yes
Any breed restrictions? No
Dog bins? No
Area for walking dogs? Off Site
Static caravans? No
Cost of static?
Mobile caravans? Yes
Cost of mobile? From £12.00 per night
Tents? Yes
Cost of tent pitch? From £8.00 per night
Electricity at the pitch? Yes
Showers? Yes
Onsite Entertainment? Yes
Opening times? 1st March - End November
Comments: Dogs must be kept on a lead. There is a guest house there that has a bar and some entertainment.

Eastfields Park

Address: Chapel Point, Chapel St. Leonards, Skegness, Lincolnshire PE24 5UX
Telephone: 01754 874499
Website:
Extra charge for dogs? No
Any breed restrictions? No
Dog bins? No
Area for walking dogs? Yes
Static caravans? No
Cost of static?
Mobile caravans? Yes
Cost of mobile? From £18.00 per night with electric
Tents? No
Cost of tent pitch?
Electricity at the pitch? Yes
Showers? Yes
Onsite Entertainment? No
Opening times? Mid March - End October
Comments: Dogs must be kept on a lead. There is a fishing lake on site.

Eastview Caravan Park

Address: Trunch Lane, Chapel St. Leonards, Skegness, Lincolnshire PE24 5TU
Telephone: 01754 875324
Website:
Extra charge for dogs? No
Any breed restrictions? No
Dog bins? No
Area for walking dogs? Yes
Static caravans? No
Cost of static?
Mobile caravans? Yes
Cost of mobile? From £19.00 per night
Tents? Yes
Cost of tent pitch? From £16.00 per night
Electricity at the pitch? Yes
Showers? Yes
Onsite Entertainment? No
Opening times? March - End October
Comments: Only 1 dog per pitch.

Eastwood House

Address: Fulletby, Horncastle, Lincolnshire LN9 6JY
Telephone: 01507 533401
Website:
Extra charge for dogs? No
Any breed restrictions? Yes
Dog bins? No
Area for walking dogs? Yes
Static caravans? No
Cost of static?
Mobile caravans? Yes
Cost of mobile? From £8.50 per night
Tents? No
Cost of tent pitch?
Electricity at the pitch? Yes
Showers? No
Onsite Entertainment? No
Opening times? All Year
Comments: No Dangerous Breeds. Dogs must be kept on a lead.

Ferry Hill Farm

Address: Ferry Rd, Fiskerton, Lincoln, Lincolnshire LN3 4HU
Telephone: 01526 399610
Website: www.ferryhillfarm.co.uk
Extra charge for dogs? No
Any breed restrictions? No
Dog bins? Yes
Area for walking dogs? Yes
Static caravans? No
Cost of static?
Mobile caravans? Yes
Cost of mobile? From £5.00 per night
Tents? Yes
Cost of tent pitch? From £5.00 per night
Electricity at the pitch? Yes
Showers? Yes
Onsite Entertainment? No
Opening times? Easter - 18th December
Comments: Small Dogs preferred.

Foremans Bridge Caravan Park

Address: Ambridge, Sutton Rd, Sutton St. James, Spalding, Lincolnshire PE12 0HU
Telephone: 01945 440346
Website: www.foremans-bridge.co.uk
Extra charge for dogs? Yes
Any breed restrictions? No
Dog bins? Yes
Area for walking dogs? Yes
Static caravans? Yes
Cost of static? £175.00 per week
Mobile caravans? Yes
Cost of mobile? From £14.00 per night for 2 people
Tents? Yes

Cost of tent pitch? From £14.00 per night for 2 people
Electricity at the pitch? Yes
Showers? Yes
Onsite Entertainment? No
Opening times? March - Mid January

Four Acres

Address: Nutts Lane, Holbeach St Johns, Spalding, Lincolnshire PE12 8RP
Telephone: 01406 540581
Website:
Extra charge for dogs? No
Any breed restrictions? No
Dog bins? Yes
Area for walking dogs? No
Static caravans? No
Cost of static?
Mobile caravans? Yes
Cost of mobile? From £4.00 per night
Tents? Yes
Cost of tent pitch? From £4.00 per night
Electricity at the pitch? No
Showers? No
Onsite Entertainment? No
Opening times? March - October

Glebe Farm

Address: Spilby, Lincolnshire PE23 4BB
Telephone: 01790 753300
Website:
Extra charge for dogs? No
Any breed restrictions? No
Dog bins? No
Area for walking dogs? Yes
Static caravans? No
Cost of static?
Mobile caravans? Yes
Cost of mobile? From £10.00 per night
Tents? No
Cost of tent pitch?
Electricity at the pitch? Yes
Showers? Yes
Onsite Entertainment? No
Opening times? All Year

Glebe Farm

Address: West Barkwith, Market Rasen, Lincolnshire LN8 5LF
Telephone: 01673 858919
Website: www.glebeapart.co.uk
Extra charge for dogs? No
Any breed restrictions? No
Dog bins? No
Area for walking dogs? Yes
Static caravans? No
Cost of static?
Mobile caravans? Yes
Cost of mobile? From £5.00 per night
Tents? Yes
Cost of tent pitch? ?
Electricity at the pitch? No
Showers? No
Onsite Entertainment? No
Opening times? All Year

Glebe Farm

Address: Church Lane, Benniworth, Market Rasen, Lincolnshire LN8 6JP
Telephone: 01507 313231
Website: www.glebe-farm.com
Extra charge for dogs? No
Any breed restrictions? Yes
Dog bins? No
Area for walking dogs? Yes
Static caravans? No
Cost of static?
Mobile caravans? Yes
Cost of mobile? From £8.00 per night

Tents? No
Cost of tent pitch?
Electricity at the pitch? Yes
Showers? No
Onsite Entertainment? No
Opening times? All Year
Comments: No Dangerous Breeds.

Glen Lodge Touring Park

Address: Glen Lodge, Edlington Moor, Woodhall Spa, Lincolnshire LN10 6UL
Telephone: 01526 353523
Website:
Extra charge for dogs? No
Any breed restrictions? No
Dog bins? Yes
Area for walking dogs? Off Site
Static caravans? No
Cost of static?
Mobile caravans? Yes
Cost of mobile? From £13.50 per night
Tents? No
Cost of tent pitch?
Electricity at the pitch? Yes
Showers? Yes
Onsite Entertainment? No
Opening times? March - End November

Golden Sands Holiday Park

Address: Quebec Rd, Mablethorpe, Lincolnshire LN12 1QJ
Telephone: 01507 477060
Website: www.havenholidays.co.uk
Extra charge for dogs? Yes
Any breed restrictions? Yes
Dog bins? Yes
Area for walking dogs? Off Site
Static caravans? Yes
Cost of static? Prices vary as discounts may apply
Mobile caravans? Yes
Cost of mobile? Prices vary as discounts may apply
Tents? Yes
Cost of tent pitch? Prices vary as discounts may apply
Electricity at the pitch? Yes
Showers? Yes
Onsite Entertainment? Yes
Opening times? Mid March - End October
Comments: No Dangerous Breeds.

Golfers Arms (The)

Address: West Ashby, Horncastle, Lincolnshire LN9 5PP
Telephone: 01507 526800
Website:
Extra charge for dogs? No
Any breed restrictions? No
Dog bins? No
Area for walking dogs? Yes
Static caravans? No
Cost of static?
Mobile caravans? Yes
Cost of mobile? From £15.00 per night
Tents? Yes
Cost of tent pitch? From £5.00 per night
Electricity at the pitch? Yes
Showers? Yes
Onsite Entertainment? Sometimes
Opening times? All Year

Goodwin Park

Address: Goodwin House, Trunch Lane, Chapel St. Leonards, Skegness, Lincolnshire PE24 5UA
Telephone: 01754 873930
Website: www.goodwinpark.co.uk
Extra charge for dogs? £10.00 per dog

deposit which is refundable
Any breed restrictions? Yes
Dog bins? No
Area for walking dogs? Yes
Static caravans? No
Cost of static?
Mobile caravans? Yes
Cost of mobile? From £15.50 per night with electric
Tents? Yes
Cost of tent pitch? From £15.50 per night with electric
Electricity at the pitch? Yes
Showers? Yes
Onsite Entertainment? No
Opening times? March - October
Comments: No Dangerous Breeds including Alastians, Staffordshire Bull Terriers and Rottweilers.

Grange Farm

Address: Mill Lane, North Hykeham, Lincoln, Lincolnshire LN6 9PB
Telephone: 01522 684682
Website:
Extra charge for dogs? No
Any breed restrictions? Yes
Dog bins? No
Area for walking dogs? Off Site
Static caravans? No
Cost of static?
Mobile caravans? Yes
Cost of mobile? From £8.00 per night
Tents? Yes
Cost of tent pitch? From £8.00 per night
Electricity at the pitch? Yes
Showers? Yes
Onsite Entertainment? No
Opening times? All Year
Comments: No Dangerous Breeds.

Grange Leisure Park

Address: Alford Rd, Mablethorpe, Lincolnshire LN12 1NE
Telephone: 01507 472814
Website: www.grangeleisurepark.co.uk
Extra charge for dogs? No
Any breed restrictions? Yes
Dog bins? No
Area for walking dogs? Yes
Static caravans? Yes
Cost of static? From £170.00 per week
Mobile caravans? Yes
Cost of mobile? From £11.00 per night
Tents? No
Cost of tent pitch?
Electricity at the pitch? Yes
Showers? Yes
Onsite Entertainment? Yes
Opening times? 5th March - End November
Comments: No Dangerous Breeds including Alastians, Dobermans, Rottweilers and German Shepherds. They have a bar which sometimes has entertainment.

Grangemead

Address: Holton Beckering, Market Rasen, Lincolnshire LN8 5NH
Telephone: 01673 858284
Website:
Extra charge for dogs? No
Any breed restrictions? No
Dog bins? No
Area for walking dogs? Yes
Static caravans? No
Cost of static?
Mobile caravans? Yes
Cost of mobile? From £6.00 per night with electric
Tents? Yes
Cost of tent pitch? From £2.00 per night
Electricity at the pitch? Yes

Showers? No
Onsite Entertainment? No
Opening times? April - October

Grange Park

Address: ButterwickRoad, Messingham, Scunthorpe, Lincolnshire DN17 3PP
Telephone: 01724 762945
Website: www.grangepark.com
Extra charge for dogs? No
Any breed restrictions? No
Dog bins? No
Area for walking dogs? No
Static caravans? No
Cost of static?
Mobile caravans? Yes
Cost of mobile? From £10.00 per night with electric
Tents? No
Cost of tent pitch?
Electricity at the pitch? Yes
Showers? Yes
Onsite Entertainment? Yes
Opening times? All Year
Comments: Dogs must be kept on a lead. There is a club house and golf course on site.

Greenfield Caravan Park

Address: Sutton Rd, Trusthorpe, Mablethorpe, Lincolnshire LN12 2PU
Telephone: 01507 441203
Website:
Extra charge for dogs? Yes
Any breed restrictions? No
Dog bins? Yes
Area for walking dogs? Yes
Static caravans? Yes
Cost of static? From £140.00 - £270.00 per week
Mobile caravans? No
Cost of mobile?
Tents? No
Cost of tent pitch?
Electricity at the pitch? No
Showers? No
Onsite Entertainment? No
Opening times? March - 8th November
Comments: Dogs must be kept on a lead.

Hagbeach Manor Caravan Park Adults only

Address: Millgate Whaplode, Spalding, Lincolnshire PE12 6RT
Telephone: 01406 373378
Website:
Extra charge for dogs? No
Any breed restrictions? No
Dog bins? No
Area for walking dogs? Off Site
Static caravans? No
Cost of static?
Mobile caravans? Yes
Cost of mobile? From £10.00 per night
Tents? Yes
Cost of tent pitch? From £10.00 per night
Electricity at the pitch? Yes
Showers? Yes
Onsite Entertainment? No
Opening times? March - November

Happy Days Leisure

Address: Trunch Lane, Chapel St. Leonards, Skegness, Lincolnshire PE24 5TU
Telephone: 01754 872341
Website: www.happydaysleisure.com
Extra charge for dogs? Yes
Any breed restrictions? No
Dog bins? Yes

Area for walking dogs? No
Static caravans? Yes
Cost of static? From £199.00 per week
Mobile caravans? No
Cost of mobile?
Tents? No
Cost of tent pitch?
Electricity at the pitch? No
Showers? No
Onsite Entertainment? Yes (High Season)
Opening times? Easter - September
Comments: Maximum of 2 Dogs.

Hardys Touring Site

Address: Sea Lane, Ingoldmells, Skegness, Lincolnshire PE25 1NU
Telephone: 01754 874071
Website:
Extra charge for dogs? No
Any breed restrictions? No
Dog bins? No
Area for walking dogs? Yes
Static caravans? No
Cost of static?
Mobile caravans? Yes
Cost of mobile? From £16.00 per night with electric
Tents? No
Cost of tent pitch?
Electricity at the pitch? Yes
Showers? Yes
Onsite Entertainment? No
Opening times? Easter - End October
Comments: Dogs must be kept on a lead.

Hartsholme Country Park Campsite

Address: Skellingthorpe Rd, Lincoln, Lincolnshire LN6 0EY
Telephone: 01522 873578
Website: www.lincoln.gov.uk
Extra charge for dogs? No
Any breed restrictions? No
Dog bins? Yes
Area for walking dogs? No
Static caravans? No
Cost of static?
Mobile caravans? Yes
Cost of mobile? From £12.90 per night with electric
Tents? Yes
Cost of tent pitch? From £6.40 per night for 2 people
Electricity at the pitch? Yes
Showers? Yes
Onsite Entertainment? No
Opening times? 1st March - 31st October (November - Weekends only and 1st Week December)

Haven Holidays

Address: Golden Sands Holiday Park, Mablethorpe, Lincolnshire LN12 1QJ
Telephone: 0871 2301900
Website: www.haven.com
Extra charge for dogs? Yes
Any breed restrictions? Yes
Dog bins? Yes
Area for walking dogs? Off Site
Static caravans? Yes
Cost of static? Prices vary as discount may apply
Mobile caravans? Yes
Cost of mobile? Prices vary as discount may apply
Tents? Yes
Cost of tent pitch? Prices vary as discount may apply
Electricity at the pitch? Yes
Showers? Yes
Onsite Entertainment? Yes
Opening times? Easter - October

Comments: Maximum of 2 dogs. No Dangerous Breeds.

Hawthorn Farm

Address: Crabtree Lane, Sutton on Sea, Mablethorpe, Lincolnshire LN12 2RS

Telephone: 01507 441503

Website: www.caravanclub.co.uk

Extra charge for dogs? No

Any breed restrictions? No

Dog bins? Yes

Area for walking dogs? Off Site

Static caravans? No

Cost of static?

Mobile caravans? Yes

Cost of mobile? From £15.00 per night

Tents? No

Cost of tent pitch?

Electricity at the pitch? Yes

Showers? Yes

Onsite Entertainment? No

Opening times? March - October

Comments: Dogs must be on a lead. Have to be Members.

Herons Mead Fishing Lake and Touring Park

Address: Marsh Lane, Orby, Lincolnshire PE24 5JA

Telephone: 01754 811340

Website: www.heronsmeadtouringpark.co.uk

Extra charge for dogs? Yes

Any breed restrictions? Yes

Dog bins? Yes

Area for walking dogs? Yes

Static caravans? No

Cost of static?

Mobile caravans? Yes

Cost of mobile? From £15.00 per night with electric for 2 people

Tents? Yes

Cost of tent pitch? From £15.00 per night with electric for 2 people

Electricity at the pitch? Yes

Showers? Yes

Onsite Entertainment? No

Opening times? 1st March - 1st October

Comments: Maximum 1 dog. No Dangerous Breeds. There is a fishing lake.

Highfield Farm

Address: Old Bolingbroke, Spilsby, Lincolnshire PE23 4EP

Telephone: 01790 763279

Website:

Extra charge for dogs? No

Any breed restrictions? No

Dog bins? No

Area for walking dogs? Yes

Static caravans? No

Cost of static?

Mobile caravans? Yes

Cost of mobile? From £6.00 per night with electric

Tents? Yes

Cost of tent pitch? From £5.00 per night

Electricity at the pitch? Yes

Showers? No

Onsite Entertainment? No

Opening times? All Year

Holme Lea

Address: Main Road, South Reston, Louth, Lincolnshire LN11 8JQ

Telephone: 01507 450646

Website:

Extra charge for dogs? No

Any breed restrictions? No

Dog bins? No

Area for walking dogs? No
Static caravans? No
Cost of static?
Mobile caravans? Yes
Cost of mobile? From £7.00 per night for 2 people
Tents? Yes
Cost of tent pitch? From £7.00 per night for 2 people
Electricity at the pitch? No
Showers? No
Onsite Entertainment? No
Opening times? June - October (Depending on weather)

Comments: Dogs must be kept on a lead.

Homelands Caravan Park

Address: Sea Road, Anderby, Skegness, Lincolnshire PE24 5YB

Telephone: 01507 490511

Website:

Extra charge for dogs? Yes
Any breed restrictions? No
Dog bins? No
Area for walking dogs? No
Static caravans? Yes
Cost of static? From £120.00 per week
Mobile caravans? Yes
Cost of mobile? From £10.00 per night
Tents? No
Cost of tent pitch?
Electricity at the pitch? Yes
Showers? Yes
Onsite Entertainment? No
Opening times? 1st March - End October (will open by appointment in November)

Comments: Great walks on beach for dogs.

Hopeville

Address: Kirmond Road, Binbrook, Market Rasen, Lincolnshire LN8 6HY

Telephone: 01472 398462

Website:

Extra charge for dogs? No
Any breed restrictions? No
Dog bins? No
Area for walking dogs? Off Site
Static caravans? No
Cost of static?
Mobile caravans? Yes
Cost of mobile? From £6.50 per night
Tents? Yes
Cost of tent pitch? From £4.50 per night
Electricity at the pitch? Yes
Showers? Yes
Onsite Entertainment? No
Opening times? All Year

Ingleby Arms

Address: 42 High Street, Marton, Gainsborough, Lincolnshire DN21 5AH

Telephone: 01427 718246

Website:

Extra charge for dogs? No
Any breed restrictions?
Dog bins? No
Area for walking dogs? Yes
Static caravans? No
Cost of static?
Mobile caravans? Yes
Cost of mobile? From £7.50 inc elec
Tents? Yes
Cost of tent pitch? From £7.50 inc elec
Electricity at the pitch? Yes
Showers? No
Onsite Entertainment? Pub
Opening times? All year

J and J Simpson

Address: Orby Rd, Addlethorpe, Skegness, Lincolnshire PE24 4TR
Telephone: 01754 872598
Website:
Extra charge for dogs? No
Any breed restrictions? No
Dog bins? Yes
Area for walking dogs? Yes
Static caravans? No
Cost of static?
Mobile caravans? Yes
Cost of mobile? From £16.00 per night
Tents? Yes
Cost of tent pitch? From £10.00 per night
Electricity at the pitch? Yes (Not Tents)
Showers? Yes
Onsite Entertainment? Yes
Opening times? March - October
Comments: Dogs must be kept on a lead.

Jolly Common Caravan Park (Adults Only)

Address: Sea Lane, Huttoft, Lincolnshire LN13 9RW
Telephone: 01507 490236
Website: www.jollycommoncaravanpark.co.uk
Extra charge for dogs? Yes
Any breed restrictions? No
Dog bins? Yes
Area for walking dogs? Off Site
Static caravans? No
Cost of static?
Mobile caravans? Yes
Cost of mobile? From £13.00 per night
Tents? No
Cost of tent pitch?
Electricity at the pitch? Yes
Showers? Yes
Onsite Entertainment? No
Opening times? 15th March - 15th October
Comments: Dogs must be kept on a lead. Maximum 2 dogs.

Jubilee Park

Address: Stixwould Rd, Woodhall Spa, Lincolnshire LN10 6QH
Telephone: 01526 352448
Website:
Extra charge for dogs? No
Any breed restrictions? No
Dog bins? Yes
Area for walking dogs? Off Site
Static caravans? No
Cost of static?
Mobile caravans? Yes
Cost of mobile? From £12.30 - £14.75 per night for 2 people with electric
Tents? Yes
Cost of tent pitch? From £9.85 - £12.35 per night for 2 people
Electricity at the pitch? Yes
Showers? Yes
Onsite Entertainment? No
Opening times? Easter - End October

Keal Lodge Caravan Club

Address: Back Lane, Deeping St James, Lincolnshire PE6 8RT
Telephone: 01778 346946
Website: www.keallodge.co.uk
Extra charge for dogs? No
Any breed restrictions? No
Dog bins? Yes
Area for walking dogs? Yes
Static caravans? No
Cost of static?
Mobile caravans? Yes
Cost of mobile? From £10.75 per night

with electric
Tents? No
Cost of tent pitch?
Electricity at the pitch? Yes
Showers? No
Onsite Entertainment? No
Opening times? All Year

Kellaway Park

Address: Marton Road, Sturton by Stow, Lincoln, Lincolnshire LN1 2AH
Telephone: 01427 787774
Website: www.kellawaypark.co.uk
Extra charge for dogs? No
Any breed restrictions? No
Dog bins? No
Area for walking dogs? No
Static caravans? No
Cost of static?
Mobile caravans? Yes
Cost of mobile? From £8.00 per night
Tents? Yes
Cost of tent pitch? From £8.00 per night
Electricity at the pitch? Yes
Showers? Yes
Onsite Entertainment? No
Opening times? Easter - End October (longer if weather permits)
Comments: Adults only.

Lakeside Caravan Park

Address: Alford Road, Sutton-on-Sea, Lincolnshire LN12 2RW
Telephone: 01507 443355
Website: www.knowlesleisure.com
Extra charge for dogs? No
Any breed restrictions? No
Dog bins? Yes
Area for walking dogs? Yes
Static caravans? Yes
Cost of static? From £200.00 - £300.00 per week
Mobile caravans? Yes
Cost of mobile? From £14.00 per night with electric
Tents? Yes
Cost of tent pitch? From £10.00 per night
Electricity at the pitch? Yes
Showers? Yes
Onsite Entertainment? No
Opening times? 15th March - End October

Lakeside Fishery

Address: Baumber, Horncastle, Lincolnshire LN9 5NW
Telephone: 01507 578330
Website: www.lakesidefishery.co.uk
Extra charge for dogs? No
Any breed restrictions? No
Dog bins? Yes
Area for walking dogs? Yes
Static caravans? No
Cost of static?
Mobile caravans? Yes
Cost of mobile? From £8.00 per night
Tents? Yes
Cost of tent pitch? From £6.00 per night
Electricity at the pitch? Yes
Showers? No
Onsite Entertainment? No
Opening times? March - October

Lakeside Park

Address: Warren Rd, North Somercotes, Louth, Lincolnshire LN11 7RB
Telephone: 01507 358428
Website: www.donamottparks.com
Extra charge for dogs? Yes
Any breed restrictions? No

Dog bins? Yes
Area for walking dogs? Yes
Static caravans? No
Cost of static?
Mobile caravans? Yes
Cost of mobile? From £15.00 per night
Tents? No
Cost of tent pitch?
Electricity at the pitch? Yes
Showers? Yes
Onsite Entertainment? Yes
Opening times? March - November

Little End Corner Caravan Site

Address: Holton Road, Tetney, Grimsby, Lincolnshire DN36 5LW
Telephone: 07715 451976
Website:
Extra charge for dogs? No
Any breed restrictions? No
Dog bins? Yes
Area for walking dogs? Yes
Static caravans? No
Cost of static?
Mobile caravans? Yes
Cost of mobile? From £9.00 per night
Tents? No
Cost of tent pitch?
Electricity at the pitch? Yes
Showers? No
Onsite Entertainment? No
Opening times? All Year

Low Farm Touring Park

Address: Low Farm, Spring Lane, Folkingham, Sleaford, Lincolnshire NG34 0SJ
Telephone: 01529 497322
Website: www.lowfarmpark.com
Extra charge for dogs? No
Any breed restrictions? No
Dog bins? No
Area for walking dogs? Off Site
Static caravans? No
Cost of static?
Mobile caravans? Yes
Cost of mobile? From £12.00 per night with electric
Tents? Yes
Cost of tent pitch? From £9.00 per night
Electricity at the pitch? Yes
Showers? Yes
Onsite Entertainment? No
Opening times? Easter - End September

Lowis Farm

Address: Eau Bank, North Somercotes, Lincolnshire LN11 7LN
Telephone: 07958 805286
Website:
Extra charge for dogs? No
Any breed restrictions? No
Dog bins? Yes
Area for walking dogs? Yes
Static caravans? No
Cost of static?
Mobile caravans? Yes
Cost of mobile? From £8.00 per night with electric
Tents? No
Cost of tent pitch?
Electricity at the pitch? Yes
Showers? No
Onsite Entertainment? Yes
Opening times? March - End November
Comments: There is a fishing lake on site.

Manor Farm Caravan Park

Address: Manor Farm, Mumby Rd, Alford, Lincolnshire LN13 9RF

Telephone: 01507 490372

Website:

Extra charge for dogs? Yes

Any breed restrictions? No

Dog bins? Yes

Area for walking dogs? Yes

Static caravans? No

Cost of static?

Mobile caravans? Yes

Cost of mobile? From £12.00 per night

Tents? Yes

Cost of tent pitch? From £12.00 per night

Electricity at the pitch? Yes

Showers? Yes

Onsite Entertainment? No

Opening times? March - October

Market Rasen Racecourse Ltd

Address: Legsby Road, Market Rasen, Lincolnshire LN8 3EA

Telephone: 01673 843434

Website:

Extra charge for dogs? No

Any breed restrictions? No

Dog bins? Yes

Area for walking dogs? Yes

Static caravans? No

Cost of static?

Mobile caravans? Yes

Cost of mobile? From £4.00 per pitch £3.70 per adult £1.30 per child over 5 years

Tents? Yes

Cost of tent pitch? From £2.00 per pitch £3.70 per adult £1.30 per child over 5 years

Electricity at the pitch? Yes

Showers? Yes

Onsite Entertainment? No

Opening times? March - October

Comments: Prices are for members only. Extra £6.00 per pitch if non members.

Meadowlands Lodge Park

Address: Monksthorpe, Great Steeping, Spilsby, Lincolnshire PE23 5PP

Telephone: 01754 830794

Website:

Extra charge for dogs? No

Any breed restrictions? No

Dog bins? Yes

Area for walking dogs? Yes

Static caravans? No

Cost of static?

Mobile caravans? Yes

Cost of mobile? From £8.50 per night

Tents? Yes

Cost of tent pitch? From £8.50 per night

Electricity at the pitch? Yes

Showers? Yes

Onsite Entertainment? No

Opening times? All Year

Merryfield Caravan Park

Address: South Road, Skegness, Lincolnshire PE24 5TL

Telephone: 01754 872286

Website: www.coastfieldleisureltd.co.uk

Extra charge for dogs? Yes

Any breed restrictions? Yes

Dog bins? No

Area for walking dogs? Yes

Static caravans? Yes

Cost of static? From £210.00 per week

Mobile caravans? No

Cost of mobile?

Tents? No
Cost of tent pitch?
Electricity at the pitch? No
Showers? No
Onsite Entertainment? Yes
Opening times? March - End October
Comments: No Dangerous Breeds.

Midville Holiday Park

Address: Stickney, Lincolnshire PE22 8HW
Telephone: 01205 270316
Website:
Extra charge for dogs? No
Any breed restrictions? No
Dog bins? No
Area for walking dogs? Off Site
Static caravans? No
Cost of static?
Mobile caravans? Yes
Cost of mobile? From £12.00 per night
Tents? Yes
Cost of tent pitch? From £12.00 per night
Electricity at the pitch? Yes
Showers? Yes
Onsite Entertainment? Off Site
Opening times? March - November
Comments: There is a pub next door that has entertainment on a Saturday Evening.

Mill House Farm

Address: Mill Farm, Moor Rd, Walesby, Market Rasen, Lincolnshire LN8 3UR
Telephone: 01673 838495
Website:
Extra charge for dogs? No
Any breed restrictions? No
Dog bins? Yes
Area for walking dogs? Yes
Static caravans? No
Cost of static?
Mobile caravans? Yes
Cost of mobile? From £9.00 per night
Tents? Yes
Cost of tent pitch? From £5.00 for 1 man tent/ £8.50 for all others per night
Electricity at the pitch? Yes
Showers? Yes
Onsite Entertainment? No
Opening times? April - October
Comments: Dogs must be kept on a lead.

Mrs G Bradbury

Address: Grange Farm, Fulstow, Louth, Lincolnshire LN11 0XX
Telephone: 01507 363229
Website:
Extra charge for dogs? No
Any breed restrictions? No
Dog bins? No
Area for walking dogs? Yes
Static caravans? No
Cost of static?
Mobile caravans? Yes
Cost of mobile? From £8.50 per night with electric
Tents? Yes
Cost of tent pitch? From £6.00 per night
Electricity at the pitch? Yes
Showers? No
Onsite Entertainment? No
Opening times? March - November

Navenby Lane Farm

Address: Bassingham, Lincolnshire LN5 9JF
Telephone: 01522 788740
Website: www.thecampingandcaravanningclub.co.uk
Extra charge for dogs? No
Any breed restrictions? No

Dog bins? No
Area for walking dogs? Yes
Static caravans? No
Cost of static?
Mobile caravans? Yes
Cost of mobile? From £5.00 per night
Tents? Yes
Cost of tent pitch? From £4.00 per night
Electricity at the pitch? No
Showers? No
Onsite Entertainment? No
Opening times? All Year

Nos 1-3 Main Road

Address: East Kirkby, Nr Spilsby, Lincolnshire PE23 4BY
Telephone: 01790 763733
Website: www.thecampingand caravanningclub.co.uk
Extra charge for dogs? No
Any breed restrictions? Yes
Dog bins? No
Area for walking dogs? Yes
Static caravans? No
Cost of static?
Mobile caravans? Yes
Cost of mobile? From £10.00 per night with electric
Tents? Yes
Cost of tent pitch? From £7.00 per night
Electricity at the pitch? Yes
Showers? Yes
Onsite Entertainment? No
Opening times? All Year
Comments: No Dangerous Breeds. Must be members of The Camping and Caravan Club.

Oakhill Leisure

Address: Oakhill Farm, Swinderby, Lincoln, Lincolnshire LN6 9QG
Telephone: 01522 868771
Website:
Extra charge for dogs? Yes
Any breed restrictions? No
Dog bins? Yes
Area for walking dogs? Yes
Static caravans? No
Cost of static?
Mobile caravans? Yes
Cost of mobile? From £8.50 per night
Tents? Yes
Cost of tent pitch? From £7.50 per night
Electricity at the pitch? Yes
Showers? Yes
Onsite Entertainment? No
Opening times? All Year

Oham Lakes

Address: Main Road, Maltby le Marsh, Alford, Lincolnshire LN13 0JP
Telephone: 01507 450623
Website: www.fisheries.co.uk/oham
Extra charge for dogs? No
Any breed restrictions? No
Dog bins? Yes
Area for walking dogs? Yes
Static caravans? Yes
Cost of static? From £250.00 per week
Mobile caravans? Yes
Cost of mobile? From £15.00 per night fully inclusive
Tents? Yes
Cost of tent pitch? From £10.00 per night
Electricity at the pitch? Yes
Showers? Yes
Onsite Entertainment? Yes
Opening times? All Year
Comments: Dogs must be kept under control. There is a fishing lake on site.

Orchard Caravan Park

Address: The Orchards, Frampton Fen Lane, Hubberts Bridge, Boston, Lincolnshire PE20 3QU
Telephone: 01205 290328
Website:
Extra charge for dogs? No
Any breed restrictions? No
Dog bins? Yes
Area for walking dogs? Off Site
Static caravans? Yes
Cost of static? From £220.00 per week
Mobile caravans? Yes
Cost of mobile? From £14.00 per night for 2 people
Tents? Yes
Cost of tent pitch? From £14.00 per night for 2 people
Electricity at the pitch? Yes
Showers? Yes
Onsite Entertainment? Yes
Opening times? All Year
Comments: Dogs must be kept on a lead on site. There is a bar, café and shop on site.

Orchard Caravan Park

Address: Witham Bank, Chapel Hill, Lincoln, Lincolnshire LN4 4PZ
Telephone: 01526 342414
Website: www.orchardcaravanpark.moonfruit.com
Extra charge for dogs? No
Any breed restrictions? No
Dog bins? No
Area for walking dogs? Yes
Static caravans? Yes
Cost of static? From £110.00 per week
Mobile caravans? Yes
Cost of mobile? From £14.00 per night
Tents? Yes
Cost of tent pitch? From £10.00 per night
Electricity at the pitch? Yes
Showers? Yes
Onsite Entertainment? Yes
Opening times? February - December
Comments: Dogs must be kept on a lead. There is a Clubhouse and Swimming Pool on site.

Orchard Park

Address: Walls Lane, Ingoldmells, Skegness, Lincolnshire PE25 1JF
Telephone: 01754 765446
Website: www.orchpark.co.uk
Extra charge for dogs? Yes
Any breed restrictions? Yes
Dog bins? Yes
Area for walking dogs? Yes
Static caravans? No
Cost of static?
Mobile caravans? Yes
Cost of mobile? From £16.00 including electric
Tents? No
Cost of tent pitch?
Electricity at the pitch? Yes
Showers? Yes
Onsite Entertainment? Yes
Opening times? End March - End October
Comments: There is a bar and a games room on site.

Pigeon Cottage Caravan and Camping Site

Address: Conisholme Road, North Somercotes, Lincolnshire LN11 7PS
Telephone: 01507 359063
Website: www.pigeoncottage.co.uk
Extra charge for dogs? No
Any breed restrictions? No

Dog bins? No
Area for walking dogs? Yes
Static caravans? No
Cost of static?
Mobile caravans? Yes
Cost of mobile? From £10.00 per night £15.00 with electric
Tents? Yes
Cost of tent pitch? From £10.00 per night £15.00 with electric
Electricity at the pitch? Yes
Showers? Yes
Onsite Entertainment? Yes
Opening times? All Year
Comments: There are 2 Fishing Lakes on site.

Pilgrimsway Campsite

Address: The Grange, Church Green Rd, Fishtoft, Boston, Lincolnshire PE21 0QY
Telephone: 01205 366646
Website: www.pilgrimsway-caravanand camping.com
Extra charge for dogs? No
Any breed restrictions? No
Dog bins? No
Area for walking dogs? Off Site
Static caravans? No
Cost of static?
Mobile caravans? Yes
Cost of mobile? From £14.50 per night with electric for 2 people
Tents? Yes
Cost of tent pitch? From £14.50 per night with electric for 2 people
Electricity at the pitch? Yes
Showers? Yes
Onsite Entertainment? No
Opening times? All Year

Pinetrees Caravan Park

Address: Croft Bank, Croft, Skegness, Lincolnshire PE24 4RE
Telephone: 01754 762949
Website: www.pinetreesholidays.co.uk
Extra charge for dogs? Yes
Any breed restrictions? No
Dog bins? Yes
Area for walking dogs? Yes
Static caravans? Yes
Cost of static? From £175.00 per week
Mobile caravans? Yes
Cost of mobile? From £8.50 per night
Tents? Yes
Cost of tent pitch? From £10.00 per night
Electricity at the pitch? Yes
Showers? Yes
Onsite Entertainment? Yes
Opening times? 1st March - End November

Poachers Patch

Address: Long Meadow, High Street, Brant Broughton, Lincoln, Lincolnshire LN5 0SL
Telephone: 01400 272476
Website:
Extra charge for dogs? No
Any breed restrictions? No
Dog bins? No
Area for walking dogs? Yes
Static caravans? No
Cost of static?
Mobile caravans? Yes
Cost of mobile? From £8.00 per night with electric
Tents? Yes
Cost of tent pitch? From £5.00 per night
Electricity at the pitch? Yes

Showers? No
Onsite Entertainment? No
Opening times? All Year

Poplar Farm

Address: Donington Road, Kirton End, Boston, Lincolnshire PE20 3HL
Telephone: 01205 722692
Website: www.poplarsfarm.i12.com
Extra charge for dogs? No
Any breed restrictions? No
Dog bins? Yes
Area for walking dogs? Off Site
Static caravans? No
Cost of static?
Mobile caravans? Yes
Cost of mobile? From £9.00 per night
Tents? No
Cost of tent pitch?
Electricity at the pitch? Yes
Showers? No
Onsite Entertainment? No
Opening times? All Year
Comments: Dogs must be kept on a lead.

Prospect Farm

Address: Waltham Road, Brigsley, Grimsby, Lincolnshire DN37 0RQ
Telephone: 01472 826491
Website: www.prospectfarm.co.uk
Extra charge for dogs? No
Any breed restrictions? No
Dog bins? No
Area for walking dogs? Off Site
Static caravans? No
Cost of static?
Mobile caravans? Yes
Cost of mobile? From £14.00 per night
Tents? Yes
Cost of tent pitch? From £14.00 per night
Electricity at the pitch? Yes
Showers? Yes
Onsite Entertainment? No
Opening times? All Year
Comments: Dogs have to be kept on a lead.

Ravenna Holiday Park

Address: Occupation Rd, Anderby Creek, Skegness, Lincolnshire PE24 5XP
Telephone: 01754 872966
Website:
Extra charge for dogs? Yes
Any breed restrictions? Yes
Dog bins? No
Area for walking dogs? Yes
Static caravans? Yes
Cost of static? From £175.00 - £420.00 per week
Mobile caravans? No
Cost of mobile?
Tents? No
Cost of tent pitch?
Electricity at the pitch?
Showers?
Onsite Entertainment? No
Opening times? All Year
Comments: No Dangerous Breeds. Maximum of 2 Dogs.

Richmond Holiday Park

Address: Skegness, Lincolnshire PE25 3TQ
Telephone: 01754 762097
Website: www.salesatrichmondholidays.com
Extra charge for dogs? Yes
Any breed restrictions? No
Dog bins? Yes
Area for walking dogs? Off Site

Static caravans? Yes
Cost of static? From £190.00 per week
Mobile caravans? Yes
Cost of mobile? From £14.50 per night
Tents? No
Cost of tent pitch?
Electricity at the pitch? Yes
Showers? Yes
Onsite Entertainment? Yes
Opening times? March - November
Comments: Maximum of 2 dogs.

Robin Hood Leisure

Address: South Rd, Chapel St. Leonards, Skegness, Lincolnshire PE24 5TR
Telephone: 01754 874444
Website: www.robinhoodleisure.com
Extra charge for dogs? Yes
Any breed restrictions? No
Dog bins? Yes
Area for walking dogs? Yes
Static caravans? Yes
Cost of static? Private vans only for rental
Mobile caravans? Yes
Cost of mobile? From £11.00 per night with electric
Tents? Yes
Cost of tent pitch? From £11.00 per night with electric
Electricity at the pitch? Yes
Showers? Yes
Onsite Entertainment? Yes
Opening times? March - End October

Ronam Cottage

Address: Pinfold Lane, Anderby, Skegness, Lincolnshire PE24 5YA
Telephone: 01507 490750
Website:
Extra charge for dogs? No
Any breed restrictions? No
Dog bins? Yes
Area for walking dogs? Yes
Static caravans? No
Cost of static?
Mobile caravans? Yes
Cost of mobile? From £8.50 per night with electric
Tents? Yes
Cost of tent pitch? From £8.50 per night with electric
Electricity at the pitch? Yes
Showers? Yes
Onsite Entertainment? No
Opening times? All Year
Comments: Dogs must be kept on a lead.

Ryland Grange Farm

Address: Fulbeck Heath, Grantham, Lincolnshire NG32 3HJ
Telephone: 01400 261745
Website:
Extra charge for dogs? No
Any breed restrictions? No
Dog bins? No
Area for walking dogs? Yes
Static caravans? No
Cost of static?
Mobile caravans? Yes
Cost of mobile? From £8.00 per night
Tents? Yes
Cost of tent pitch? From £8.00 per night
Electricity at the pitch? Yes
Showers? No
Onsite Entertainment? No
Opening times? All Year

Saltfleetby Fisheries Caravan Park

Address: The Fisheries, Main Rd, Saltfleetby, Louth, Lincolnshire LN11 7SS
Telephone: 01507 338272

Website: www.saltfleetbyfisheries.co.uk
Extra charge for dogs? Yes
Any breed restrictions? No
Dog bins? Yes
Area for walking dogs? Yes
Static caravans? No
Cost of static?
Mobile caravans? Yes
Cost of mobile? From £10.00 per night
Tents? Yes
Cost of tent pitch? From £10.00 per night
Electricity at the pitch? Yes
Showers? Yes
Onsite Entertainment? No
Opening times? March - November
Comments: There is a fishing lake on site.

Seacroft Holiday Estates Ltd

Address: Sutton Rd, Trusthorpe, Mablethorpe, Lincolnshire LN12 2PN
Telephone: 01507 472421
Website: www.seacroftcaravanpark.co.uk
Extra charge for dogs? Yes
Any breed restrictions? No
Dog bins? No
Area for walking dogs? Off Site
Static caravans? Yes
Cost of static? From £270.00 per week
Mobile caravans? Yes
Cost of mobile? From £13.50 per night
Tents? No
Cost of tent pitch?
Electricity at the pitch? Yes
Showers? Yes
Onsite Entertainment? Yes
Opening times? March - November
Comments: There is a Clubhouse on site.

Short Ferry Caravan Park

Address: Ferry Rd, Fiskerton, Lincoln, Lincolnshire LN3 4HU
Telephone: 01526 398021
Website: www.shortferry.co.uk
Extra charge for dogs? No
Any breed restrictions? No
Dog bins? No
Area for walking dogs? Yes
Static caravans? No
Cost of static?
Mobile caravans? Yes
Cost of mobile? From £17.00 per night with electric, awning, up to 6 people and 2 dogs.
Tents? Yes
Cost of tent pitch?
Electricity at the pitch? Yes
Showers? Yes
Onsite Entertainment? Yes
Opening times? All Year
Comments: There is a pub and swimming pool on site.

Silver Beach Caravan Park

Address: Ingoldmells, Lincolnshire PE25 1LX
Telephone: 01754 872528
Website:
Extra charge for dogs? No
Any breed restrictions? No
Dog bins? No
Area for walking dogs? No
Static caravans? No
Cost of static?
Mobile caravans? Yes
Cost of mobile? From £16.00 per night
Tents? No
Cost of tent pitch?
Electricity at the pitch? Yes
Showers? Yes

Onsite Entertainment? No

Opening times? Mid March - End October (Weather Permitting)

Comments: There is a Supermarket and Launderette on site. No Caravans over 18ft and no Awnings.

Silver Birches Caravan Park

Address: Waterside Road, Barton-upon-Humber, Lincolnshire DN18 5BA

Telephone: 01652 632509

Website: www.silverbirchescaravanpark.co.uk

Extra charge for dogs? Yes

Any breed restrictions? No

Dog bins? No

Area for walking dogs? Off Site

Static caravans? No

Cost of static?

Mobile caravans? Yes

Cost of mobile? From £14.00 per night with electric for 2 people

Tents? Yes

Cost of tent pitch? From £14.00 per night for 2 people + car

Electricity at the pitch? Yes

Showers? Yes

Onsite Entertainment? No

Opening times? All Year

Silverhill Caravan Park

Address: Roman Bank, Lutton Gowts, Lutton, Spalding, Lincolnshire PE12 9LQ

Telephone: 01406 365673

Website: www.silverhillcaravanpark.co.uk

Extra charge for dogs? No

Any breed restrictions? No

Dog bins? Yes

Area for walking dogs? Yes

Static caravans? Yes

Cost of static? From £150.00 - £250.00 per week

Mobile caravans? No

Cost of mobile?

Tents? No

Cost of tent pitch?

Electricity at the pitch?

Showers?

Onsite Entertainment? No

Opening times? 1st March - 31st December

Skegness Sands Touring Site

Address: Winthorpe Avenue, Skegness, Lincolnshire PE25 1QZ

Telephone: 01754 761484

Website: www.skegness-sands.co.uk

Extra charge for dogs? No

Any breed restrictions? No

Dog bins? No

Area for walking dogs? Yes

Static caravans? No

Cost of static?

Mobile caravans? Yes

Cost of mobile? From £14.00 - £20.50 per night for members

Tents? No

Cost of tent pitch?

Electricity at the pitch? Yes

Showers? Yes

Onsite Entertainment? No

Opening times? All Year

Comments: Is a part of The Caravan Club.

Skegness Water Leisure Park

Address: Walls Lane, Ingoldmells, Skegness, Lincolnshire PE25 1JF

Telephone: 01754 769019

Website: www.skegnesswaterleisurepark.co.uk

Extra charge for dogs? Yes

Any breed restrictions? No

Dog bins? Yes
Area for walking dogs? Yes
Static caravans? No
Cost of static?
Mobile caravans? Yes
Cost of mobile? From £15.00 per night
Tents? Yes
Cost of tent pitch? From £15.00 per night
Electricity at the pitch? Yes
Showers? Yes
Onsite Entertainment? Yes
Opening times? 1st Sat March - 3rd Sat October

Southview Leisure Park

Address: Burgh Road, Skegness, Lincolnshire PE25 2LA
Telephone: 01754 896000
Website: www.southview-leisure.com
Extra charge for dogs? Yes
Any breed restrictions? No
Dog bins? Yes
Area for walking dogs? Yes
Static caravans? Yes
Cost of static? Prices vary as discounts may apply
Mobile caravans? Yes
Cost of mobile? From £18.00 per night with electric
Tents? No
Cost of tent pitch?
Electricity at the pitch? Yes
Showers? Yes
Onsite Entertainment? Yes
Opening times? March - November

St Edmund Orchard Park Caravan and Camping Park

Address: Sutton, Lincolnshire PE12 0LT
Telephone: 01945 700482
Website: www.orchardviewholidays.com
Extra charge for dogs? No
Any breed restrictions? No
Dog bins? Yes
Area for walking dogs? Yes
Static caravans? Yes
Cost of static? From £180.00 per week
Mobile caravans? Yes
Cost of mobile? From £9.00 - £12.00 per night
Tents? Yes
Cost of tent pitch? From £9.00 - £12.00 per night
Electricity at the pitch? Yes
Showers? Yes
Onsite Entertainment? No
Opening times? Mid March - End October
Comments: Dogs must be kept on a lead. There is a small quiet lounge area with a bar on site.

Stable Farm

Address: Short Drove, Gosberton Clough, Spalding, Lincolnshire PE11 4JT
Telephone: 07709 064651
Website:
Extra charge for dogs? No
Any breed restrictions? No
Dog bins? Yes
Area for walking dogs? Yes
Static caravans? No
Cost of static?
Mobile caravans? Yes
Cost of mobile? From £6.00 per night
Tents? Yes
Cost of tent pitch? From £5.00 per night
Electricity at the pitch? Yes
Showers? No

Onsite Entertainment? No

Opening times? All Year

Comments: Dogs must be kept on a lead.

Stocks Hill Cottage

Address: Woodhall Road, Stixwould, Woodhall Spa, Lincolnshire LN10 5HL

Telephone: 01526 354744

Website:

Extra charge for dogs? No

Any breed restrictions? No

Dog bins? No

Area for walking dogs? Yes

Static caravans? No

Cost of static?

Mobile caravans? Yes

Cost of mobile? From £8.00 per night with electric

Tents? Yes

Cost of tent pitch? From £5.00 per night

Electricity at the pitch? Yes

Showers? No

Onsite Entertainment? No

Opening times? March - End September

Comments: Dogs must be kept on a lead.

Stockmoor Farm

Address: Stockmoor Lane, Market Rasen, Lincolnshire LN8 3TT

Telephone: 01673 842340

Website: www.5van.co.uk

Extra charge for dogs? No

Any breed restrictions? No

Dog bins? No

Area for walking dogs? Yes

Static caravans? No

Cost of static?

Mobile caravans? Yes

Cost of mobile? From £11.00 per night with electric

Tents? No

Cost of tent pitch?

Electricity at the pitch? Yes

Showers? No

Onsite Entertainment? No

Opening times? March - October (CL Site) All Year is available

Comments: Members of The Caravan Club only. Adults only.

Sunkist Caravan Park

Address: Sea Rd, Skegness, Lincolnshire PE24 5XW

Telephone: 01754 872374

Website: www.funkistcaravanpark.co.uk

Extra charge for dogs? No

Any breed restrictions? No

Dog bins? No

Area for walking dogs? No

Static caravans? Yes

Cost of static? From £220.00 per week

Mobile caravans? No

Cost of mobile?

Tents? No

Cost of tent pitch?

Electricity at the pitch? No

Showers? No

Onsite Entertainment? No

Opening times? March - October

Sunnydale Holiday Park

Address: Sunnydale Caravan Park, Sea Lane, Saltfleet, Louth, Lincolnshire LN11 7RP

Telephone: 01507 338100

Website: www.park-resorts.com

Extra charge for dogs? Yes

Any breed restrictions? Yes

Dog bins? Yes
Area for walking dogs? Yes
Static caravans? Yes
Cost of static? From £199.00 - £639.00 per week
Mobile caravans? Yes
Cost of mobile? From £10.00 per night
Tents? No
Cost of tent pitch?
Electricity at the pitch? Yes
Showers? Yes
Onsite Entertainment? Yes
Opening times? March - October
Comments: No Dangerous Breeds.

Suzeden

Address: Trent Port Road, Marton, Gainsborough, Lincolnshire DN21 5AP
Telephone: 07815 187375
Website:
Extra charge for dogs? Yes
Any breed restrictions? No
Dog bins? Yes
Area for walking dogs? No
Static caravans? No
Cost of static?
Mobile caravans? Yes
Cost of mobile? From £3.00 per person per night
Tents? Yes
Cost of tent pitch? From £3.00 per person per night
Electricity at the pitch? No
Showers? No
Onsite Entertainment? No
Opening times? All Year

Sycamore Farm Caravan and Camping

Address: Chalk Lane, Burgh-le-marsh, Skegness, Lincolnshire PE24 5HN
Telephone: 01754 810833
Website: www.sycamorefarm.net
Extra charge for dogs? Yes
Any breed restrictions? No
Dog bins? No
Area for walking dogs? Yes
Static caravans? Yes
Cost of static? From £175.00 per week
Mobile caravans? Yes
Cost of mobile? From £11.00 per night with electric
Tents? Yes
Cost of tent pitch? From £11.00 per night with electric
Electricity at the pitch? Yes
Showers? Yes
Onsite Entertainment? No
Opening times? 1st March - End November (Statics) 1st March - End October (Touring)
Comments: There is a launderette, a shop and a fishing lake on site.

Taggs Caravan Site

Address: 178, Wainfleet Rd, Skegness, Lincolnshire PE25 2ER
Telephone: 01754 764280
Website:
Extra charge for dogs? No
Any breed restrictions? No
Dog bins? No
Area for walking dogs? Off Site
Static caravans? No
Cost of static?
Mobile caravans? Yes
Cost of mobile? From £13.00 per night with electric
Tents? No
Cost of tent pitch?
Electricity at the pitch? Yes

Showers? Yes

Onsite Entertainment? Yes

Opening times? March - End October

Comments: There is a Clubhouse on site.

Tallington Lakes

Address: Barholm Road, Tallington, Stamford, Lincolnshire PE9 4RJ

Telephone: 01778 347000

Website: www.tallington.com

Extra charge for dogs? Yes

Any breed restrictions? No

Dog bins? Yes

Area for walking dogs? Off Site

Static caravans? No

Cost of static?

Mobile caravans? Yes

Cost of mobile? From £11.00 per night

Tents? Yes

Cost of tent pitch? From £7.00 per night

Electricity at the pitch? Yes

Showers? Yes

Onsite Entertainment? Sometimes

Opening times? All Year

Comments: Maxium of 2 dogs.

Tetford Country Cottages

Address: East Road, Tetford, Lincolnshire LN9 6QQ

Telephone: 01507 533276

Website: www.tetfordcountrycottages.co.uk

Extra charge for dogs? Yes

Any breed restrictions? No

Dog bins? Yes

Area for walking dogs? Yes

Static caravans? No

Cost of static?

Mobile caravans? Yes

Cost of mobile? From £7.00 per night

Tents? Yes

Cost of tent pitch? From £7.00 per night

Electricity at the pitch? Yes

Showers? Yes

Onsite Entertainment? No

Opening times? All Year (Weather Permitting)

Comments: Maximum 2 dogs. Dogs must be able to socialise. Must be member of The Camping and Caravan Club. There is a Tearoom on site.

The Camping and Caravanning Club

Address: Wellsyke Lane, Kirkby On Bain, Woodhall Spa, Lincolnshire LN10 6YU

Telephone: 01526 352911

Website: www.thecampingandcaravanningclub.co.uk

Extra charge for dogs? No

Any breed restrictions? No

Dog bins? Yes

Area for walking dogs? Yes

Static caravans? No

Cost of static?

Mobile caravans? Yes

Cost of mobile? From £5.15 per person per night for members

Tents? Yes

Cost of tent pitch? From £5.15 per person per night for members

Electricity at the pitch? Yes

Showers? Yes

Onsite Entertainment? No

Opening times? Mid March - 3rd November

The Caravan Club Ltd

Address: Hawthorn Farm Caravan Club Site, Crabtree Lane, Sutton-on-Sea, Mablethorpe, Lincolnshire LN12 2RS

Telephone: 01507 441503

Website: www.thecaravanclub.co.uk

Extra charge for dogs? No

Any breed restrictions? No

Dog bins? Yes

Area for walking dogs? No

Static caravans? No

Cost of static? From £4.60 per person + £4.80 per pitch

Mobile caravans? Yes

Cost of mobile? From £4.60 per person + £4.80 per pitch

Tents? No

Cost of tent pitch? From £4.60 per person + £4.80 per pitch

Electricity at the pitch? Yes

Showers? Yes

Onsite Entertainment? No

Opening times? March - November

Comments: Must be members of The Caravan Club.

The Hare and Hounds

Address: Main Street, Greatford, nr Stamford, Lincolnshire PE9 4QA

Telephone: 01778 560332

Website: www.hareandhoundsgreatford.com

Extra charge for dogs? No

Any breed restrictions? No

Dog bins? No

Area for walking dogs? Off Site

Static caravans? No

Cost of static?

Mobile caravans? Yes

Cost of mobile? From £5.00 per night

Tents? Yes

Cost of tent pitch? From £5.00 per night

Electricity at the pitch? Yes

Showers? No

Onsite Entertainment? Yes

Opening times? All Year

Comments: There is a pub on site.

The Hawthorns

Address: Low Road, Croft, Skegness, Lincolnshire PE24 4RY

Telephone: 01754 880416

Website:

Extra charge for dogs? No

Any breed restrictions? No

Dog bins? No

Area for walking dogs? Yes

Static caravans? No

Cost of static?

Mobile caravans? Yes

Cost of mobile? From £3.00 per night

Tents? Yes

Cost of tent pitch? From £2.50 per night

Electricity at the pitch? No

Showers? No

Onsite Entertainment? No

Opening times? Easter - October

Comments: Dogs must be kept on a lead.

The Old Stables

Address: Well, Alford, Lincolnshire LN13 0EU

Telephone: 01507 462167

Website: www.thecampingandcaravanningclub.co.uk

Extra charge for dogs? No

Any breed restrictions? No

Dog bins? No

Area for walking dogs? Yes
Static caravans? No
Cost of static?
Mobile caravans? Yes
Cost of mobile? From £8.00 per night
Tents? Yes
Cost of tent pitch? From £6.00 per night
Electricity at the pitch? Yes
Showers? Yes
Onsite Entertainment? No
Opening times? April - October

Comments: Have to be a member of the Camping and Caravanning Club.

The Paddocks Caravan Club

Address: Northgate West Pinchbeck, Spalding, Lincolnshire PE11 3TB

Telephone: 01775 640573

Website:

Extra charge for dogs? No
Any breed restrictions? No
Dog bins? No
Area for walking dogs? Yes
Static caravans? No
Cost of static?
Mobile caravans? Yes
Cost of mobile? From £8.00 per night
Tents? Yes
Cost of tent pitch? From £8.00 per night
Electricity at the pitch? Yes
Showers? Yes
Onsite Entertainment? No
Opening times? Easter - End October

The Rutland Arms Dirty Duck Caravan Site

Address: Woolsthorpe by Belvoir, Grantham, Lincolnshire NG32 1NY

Telephone: 01476 870111

Website:

Extra charge for dogs? No
Any breed restrictions? No
Dog bins? No
Area for walking dogs? No
Static caravans? No
Cost of static?
Mobile caravans? Yes
Cost of mobile? From £14.00 per night
Tents? Yes
Cost of tent pitch? From £14.00 per night
Electricity at the pitch? Yes
Showers? Yes
Onsite Entertainment? Yes
Opening times? All Year

Comments: There is a pub on site.

The Ship Inn

Address: 109 Sea Road, Chapel St Leonards, Skegness, Lincolnshire PE24 5RX

Telephone: 01754 872640

Website:

Extra charge for dogs? No
Any breed restrictions? Yes
Dog bins? Off Site
Area for walking dogs? Off Site
Static caravans? No
Cost of static?
Mobile caravans? Yes
Cost of mobile? From £13.00 per night
Tents? Yes
Cost of tent pitch? From £10.00 per night
Electricity at the pitch? Yes
Showers? Yes
Onsite Entertainment? Yes
Opening times? March - October

Comments: Dogs must be kept on a lead. No Dangerous Breeds. There is a pub on site. Must be member of Camping and Caravan Club.

The Villa

Address: Main Road, Keal Cotes, Spilsby, Lincolnshire PE23 4AG
Telephone: 01790 763240
Website:
Extra charge for dogs? No
Any breed restrictions? No
Dog bins? No
Area for walking dogs? Yes
Static caravans? No
Cost of static?
Mobile caravans? Yes
Cost of mobile? From £10.00 per night
Tents? Yes
Cost of tent pitch? ?
Electricity at the pitch? Yes
Showers? No
Onsite Entertainment? No
Opening times? All Year
Comments: Dogs must be kept on a lead.

The Windmill Inn

Address: Ingham, Lincoln, Lincolnshire LN1 2YQ
Telephone: 01522 730249
Website:
Extra charge for dogs? No
Any breed restrictions? No
Dog bins? No
Area for walking dogs? Off Site
Static caravans? No
Cost of static?
Mobile caravans? Yes
Cost of mobile? From £3.00 per night
Tents? No
Cost of tent pitch?
Electricity at the pitch? No
Showers? No
Onsite Entertainment? Yes
Opening times? All Year
Comments: Pub on site open 4 nights a week.

The Wishing Well Inn

Address: Main Street, Dyke, Nr Bourne, Lincolnshire PE10 0AF
Telephone: 01778 422970
Website: www.kellytaverns.com
Extra charge for dogs? No
Any breed restrictions? No
Dog bins? No
Area for walking dogs? Yes
Static caravans? No
Cost of static?
Mobile caravans? Yes
Cost of mobile? From £10.00 per night with electric
Tents? Yes
Cost of tent pitch? From £5.00 per night
Electricity at the pitch? Yes
Showers? No
Onsite Entertainment? No
Opening times? All Year
Comments: Dogs must be kept on a lead.

The Wood Farm

Address: Bar Green Lane, East Fen Side, Stickney, Boston, Lincolnshire PE22 8BZ
Telephone: 01205 480687
Website:
Extra charge for dogs? No
Any breed restrictions? No
Dog bins? Yes
Area for walking dogs? Yes
Static caravans? Yes
Cost of static? From £295.00 per week
Mobile caravans? Yes
Cost of mobile? From £10.00 per night

Tents? Yes
Cost of tent pitch? From £10.00 per night
Electricity at the pitch? Yes
Showers? Yes
Onsite Entertainment? No
Opening times? All Year
Comments: There is a fishing lake on site.

Thorpe Park Holiday Centre

Address: Cleethorpes, Lincolnshire DN35 0PW
Telephone: 01472 813395
Website: www.havenholidays.co.uk
Extra charge for dogs? Yes
Any breed restrictions? No
Dog bins? Yes
Area for walking dogs? Yes
Static caravans? Yes
Cost of static? Prices vary as discounts may apply
Mobile caravans? Yes
Cost of mobile? Prices vary as discounts may apply
Tents? Yes
Cost of tent pitch? Prices vary as discounts may apply
Electricity at the pitch? Yes
Showers? Yes
Onsite Entertainment? Yes
Opening times? 1st March - 31st October
Comments: Dogs must be kept on a lead. Maximum 2 dogs.

Tomlinsons Leisure Park

Address: South Rd, Chapel St. Leonards, Skegness, Lincolnshire PE24 5TL
Telephone: 01754 872241
Website: www.tomlinsons-leisure.co.uk
Extra charge for dogs? Yes
Any breed restrictions? No
Dog bins? No
Area for walking dogs? Off Site
Static caravans? Yes
Cost of static? From £160.00 per week
Mobile caravans? No
Cost of mobile?
Tents? No
Cost of tent pitch?
Electricity at the pitch? No
Showers? No
Onsite Entertainment? Yes
Opening times? Easter - October
Comments: Maximum 1 dog per unit. Dogs must be kept on a lead. There is a Clubhouse on site.

Topos Farm

Address: Great Steeping Aerodrome, Spilsby, Lincolnshire PE23 5PP
Telephone: 07789 154937
Website:
Extra charge for dogs? No
Any breed restrictions? Yes
Dog bins? No
Area for walking dogs? Off Site
Static caravans? No
Cost of static?
Mobile caravans? Yes
Cost of mobile? From £5.00 per night
Tents? Yes
Cost of tent pitch? From £5.00 per night
Electricity at the pitch? Yes
Showers? Yes
Onsite Entertainment? No
Opening times? All Year
Comments: No Big Dogs.

Trusthorpe Spring Leisure Park

Address: Mile Lane, Trusthorpe, Mablethorpe, Lincolnshire LN12 2QQ

Telephone: 01507 441384
Website:
Extra charge for dogs? No
Any breed restrictions? No
Dog bins? Yes
Area for walking dogs? Yes
Static caravans? No
Cost of static?
Mobile caravans? Yes
Cost of mobile? From £18.00 per night
Tents? No
Cost of tent pitch?
Electricity at the pitch? Yes
Showers? Yes
Onsite Entertainment? Yes
Opening times? 1st March - 31st October
Comments: Maximum 1 dog.

Waggon and Horses

Address: Main Road, Louth, Lincolnshire LN11 8JQ
Telephone: 01507 450364
Website: www.waggonandhorsesreston.co.uk
Extra charge for dogs? No
Any breed restrictions? No
Dog bins? No
Area for walking dogs? Yes
Static caravans? No
Cost of static?
Mobile caravans? Yes
Cost of mobile? From £10.00 per night
Tents? Yes
Cost of tent pitch? From £7.50 per night
Electricity at the pitch? Yes
Showers? No
Onsite Entertainment? Yes
Opening times? All Year

Walesby Woodlands Caravan Park

Address: Walesby, Market Rasen, Lincolnshire LN8 3UN
Telephone: 01673 843285
Website:
Extra charge for dogs? No
Any breed restrictions? No
Dog bins? No
Area for walking dogs? Off Site
Static caravans? No
Cost of static?
Mobile caravans? Yes
Cost of mobile? From £15.00 per night with electric
Tents? Yes
Cost of tent pitch? From £13.00 per night for 2 people + car
Electricity at the pitch? Yes
Showers? Yes
Onsite Entertainment? Yes
Opening times? March - End October
Comments: Café on site.

Walnut Lake Lodges and Camping

Address: Main Road, Algarkirk, Boston, Lincolnshire PE20 2LQ
Telephone: 01205 460482
Website: www.walnutlakes.co.uk
Extra charge for dogs? No
Any breed restrictions? Yes
Dog bins? No
Area for walking dogs? Yes
Static caravans? No
Cost of static?
Mobile caravans? Yes
Cost of mobile? From £10.00 per night
Tents? No
Cost of tent pitch?
Electricity at the pitch? Yes
Showers? Yes

Onsite Entertainment? No

Opening times? Easter - End September

Comments: No Dangerous Breeds.

Walshs Holiday Park

Address: Roman Bank, Skegness, Lincolnshire PE25 1QP

Telephone: 01754 764485

Website:

Extra charge for dogs? No

Any breed restrictions? Yes

Dog bins? Yes

Area for walking dogs? Yes

Static caravans? Yes

Cost of static? From £100.00 per week

Mobile caravans? No

Cost of mobile?

Tents? No

Cost of tent pitch?

Electricity at the pitch? No

Showers? No

Onsite Entertainment? No

Opening times? Mid March - End October

Comments: Maximum 2 dogs. Don't allow very large breeds. Don't allow groups of young people.

Waterfront Country Park

Address: Gainsborough, Lincolnshire DN10 4ET

Telephone: 01427 890000

Website:

Extra charge for dogs? Yes

Any breed restrictions? No

Dog bins? Yes

Area for walking dogs? Yes

Static caravans? No

Cost of static?

Mobile caravans? Yes

Cost of mobile? From £9.00 per night with electric

Tents? No

Cost of tent pitch?

Electricity at the pitch? Yes

Showers? No

Onsite Entertainment? No

Opening times? All Year

Comments: There is a pub next door.

Waterside Leisure Park

Address: Anchor Lane, Ingoldmells, Skegness, Lincolnshire PE25 1LX

Telephone: 01754 874837

Website: www.blueanchor.biz

Extra charge for dogs? No

Any breed restrictions? No

Dog bins? No

Area for walking dogs? Off Site

Static caravans? No

Cost of static?

Mobile caravans? Yes

Cost of mobile? From £15.00 per night

Tents? No

Cost of tent pitch?

Electricity at the pitch? Yes

Showers? Yes

Onsite Entertainment? No

Opening times? Mid March - End October

Comments: Dogs must be kept on a lead. There is a shop and a fishing lake on site.

West End Farm Caravan Park

Address: Carlton Rd, South Reston, Louth, Lincolnshire LN11 8JN

Telephone: 01507 450949

Website: www.westendfarm.co.uk

Extra charge for dogs? No

Any breed restrictions? No

Dog bins? No

Area for walking dogs? Off Site
Static caravans? No
Cost of static?
Mobile caravans? Yes
Cost of mobile? From £12.00 per night with electric for 2 people
Tents? Yes
Cost of tent pitch? From £9.00 per night
Electricity at the pitch? Yes
Showers? Yes
Onsite Entertainment? No
Opening times? Easter - October

West Lodge Lakes

Address: Whisby Moor, Lincoln, Lincolnshire LN6 9BY
Telephone: 01522 681720
Website:
Extra charge for dogs? Yes
Any breed restrictions? ?
Dog bins? No
Area for walking dogs? Yes
Static caravans? No
Cost of static?
Mobile caravans? Yes
Cost of mobile? From £10.00 per night
Tents? Yes
Cost of tent pitch? From £5.00 per night
Electricity at the pitch? Yes
Showers? Yes
Onsite Entertainment? No
Opening times? All Year

Westlea Caravan Site

Address: Ingoldmells Rd, Burgh Le Marsh, Skegness, Lincolnshire PE24 5HE
Telephone: 01754 810570
Website: www.westleacaravanpark.co.uk
Extra charge for dogs? No
Any breed restrictions? No
Dog bins? No
Area for walking dogs? Off Site
Static caravans? No
Cost of static?
Mobile caravans? Yes
Cost of mobile? From £10.00 per night with electric
Tents? Yes
Cost of tent pitch? From £10.00 per night with electric
Electricity at the pitch? Yes
Showers? Yes
Onsite Entertainment? No
Opening times? March - End October

West Pinchbeck Village Hall

Address: Six House Bank, West Pinchbeck, Spalding, Lincolnshire PE11 3QG
Telephone: 01775 640271
Website:
Extra charge for dogs? No
Any breed restrictions? No
Dog bins? No
Area for walking dogs? Off Site
Static caravans? No
Cost of static?
Mobile caravans? Yes
Cost of mobile? From £4.00 per night
Tents? Yes
Cost of tent pitch? From £4.00 per night
Electricity at the pitch? No
Showers? No
Onsite Entertainment? No
Opening times? All Year

White Cat Caravan and Camping Park

Address: The Cottage, Shaws Lane, Old Leake, Boston, Lincolnshire PE22 9LQ
Telephone: 01205 870121
Website: www.whitecatpark.com

Extra charge for dogs? Yes
Any breed restrictions? No
Dog bins? Yes
Area for walking dogs? Yes
Static caravans? Yes
Cost of static? From £290.00 per week
Mobile caravans? Yes
Cost of mobile? From £11.00 per night
Tents? Yes
Cost of tent pitch? From £11.00 per night
Electricity at the pitch? Yes
Showers? Yes
Onsite Entertainment? No
Opening times? April - October

White Horse Caravan Park

Address: Classification: Caravan Parks Dunston Fen, Metheringham, Lincoln, Lincolnshire LN4 3AP
Telephone: 01526 399919
Website: www.knowlesleisure.com
Extra charge for dogs? No
Any breed restrictions? No
Dog bins? Yes
Area for walking dogs? Yes
Static caravans? Yes
Cost of static? From £150.00 - £200.00 per week
Mobile caravans? No
Cost of mobile?
Tents? No
Cost of tent pitch?
Electricity at the pitch? No
Showers? No
Onsite Entertainment? No
Opening times? February - December
Comments: There is a pub on site.

White House Farm

Address: Hobhole Bank, New Leake, Boston, Lincolnshire PE22 8JH
Telephone: 01205 270440
Website: www.whitehousefarm.biz
Extra charge for dogs? No
Any breed restrictions? No
Dog bins? Yes
Area for walking dogs? Off Site
Static caravans? No
Cost of static?
Mobile caravans? Yes
Cost of mobile? From £6.00 per night
Tents? Yes
Cost of tent pitch? From £6.00 per night
Electricity at the pitch? Yes
Showers? No
Onsite Entertainment? No
Opening times? All Year

Willow Holt Caravan and Camping Park

Address: Lodge Rd, Tattershall, Lincoln, Lincolnshire LN4 4JS
Telephone: 01526 343111
Website: www.willowholt.co.uk
Extra charge for dogs? Yes
Any breed restrictions? No
Dog bins? No
Area for walking dogs? Yes
Static caravans? No
Cost of static?
Mobile caravans? Yes
Cost of mobile? From £12.00 - £16.00 per night
Tents? Yes
Cost of tent pitch? From £12.00 - £16.00 per night
Electricity at the pitch? Yes
Showers? Yes

Onsite Entertainment? No
Opening times? March - October

Winceby House Farm

Address: Horncastle, Lincolnshire LN9 6PB
Telephone: 01507 588249
Website:
Extra charge for dogs? No
Any breed restrictions? No
Dog bins? No
Area for walking dogs? No
Static caravans? No
Cost of static?
Mobile caravans? Yes
Cost of mobile? From £5.00 per night
Tents? Yes
Cost of tent pitch? From £5.00 per night
Electricity at the pitch? No
Showers? No
Onsite Entertainment? No
Opening times? All Year

Windcatch Holiday Park

Address: 11 Kellett Gate, Low Fulney, Spalding, Lincolnshire PE12 6EH
Telephone: 01775 718171
Website: www.windcatchcaravanpark.co.uk
Extra charge for dogs? No
Any breed restrictions? No
Dog bins? No
Area for walking dogs? Yes
Static caravans? No
Cost of static?
Mobile caravans? Yes
Cost of mobile? From £8.50 per night with electric
Tents? Yes
Cost of tent pitch? From £7.00 per night with electric
Electricity at the pitch? Yes
Showers? Yes
Onsite Entertainment? No
Opening times? All Year
Comments: There is a shop on site.

Windmill Farm Caravan Park

Address: Bourne, Lincolnshire PE6 9PX
Telephone: 01775 640215
Website: www.windmill-farm-caravan-park.com
Extra charge for dogs? No
Any breed restrictions? Yes
Dog bins? No
Area for walking dogs? Yes
Static caravans? No
Cost of static?
Mobile caravans? Yes
Cost of mobile? From £11.00 per night
Tents? Yes
Cost of tent pitch? From £9.00 per night
Electricity at the pitch? Yes
Showers? Yes
Onsite Entertainment? No
Opening times? All Year
Comments: No Dangerous Breeds.

Woodlands Waters Ltd

Address: Willoughby Rd, Ancaster, Grantham, Lincolnshire NG32 3RT
Telephone: 01400 230888
Website: www.woodlandwaters.co.uk
Extra charge for dogs? Yes
Any breed restrictions? No
Dog bins? No
Area for walking dogs? Yes
Static caravans? No
Cost of static?

Mobile caravans? Yes
Cost of mobile? From £12.00 per night
Tents? Yes
Cost of tent pitch? From £12.00 per night
Electricity at the pitch? Yes
Showers? Yes
Onsite Entertainment? Yes
Opening times? All Year
Comments: There is a bar and restaurant on site.

Woodthorpe Hall Leisure Park

Address: Woodthorpe Hall, Woodthorpe, Nr Alford, Lincolnshire LN13 0DD
Telephone: 01507 450294
Website: www.wooodthorpehall leisure.co.uk
Extra charge for dogs? Yes
Any breed restrictions? No
Dog bins? Yes
Area for walking dogs? Yes
Static caravans? Yes
Cost of static? From £175.00 per week
Mobile caravans? Yes
Cost of mobile? From £12.00 - £16.00 per night with electric
Tents? Yes
Cost of tent pitch? From £12.00 - £16.00 per night with electric
Electricity at the pitch? Yes
Showers? Yes
Onsite Entertainment? Yes
Opening times? 1st March - 3rd January

Bluebell Farm Holidays

Address: Rectory Road, Anderby, Skegness, Lincolnshire PE24 5YF
Telephone: 01507 490007
Website:
Extra charge for dogs? Yes
Any breed restrictions? No
Dog bins? Yes
Area for walking dogs? Yes
Static caravans? No
Cost of static?
Mobile caravans? Yes
Cost of mobile? From £5.00 per night
Tents? Yes
Cost of tent pitch? From £5.00 per night
Electricity at the pitch? Yes
Showers? Yes
Onsite Entertainment? No
Opening times? All Year

Havenhouse Farm

Address: Croft Marsh Lane, Croft, Skegness, Lincolnshire PE24 4AR
Telephone: 01754 881555
Website: www.havenhousefarm.co.uk
Extra charge for dogs? Yes
Any breed restrictions? No
Dog bins? Yes
Area for walking dogs? Yes
Static caravans? No
Cost of static?
Mobile caravans? Yes
Cost of mobile? From £8.00 per night
Tents? Yes
Cost of tent pitch? From £6.00 per night
Electricity at the pitch? Yes
Showers? Yes
Onsite Entertainment? Yes
Opening times? 1st March - End October
Comments: They are licensed and they serve food. There is also fishing on site.

Holivans Ltd

Address: Quebec Rd, Mablethorpe, Lincolnshire LN12 1QH

Telephone: 01507 473327
Website: www.holivans.co.uk
Extra charge for dogs? No
Any breed restrictions? No
Dog bins? No
Area for walking dogs? Off Site
Static caravans? No
Cost of static?
Mobile caravans? Yes
Cost of mobile? From £15.00 - £17.00 per night
Tents? No
Cost of tent pitch?
Electricity at the pitch? Yes
Showers? Yes
Onsite Entertainment? No
Opening times? March - October

Hunters Lodge

Address: Roman Road, Moulton Chapel, Spalding, Lincolnshire PE12 0XA
Telephone: 01406 380289
Website: www.hunterslodgecaravansite.co.uk
Extra charge for dogs? No
Any breed restrictions? No
Dog bins? No
Area for walking dogs? No
Static caravans? No
Cost of static?
Mobile caravans? Yes
Cost of mobile? From £7.00 per night
Tents? Yes
Cost of tent pitch? From £7.00 per night
Electricity at the pitch? Yes
Showers? No
Onsite Entertainment? No
Opening times? April - October

Inglenook Caravan Park

Address: Ingoldmells, Lincolnshire PE25 1LL
Telephone: 01507 490365
Website:
Extra charge for dogs? No
Any breed restrictions? No
Dog bins? Yes
Area for walking dogs? Off Site
Static caravans? No
Cost of static?
Mobile caravans? Yes
Cost of mobile? From £12.00 per night with electric
Tents? No
Cost of tent pitch?
Electricity at the pitch? Yes
Showers? Yes
Onsite Entertainment? No
Opening times? Begin March - End November

Ladysmith Farm

Address: Bracebridge Heath, Lincoln, Lincolnshire LN4 2JA
Telephone: 01522 720512
Website:
Extra charge for dogs? No
Any breed restrictions? No
Dog bins? No
Area for walking dogs? Yes
Static caravans? No
Cost of static?
Mobile caravans? Yes
Cost of mobile? From £5.00 per night
Tents? Yes
Cost of tent pitch? From £5.00 per night
Electricity at the pitch? No
Showers? No

Onsite Entertainment? No

Opening times? All Year

Lincolnshire Lanes

Address: Manor Farm, East Firsby, Market Rasen, Lincolnshire LN8 2DB

Telephone: 01673 878258

Website: www.lincolnshire-lanes.com

Extra charge for dogs? No

Any breed restrictions? No

Dog bins? No

Area for walking dogs? Yes

Static caravans? No

Cost of static?

Mobile caravans? Yes

Cost of mobile? From £8.00 per night

Tents? Yes

Cost of tent pitch? From £7.00 per night

Electricity at the pitch? Yes

Showers? Yes

Onsite Entertainment? No

Opening times? All Year

Little Eden

Address: 112 Horncastle Road, Woodhall Spa, Lincolnshire LN10 6UX

Telephone: 01526 352847

Website:

Extra charge for dogs? No

Any breed restrictions? No

Dog bins? No

Area for walking dogs? Off Site

Static caravans? No

Cost of static?

Mobile caravans? Yes

Cost of mobile? From £7.00 per night including electric

Tents? Yes

Cost of tent pitch? From £5.50 per night

Electricity at the pitch? Yes

Showers? No

Onsite Entertainment? No

Opening times? All Year

Comments: Dogs must be kept on a lead. Must be members of the Camping and Caravanning Club can join on site.

Lowfields Holiday & Fishing Retreat

Address: Lowfields Grange, Eagle Rd, North Scarle, Lincoln, Lincolnshire LN6 9EN

Telephone: 01522 778717

Website: www.lowfields-retreat.co.uk

Extra charge for dogs? Yes

Any breed restrictions? No

Dog bins? Yes

Area for walking dogs? Yes

Static caravans? Yes

Cost of static? From £243.00 per week

Mobile caravans? No

Cost of mobile?

Tents? No

Cost of tent pitch?

Electricity at the pitch? No

Showers? No

Onsite Entertainment? No

Opening times? March - November

Comments: There is fishing on site.

Mill Farm

Address: Wrangle Bank, Wrangle, Boston, Lincolnshire PE22 9DT

Telephone: 01754 820053

Website: www.millfarmleisure.co.uk

Extra charge for dogs? No

Any breed restrictions? No

Dog bins? No

Area for walking dogs? Yes

Static caravans? No

Cost of static?

Mobile caravans? Yes

Cost of mobile? From £12.00 per night
Tents? Yes
Cost of tent pitch? From £12.00 per night
Electricity at the pitch? Yes
Showers? Yes
Onsite Entertainment? No
Opening times? All Year
Comments: Dogs must be kept on a lead.

New Delights Caravan Park

Address: Windy Ridge, New Delights, Tetney, Grimsby, Lincolnshire DN36 5PA
Telephone: 01472 813741
Website:
Extra charge for dogs? No
Any breed restrictions? Yes
Dog bins? No
Area for walking dogs? Off Site
Static caravans? No
Cost of static?
Mobile caravans? Yes
Cost of mobile? From £8.00 per night
Tents? No
Cost of tent pitch?
Electricity at the pitch? Yes
Showers? No
Onsite Entertainment? No
Opening times? End March - End September
Comments: No Dangerous Breeds. Dogs must be kept on a lead on site.

North Shore Holiday Centre

Address: Elmhirst Avenue, Roman Bank, Skegness, Lincolnshire PE25 1SL
Telephone: 01754 763815
Website: www.northshore-skegness.co.uk
Extra charge for dogs? Yes
Any breed restrictions? No
Dog bins? Yes
Area for walking dogs? Yes
Static caravans? Yes
Cost of static? From £215.00 per week
Mobile caravans? Yes
Cost of mobile? From £16.00 per night
Tents? No
Cost of tent pitch?
Electricity at the pitch? Yes
Showers? Yes
Onsite Entertainment? Yes
Opening times? March - Beg November
Comments: There is a Clubhouse on site.

Orchard View Caravan & Camping Park

Address: 102, Broadgate, Sutton St. Edmund, Spalding, Lincolnshire PE12 0LT
Telephone: 01945 700482
Website: www.orchardviewholidays.com
Extra charge for dogs? No
Any breed restrictions? No
Dog bins? Yes
Area for walking dogs? Yes
Static caravans? Yes
Cost of static? From £186.00 per week
Mobile caravans? Yes
Cost of mobile? From £9.00 per night
Tents? Yes
Cost of tent pitch? From £9.00 per night
Electricity at the pitch? Yes
Showers? Yes
Onsite Entertainment? Yes
Opening times? Mid March - End October

Comments: There is a lounge and bar on site but no entertainment.

Roach Farm Park Caravan Site

Address: Burgh Rd, Skegness, Lincolnshire PE25 2RA

Telephone: 01754 898049

Website: www.coastfieldleisure.co.uk

Extra charge for dogs? No

Any breed restrictions? Yes

Dog bins? No

Area for walking dogs? Yes

Static caravans? No

Cost of static?

Mobile caravans? Yes

Cost of mobile? From £14.00 per night for 5 people, electric and awning

Tents? Yes

Cost of tent pitch? From £12.00 per night

Electricity at the pitch? Yes

Showers? Yes

Onsite Entertainment? Yes

Opening times? All Year

Comments: No Dangerous or very Large Breeds. There is fishing on site.

Rod & Line Caravan Park

Address: Lymn Bank East, Thorpe St. Peter, Skegness, Lincolnshire PE24 4PJ

Telephone: 01754 880494

Website:

Extra charge for dogs? No

Any breed restrictions? No

Dog bins? No

Area for walking dogs? Off Site

Static caravans? Yes

Cost of static? From £200.00 per week

Mobile caravans? No

Cost of mobile?

Tents? No

Cost of tent pitch?

Electricity at the pitch? No

Showers? No

Onsite Entertainment? No

Opening times? March - October

The Camping & Caravanning Club

Address: Highfield, 120, Church Lane, Mablethorpe, Lincolnshire LN12 2NU

Telephone: 01507 472374

Website: www.thecampingand caravanningclub.co.uk

Extra charge for dogs? No

Any breed restrictions? No

Dog bins? ?

Area for walking dogs? ?

Static caravans? No

Cost of static?

Mobile caravans? Yes

Cost of mobile? From £4.40 per adult per night + £6.00 site fee if not a member

Tents? No

Cost of tent pitch?

Electricity at the pitch? Yes

Showers? Yes

Onsite Entertainment? No

Opening times? Mid March - 3rd November

Comments: There is a children's play area on site.

Sunnydale Holiday Park

Address: Sunnydale Caravan Park, Sea Lane, Saltfleet, Louth, Lincolnshire LN11 7RP

Telephone: 01507 338100

Website: www.park-resorts.com

Extra charge for dogs? Yes

Any breed restrictions? Yes

Dog bins? Yes

Area for walking dogs? Yes

Static caravans? Yes
Cost of static? From £199.00 - £639.00 per week
Mobile caravans? Yes
Cost of mobile? From £10.00 per night
Tents? No
Cost of tent pitch?
Electricity at the pitch? Yes
Showers? Yes
Onsite Entertainment? Yes
Opening times? March - October
Comments: No Dangerous Breeds.

The White Horse Inn & Caravan Park

Address: Dunston Fen, Lincolnshire LN4 3AP
Telephone: 01526 399919
Website: www.knawlesleisure.com
Extra charge for dogs? No
Any breed restrictions? No
Dog bins? Yes
Area for walking dogs? Yes
Static caravans? Yes
Cost of static? From £150.00 per week
Mobile caravans? Yes
Cost of mobile? From £14.00 per night with electric
Tents? Yes
Cost of tent pitch? From £10.00 per night
Electricity at the pitch? Yes
Showers? Yes
Onsite Entertainment? Yes
Opening times? February - December
Comments: There is a pub on site.

Laleham Camping Club

Address: Laleham Park Camping Site, Laleham, Staines, Middlesex TW18 1SS
Telephone: 01932 564149
Website: www.lalehamcampingclub.co.uk
Extra charge for dogs? No
Any breed restrictions? No
Dog bins? No
Area for walking dogs? Off Site
Static caravans? No
Cost of static?
Mobile caravans? Yes
Cost of mobile? From £6.00 per adult £3.00 per child per night
Tents? Yes
Cost of tent pitch? From £6.00 per adult £3.00 per child per night
Electricity at the pitch? Yes
Showers? Yes
Onsite Entertainment? No
Opening times? April - October
Comments: Dogs must be kept on a lead.

The Caravan Club Ltd

Address: Wyatts Covert, Denham, Uxbridge, Middlesex UB9 5DH
Telephone: 01895 832729
Website: www.thecaravanclub.co.uk
Extra charge for dogs? No
Any breed restrictions? No
Dog bins? Yes
Area for walking dogs? Off Site
Static caravans? No
Cost of static?
Mobile caravans? Yes
Cost of mobile? From £14.90 - £21.30 for 2 people per night
Tents? No
Cost of tent pitch?
Electricity at the pitch? Yes
Showers? Yes
Onsite Entertainment? No
Opening times? All Year
Comments: Members of The Caravan Club only.

Theobalds Park Camping & Caravanning Club Site

Address: Bulls Cross Ride, Waltham Cross, Enfield, Middlesex EN7 5HS
Telephone: 01992 620604
Website: www.thecampingandcaravanningclub.co.uk
Extra charge for dogs? No
Any breed restrictions? No
Dog bins? Yes
Area for walking dogs? Yes
Static caravans? No
Cost of static?
Mobile caravans? Yes
Cost of mobile? From £3.75 per night per person
Tents? Yes
Cost of tent pitch? From £3.75 per night per person
Electricity at the pitch? Yes
Showers? Yes
Onsite Entertainment? No
Opening times? March - Beg November
Comments: Dogs must be kept on a lead.

Norfolk

Abbotts Farm Clothes Optional Caravan & Camping Site

Address: Northgate West Pinchbeck, Spalding, Lincolnshire PE11 3TB
Telephone: 01362 858871
Website:
Extra charge for dogs? No
Any breed restrictions? No
Dog bins? No
Area for walking dogs? Yes
Static caravans? No
Cost of static?
Mobile caravans? Yes
Cost of mobile? From £6.00 per night
Tents? Yes
Cost of tent pitch? From £6.00 per night
Electricity at the pitch? Yes
Showers? Yes
Onsite Entertainment? No
Opening times? All Year (Weather Permitting)

Applewood Caravan & Camping Park

Address: The Grove, Banham Zoo, Kenninghall Rd, Banham, Norwich, Norfolk NR16 2HE
Telephone: 01953 888370
Website:
Extra charge for dogs? No
Any breed restrictions? No
Dog bins? Yes
Area for walking dogs? Yes
Static caravans? No
Cost of static?
Mobile caravans? Yes
Cost of mobile? From £14.00 per night
Tents? Yes
Cost of tent pitch? From £8.75 per night
Electricity at the pitch? Yes
Showers? Yes
Onsite Entertainment? Rarely
Opening times? February - October

Beeston Regis Caravan & Camping Park

Address: Cromer Rd, Beeston Regis, Cromer, Norfolk NR27 9NG
Telephone: 01263 823614
Website: www.beestonregis.co.uk
Extra charge for dogs? Yes
Any breed restrictions? No
Dog bins? Yes
Area for walking dogs? Yes
Static caravans? No
Cost of static?
Mobile caravans? Yes
Cost of mobile? From £15.00 per night for 2 people with electric
Tents? Yes
Cost of tent pitch? From £15.00 per night for 2 people with electric
Electricity at the pitch? Yes
Showers? Yes
Onsite Entertainment? No
Opening times? March - End October

Breck Farm Caravanning & Camping

Address: Weybourne, Holt, Norfolk NR25 6QL

Telephone: 01263 588236

Website: www.breckfarm.co.uk

Extra charge for dogs? No

Any breed restrictions? No

Dog bins? No

Area for walking dogs? Yes

Static caravans? No

Cost of static?

Mobile caravans? Yes

Cost of mobile? From £12.00 per night with electric

Tents? Yes

Cost of tent pitch? From £3.50 per pitch + £2.50 per person per night

Electricity at the pitch? Yes

Showers? Yes

Onsite Entertainment? No

Opening times? Easter - End October

Breckland Meadows Touring Park

Address: Lynn Rd, Swaffham, Norfolk PE37 7AY

Telephone: 01760 721246

Website: www.brecklandmeadows.co.uk

Extra charge for dogs? Yes

Any breed restrictions? No

Dog bins? Yes

Area for walking dogs? Yes

Static caravans? No

Cost of static?

Mobile caravans? Yes

Cost of mobile? From £11.75 per night

Tents? Yes

Cost of tent pitch? From £11.75 per night

Electricity at the pitch? Yes

Showers? Yes

Onsite Entertainment? No

Opening times? All Year

Breydon Water Holiday Park

Address: Burgh Castle, Great Yarmouth, Norfolk NR31 9QB

Telephone: 08716 649709

Website: www.park-resorts.com

Extra charge for dogs? Yes

Any breed restrictions? Yes

Dog bins? No

Area for walking dogs? Yes

Static caravans? Yes

Cost of static? From £209.00 per week

Mobile caravans? Yes

Cost of mobile? ?

Tents? Yes

Cost of tent pitch? ?

Electricity at the pitch? Yes

Showers? Yes

Onsite Entertainment? Yes

Opening times? March - End October

Comments: No Dangerous Breeds.

Brick Kilne Farm Caravanning & Camping

Address: Brick Kilne Farm, Swaffham Rd, Ashill, Thetford, Norfolk IP25 7BT

Telephone: 01760 441300

Website:

Extra charge for dogs? No

Any breed restrictions? No

Dog bins? No

Area for walking dogs? Yes

Static caravans? No

Cost of static?

Mobile caravans? Yes

Cost of mobile? From £6.00 per night

Tents? Yes

Cost of tent pitch? From £6.00 per night

Electricity at the pitch? Yes
Showers? Yes
Onsite Entertainment? No
Opening times? All Year
Comments: Dogs must be kept on a lead.

Brickyard Farm

Address: Grove Road, Banham, Norfolk NR16 2HQ
Telephone: 01953 887223
Website:
Extra charge for dogs? No
Any breed restrictions? Yes
Dog bins? No
Area for walking dogs? Yes
Static caravans? No
Cost of static?
Mobile caravans? Yes
Cost of mobile? From £12.00 per night with electric
Tents? Yes
Cost of tent pitch? From £10.00 per night
Electricity at the pitch? Yes
Showers? Yes
Onsite Entertainment? No
Opening times? All Year
Comments: No Dangerous Breeds.

Broad Farm Caravan Park

Address: Broad Farm, Main Road, Fleggburgh, Great Yarmouth, Norfolk NR29 3AF
Telephone: 01493 369273
Website:
Extra charge for dogs? Yes
Any breed restrictions? No
Dog bins? Yes
Area for walking dogs? Yes
Static caravans? Yes
Cost of static? ?
Mobile caravans? Yes
Cost of mobile? From £15.00 per pitch per night
Tents? Yes
Cost of tent pitch? From £8.00 per pitch per night
Electricity at the pitch? Yes
Showers? Yes
Onsite Entertainment? Yes
Opening times? May Day - End September
Comments: Dogs must be kept on a lead. There is a Clubhouse open every night during high season.

Bureside Holiday Park

Address: Boundary Farm, Oby, Great Yarmouth, Norfolk NR29 3BW
Telephone: 01493 369233
Website:
Extra charge for dogs? No
Any breed restrictions? No
Dog bins? No
Area for walking dogs? Off Site
Static caravans? No
Cost of static?
Mobile caravans? Yes
Cost of mobile? From £14.00 per night for 2 people
Tents? Yes
Cost of tent pitch? From £14.00 per night for 2 people
Electricity at the pitch? Yes
Showers? Yes
Onsite Entertainment? No
Opening times? May - September

Burgh Hall Holiday Park

Address: Lords Lane, Burgh Castle, Great Yarmouth, Norfolk NR31 9EP

Telephone: 01493 780847

Website:

Extra charge for dogs? No

Any breed restrictions? Yes

Dog bins? No

Area for walking dogs? Yes

Static caravans? No

Cost of static?

Mobile caravans? Yes

Cost of mobile? From £15.00 per night with electric

Tents? Yes

Cost of tent pitch? From £13.00 per night

Electricity at the pitch? Yes (Not Tents)

Showers? Yes

Onsite Entertainment? Yes

Opening times? March - December

Comments: No Dangerous Breeds. There is a swimming pool and childrens play area on site. There is entertainment on a Friday and Saturday Night.

Bush House Farm

Address: Bush House Farm, Church Road, Sutton, Norfolk NR12 9SA

Telephone: 01692 580365

Website:

Extra charge for dogs? No

Any breed restrictions? No

Dog bins? No

Area for walking dogs? Off Site

Static caravans? No

Cost of static?

Mobile caravans? Yes

Cost of mobile? From £7.00 per night

Tents? No

Cost of tent pitch?

Electricity at the pitch? Yes

Showers? No

Onsite Entertainment? No

Opening times? April - October

Comments: Must be members of The Caravan Club. Dogs must be kept on a lead at all times.

Cable Gap Caravan Park

Address: Coast Rd, Bacton, Norwich, Norfolk NR12 0EW

Telephone: 01692 650667

Website: www.cablegap.co.uk

Extra charge for dogs? Yes

Any breed restrictions? Yes

Dog bins? No

Area for walking dogs? Off Site

Static caravans? Yes

Cost of static? From £150.00 per week

Mobile caravans? No

Cost of mobile?

Tents? No

Cost of tent pitch?

Electricity at the pitch? No

Showers? No

Onsite Entertainment? No

Opening times? Beg March - Mid November

Comments: No Dangerous Breeds.

California Cliffs Holiday Park

Address: Rottenstone Lane, Great Yarmouth, Norfolk NR29 3QU

Telephone: 01493 730584

Website: www.park-resorts.com

Extra charge for dogs? Yes

Any breed restrictions? Yes

Dog bins? No

Area for walking dogs? Off Site

Static caravans? Yes

Cost of static? From £160.00

Mobile caravans? No

Cost of mobile?
Tents? No
Cost of tent pitch?
Electricity at the pitch? No
Showers? No
Onsite Entertainment? Yes
Opening times? March - October
Comments: No Dangerous Breeds.

Castaways Holiday Park

Address: Paston Rd, Bacton, Norwich, Norfolk NR12 0JB
Telephone: 01692 650436
Website: www.castawaysholidaypark.co.uk
Extra charge for dogs? Yes
Any breed restrictions? No
Dog bins? Yes
Area for walking dogs? Yes
Static caravans? Yes
Cost of static? From £193.00 per week
Mobile caravans? No
Cost of mobile?
Tents? No
Cost of tent pitch?
Electricity at the pitch? No
Showers? No
Onsite Entertainment? Yes
Opening times? 1st March - 2nd January
Comments: Maximum 3 dogs.

Cavick House Farm

Address: Cavick Road, Wymondham, Norfolk NR18 9PJ
Telephone: 01953 604810
Website: www.thecaravanclub.co.uk
Extra charge for dogs? No
Any breed restrictions? No
Dog bins? No
Area for walking dogs? Off Site
Static caravans? No
Cost of static?
Mobile caravans? Yes
Cost of mobile? From £6.00 per night with electric
Tents? No
Cost of tent pitch?
Electricity at the pitch? Yes
Showers? No
Onsite Entertainment? No
Opening times? March - October
Comments: Dogs must be kept on a lead. From 2009 prices are increasing to £8.00 per pitch per night. Must be a member of the Caravan Club.

Cherry Tree Holiday Park

Address: Mill Rd, Burgh Castle, Great Yarmouth, Norfolk NR31 9QR
Telephone: 0871 6410323
Website: www.parkdeanholidays.co.uk
Extra charge for dogs? Yes
Any breed restrictions? Yes
Dog bins? Yes
Area for walking dogs? Yes
Static caravans? Yes
Cost of static? From £169.00 per week
Mobile caravans? No
Cost of mobile?
Tents? No
Cost of tent pitch?
Electricity at the pitch? No
Showers? No
Onsite Entertainment? Yes
Opening times? March - November
Comments: No Dangerous Breeds.

Claggan Caravanning & Camping

Address: Claggan, Church Road, Wreningham, Norwich, Norfolk NR16 1BA

Telephone: 01508 481798

Website:

Extra charge for dogs? No

Any breed restrictions? No

Dog bins? No

Area for walking dogs? No

Static caravans? No

Cost of static?

Mobile caravans? Yes

Cost of mobile? From £5.00 per night

Tents? Yes

Cost of tent pitch? From £5.00 per night

Electricity at the pitch? No

Showers? No

Onsite Entertainment? No

Opening times? All Year (Weather Permitting)

Comments: Dogs must be kept on a lead at all times.

Clippesby Hall

Address: Hall Lane, Clippesby, Great Yarmouth, Norfolk NR29 3BL

Telephone: 01493 367800

Website: www.clippesby.com

Extra charge for dogs? Yes

Any breed restrictions? No

Dog bins? Yes

Area for walking dogs? Yes

Static caravans? No

Cost of static?

Mobile caravans? Yes

Cost of mobile? From £10.00 per night

Tents? Yes

Cost of tent pitch? From £10.00 per night

Electricity at the pitch? Yes

Showers? Yes

Onsite Entertainment? Yes

Opening times? Easter - October

Comments: There is entertainment on site, once a week in low season, twice a week in high season.

Crossways Caravan Site

Address: Holt Road, Little Snoring, Fakenham, Norfolk NR21 0AX

Telephone: 01328 878335

Website: www.glavenvalley.co.uk

Extra charge for dogs? Yes

Any breed restrictions? No

Dog bins? Yes

Area for walking dogs? No

Static caravans? Yes

Cost of static? From £140.00 - £340.00 per week

Mobile caravans? Yes

Cost of mobile? From £7.00 - £16.00 per night with electric

Tents? Yes

Cost of tent pitch? From £7.00 - £16.00 per night with electric

Electricity at the pitch? Yes

Showers? Yes

Onsite Entertainment? No

Opening times? All Year

Deepdale Backpackers & Camping

Address: Deepdale Farm, Burnham Deepdale, King's Lynn, Norfolk PE31 8DD

Telephone: 01485 210256

Website: www.deepdalefarm.co.uk

Extra charge for dogs? No

Any breed restrictions? No

Dog bins? No

Area for walking dogs? Yes

Static caravans? No

Cost of static?

Mobile caravans? No

Cost of mobile?
Tents? Yes
Cost of tent pitch? From £4.50 per adult per night
Electricity at the pitch? No
Showers? Yes
Onsite Entertainment? No
Opening times? All Year

Deers Glade Caravan & Camping Park

Address: White Post Rd, Hanworth, Norwich, Norfolk NR11 7HN
Telephone: 01263 768633
Website: www.deersglade.co.uk
Extra charge for dogs? Yes
Any breed restrictions? No
Dog bins? Yes
Area for walking dogs? Yes
Static caravans? No
Cost of static?
Mobile caravans? Yes
Cost of mobile? From £5.50 per adult per night/£10.00 single occupancy per night
Tents? Yes
Cost of tent pitch? From £5.50 per adult per night/£10.00 single occupancy per night
Electricity at the pitch? Yes
Showers? Yes
Onsite Entertainment? No
Opening times? All Year
Comments: There is a Kennel facility from £7.00 per day.

Diglea Caravan Park Ltd

Address: 32, Beach Rd, Snettisham, King's Lynn, Norfolk PE31 7RA
Telephone: 01485 541367
Website:
Extra charge for dogs? Yes
Any breed restrictions? No
Dog bins? Yes
Area for walking dogs? Yes
Static caravans? No
Cost of static?
Mobile caravans? Yes
Cost of mobile? From £10.00 per night
Tents? Yes
Cost of tent pitch? From £10.00 per night
Electricity at the pitch? Yes
Showers? Yes
Onsite Entertainment? Yes
Opening times? April - September
Comments: Dogs must be kept on a lead. There is a small Clubhouse on site that has entertainment at weekends.

Drewery Caravan Park

Address: California Rd, California, Great Yarmouth, Norfolk NR29 3QW
Telephone: 01493 730845
Website:
Extra charge for dogs? Yes
Any breed restrictions? No
Dog bins? Yes
Area for walking dogs? Off Site
Static caravans? No
Cost of static?
Mobile caravans? Yes
Cost of mobile? From £12.00 per night with electric
Tents? Yes
Cost of tent pitch? From £10.00 per night
Electricity at the pitch? Yes
Showers? Yes
Onsite Entertainment? Yes
Opening times? April - End October
Comments: There is entertainment at weekends.

Eastern Beach Caravan Park

Address: Manor Rd, Caister-on-Sea, Great Yarmouth, Norfolk NR30 5HH

Telephone: 01493 720367

Website: www.easternbeachcaravanpark.co.uk

Extra charge for dogs? Yes

Any breed restrictions? No

Dog bins? No

Area for walking dogs? Yes

Static caravans? Yes

Cost of static? From £100.00 per week

Mobile caravans? No

Cost of mobile?

Tents? No

Cost of tent pitch?

Electricity at the pitch? No

Showers? No

Onsite Entertainment? Yes

Opening times? Week Before Easter - End October

Elm Beach Caravan Park

Address: Manor Rd, Caister-on-Sea, Great Yarmouth, Norfolk NR30 5HG

Telephone: 01493 721630

Website: www.elmbeachcaravanpark.com

Extra charge for dogs? Yes

Any breed restrictions? No

Dog bins? No

Area for walking dogs? Off Site

Static caravans? Yes

Cost of static? From £95.00 per week

Mobile caravans? No

Cost of mobile?

Tents? No

Cost of tent pitch?

Electricity at the pitch? No

Showers? No

Onsite Entertainment? No

Opening times? March - January

Fakenham Racecourse Camping & Caravan Site

Address: The Racecourse, Fakenham, Norfolk NR21 7NY

Telephone: 01328 862388

Website: www.fakenhamracecourse.co.uk

Extra charge for dogs? No

Any breed restrictions? No

Dog bins? Yes

Area for walking dogs? Yes

Static caravans? No

Cost of static?

Mobile caravans? Yes

Cost of mobile? From £4.80 per pitch £3.30 per adult per night

Tents? Yes

Cost of tent pitch? From £6.00 per night

Electricity at the pitch? Yes

Showers? Yes

Onsite Entertainment? No

Opening times? All Year

Forest Holidays

Address: Thorpe Woodland Campsite, Shadwell, Thetford, Norfolk IP24 2RX

Telephone: 01842 751042

Website: www.forestholidays.co.uk

Extra charge for dogs? Yes

Any breed restrictions? No

Dog bins? No

Area for walking dogs? Yes

Static caravans? No

Cost of static?

Mobile caravans? Yes

Cost of mobile? From £6.60 per night for 2 people

Tents? Yes
Cost of tent pitch? From £6.60 per night for 2 people
Electricity at the pitch? Yes
Showers? No
Onsite Entertainment? No
Opening times? March - October
Comments: Maximum 3 dogs per pitch. Non Members will be charged an extra £3.00.

Forest Park Caravan Site

Address: Cromer, Norfolk NR27 0JR
Telephone: 01263 513290
Website: www.forest-park.co.uk
Extra charge for dogs? Yes
Any breed restrictions? No
Dog bins? Yes
Area for walking dogs? Yes
Static caravans? No
Cost of static?
Mobile caravans? Yes
Cost of mobile? From £12.00 per night
Tents? Yes
Cost of tent pitch? From £12.00 per night
Electricity at the pitch? Yes
Showers? Yes
Onsite Entertainment? Yes
Opening times? 15th March - 15th January
Comments: Dogs must be kept on a lead.

Foxhills Caravan Club

Address: Weybourne, Holt, Norfolk NR25 7EH
Telephone: 01263 588253
Website:
Extra charge for dogs? No
Any breed restrictions? Yes
Dog bins? No
Area for walking dogs? Off Site
Static caravans? No
Cost of static?
Mobile caravans? Yes
Cost of mobile? From £9.00 per night
Tents? Yes
Cost of tent pitch? From £9.00 per night
Electricity at the pitch? Yes (Not Tents)
Showers? Yes
Onsite Entertainment? No
Opening times? All Year
Comments: No Dangerous Breeds.

Gale Cruisers

Address: Riverside, Pits Lane, Chedgrave, Norwich, Norfolk NR14 6NQ
Telephone: 01508 520275
Website: www.galeriverside.co.uk
Extra charge for dogs? No
Any breed restrictions? No
Dog bins? Yes
Area for walking dogs? Yes
Static caravans? No
Cost of static?
Mobile caravans? Yes
Cost of mobile? From £9.50 per night
Tents? No
Cost of tent pitch?
Electricity at the pitch? Yes
Showers? No
Onsite Entertainment? No
Opening times? All Year

Gatton Waters

Address: Offlynne Rd, Hillington, King's Lynn, Norfolk PE31 6BJ
Telephone: 01485 600643
Website: www.gattonwaters.co.uk
Extra charge for dogs? No
Any breed restrictions? No
Dog bins? No

Area for walking dogs? Yes
Static caravans? No
Cost of static?
Mobile caravans? Yes
Cost of mobile? From £14.00 per night with electric
Tents? Yes
Cost of tent pitch? From £14.00 per night with electric
Electricity at the pitch? Yes
Showers? Yes
Onsite Entertainment? Yes
Opening times? March - October
Comments: Maxiumum 3 Dogs. Adults only. There is a bar and restaurant on site.

Golden Beach Holiday Centre

Address: Beach Rd, Sea Palling, Norwich, Norfolk NR12 0AL
Telephone: 01692 598269
Website: www.goldenbeachpark.co.uk
Extra charge for dogs? Yes
Any breed restrictions? No
Dog bins? No
Area for walking dogs? Off Site
Static caravans? Yes
Cost of static? From £190.00 per week
Mobile caravans? Yes
Cost of mobile? From £12.00 per night
Tents? Yes
Cost of tent pitch? From £12.00 per night
Electricity at the pitch? Yes
Showers? Yes
Onsite Entertainment? No
Opening times? March - October

Grange Farm

Address: Stody, Melton Constable, Norfolk NR24 2EB
Telephone: 01263 860291
Website:
Extra charge for dogs? No
Any breed restrictions? No
Dog bins? No
Area for walking dogs? Yes
Static caravans? No
Cost of static?
Mobile caravans? Yes
Cost of mobile? From £4.00 per night
Tents? Yes
Cost of tent pitch? From £4.00 per night
Electricity at the pitch? No
Showers? No
Onsite Entertainment? No
Opening times? April - October

Grange Farm Camping & Caravans

Address: Grange Farm, Whittington, King's Lynn, Norfolk PE33 9TF
Telephone: 01366 500075
Website: www.grangefarmtouringpark.co.uk
Extra charge for dogs? No
Any breed restrictions? Yes
Dog bins? Yes
Area for walking dogs? Yes
Static caravans? No
Cost of static?
Mobile caravans? Yes
Cost of mobile? From £9.00 per pitch
Tents? Yes
Cost of tent pitch? From £9.00 per night
Electricity at the pitch? Yes
Showers? Yes
Onsite Entertainment? No
Opening times? February - December
Comments: No Dangerous Breeds.

Grange Touring Park

Address: Ormesby St. Margaret, Great Yarmouth, Norfolk NR29 3QG

Telephone: 01493 730306
Website:
Extra charge for dogs? Yes
Any breed restrictions? Yes
Dog bins? Yes
Area for walking dogs? Off Site
Static caravans? No
Cost of static?
Mobile caravans? Yes
Cost of mobile? From £11.50 per night with electric
Tents? Yes
Cost of tent pitch? From £7.50 per night
Electricity at the pitch? Yes
Showers? Yes
Onsite Entertainment? No
Opening times? March - End September
Comments: No Dangerous Breeds. There is a Hotel next door where there is food and entertainment.

Great Yarmouth Caravan Club Site

Address: Great Yarmouth, Norfolk NR30 4AU
Telephone: 01493 855223
Website: www.thecaravanclub.co.uk
Extra charge for dogs? No
Any breed restrictions? Yes
Dog bins? Yes
Area for walking dogs? Off Site
Static caravans? No
Cost of static?
Mobile caravans? Yes
Cost of mobile? From £4.30 per pitch + £3.95 per person per night
Tents? No
Cost of tent pitch?
Electricity at the pitch? Yes
Showers? Yes
Onsite Entertainment? No
Opening times? March - November
Comments: No Dangerous Breeds. Non Members will be charged an extra £7.00 per night.

Green Park Caravan Park

Address: Beach Rd, Scratby, Great Yarmouth, Norfolk NR29 3NW
Telephone: 01493 730440
Website: www.greenfarmcaravanpark.com
Extra charge for dogs? Yes
Any breed restrictions? No
Dog bins? Yes
Area for walking dogs? Off Site
Static caravans? Yes
Cost of static? From £175.00 per week
Mobile caravans? Yes
Cost of mobile? From £18.00 per night with electric
Tents? Yes
Cost of tent pitch? From £18.00 per night with electric
Electricity at the pitch? Yes
Showers? Yes
Onsite Entertainment? Yes
Opening times? 26th March - 31st October
Comments: Dogs must be kept on a lead. Entertainment is in adjourning sites.

Greenwoods Campsite

Address: Manor Farm, Tattersett, nr Fakenham, Kings Lynn, Norfolk PE31 8RS
Telephone: 07917 842371
Website: www.greenwoodscampsite.co.uk
Extra charge for dogs? Yes
Any breed restrictions? No
Dog bins? No
Area for walking dogs? Off Site
Static caravans? No
Cost of static?

Mobile caravans? Yes

Cost of mobile? From £4.00 per adults £1.00 per child under 12 years

Tents? Yes

Cost of tent pitch? From £4.00 per adults £1.00 per child under 12 years

Electricity at the pitch? Yes

Showers? Yes

Onsite Entertainment? No

Opening times? March - October

Haven Holidays

Address: Caister Holiday Park, Ormesby Rd, Caister-on-Sea, Great Yarmouth, Norfolk NR30 5NQ

Telephone: 0871 2301900

Website: www.havenholidays.co.uk

Extra charge for dogs? Yes

Any breed restrictions? Yes

Dog bins? Yes

Area for walking dogs? Off Site

Static caravans? Yes

Cost of static? Prices vary as discounts may apply

Mobile caravans? No

Cost of mobile?

Tents? No

Cost of tent pitch?

Electricity at the pitch? No

Showers? No

Onsite Entertainment? Yes

Opening times? March - 1st week November

Comments: No Dangerous Breeds. Dogs must be kept on a lead.

Haven Holidays

Address: Hopton Holiday Village, Hopton-on-Sea, Great Yarmouth, Norfolk NR31 9BW

Telephone: 0871 2301900

Website: www.havenholidays.co.uk

Extra charge for dogs? Yes

Any breed restrictions? Yes

Dog bins? Yes

Area for walking dogs? Off Site

Static caravans? Yes

Cost of static? Prices vary as discounts may apply

Mobile caravans? No

Cost of mobile?

Tents? No

Cost of tent pitch?

Electricity at the pitch? No

Showers? No

Onsite Entertainment? Yes

Opening times? March - 1st week November

Comments: No Dangerous Breeds. Dogs must be kept on a lead.

Haven Holidays

Address: Seashore Holiday Park, North Denes, Great Yarmouth, Norfolk NR30 4HG

Telephone: 0871 2301900

Website: www.havenholidays.co.uk

Extra charge for dogs? Yes

Any breed restrictions? Yes

Dog bins? Yes

Area for walking dogs? Off Site

Static caravans? Yes

Cost of static? Prices vary as discounts may apply

Mobile caravans? No

Cost of mobile?

Tents? No

Cost of tent pitch?

Electricity at the pitch? No

Showers? No

Onsite Entertainment? Yes

Opening times? March - 1st week November

Comments: No Dangerous Breeds. Dogs must be kept on a lead.

Haven Holidays

Address: Wild Duck Holiday Park, Howards Common, Belton, Great Yarmouth, Norfolk NR31 9NE
Telephone: 0871 2301900
Website: www.havenholidays.co.uk
Extra charge for dogs? Yes
Any breed restrictions? Yes
Dog bins? Yes
Area for walking dogs? Off Site
Static caravans? Yes
Cost of static? Prices vary as discounts may apply
Mobile caravans? Yes
Cost of mobile? Prices vary as discounts may apply
Tents? Yes
Cost of tent pitch? Prices vary as discounts may apply
Electricity at the pitch? Yes
Showers? Yes
Onsite Entertainment? Yes
Opening times? March - 1st week November
Comments: No Dangerous Breeds. Dogs must be kept on a lead.

Heather House Farm

Address: Heath Road, Hickling, Norwich, Norfolk NR12 0AX
Telephone: 01692 598434
Website:
Extra charge for dogs? No
Any breed restrictions? No
Dog bins? No
Area for walking dogs? Off Site
Static caravans? No
Cost of static?
Mobile caravans? Yes
Cost of mobile? From £7.00 per night
Tents? No
Cost of tent pitch?
Electricity at the pitch? No
Showers? No
Onsite Entertainment? No
Opening times? All Year
Comments: Naturists Only. It is a Caravan Club Site Location.

Highgate Farm Caravan Park

Address: Swim Road, Runham Swim, Norfolk NR29 3EH
Telephone: 01493 368133
Website:
Extra charge for dogs? No
Any breed restrictions? No
Dog bins? No
Area for walking dogs? Yes
Static caravans? No
Cost of static?
Mobile caravans? Yes
Cost of mobile? From £11.00 per night with electric
Tents? Yes
Cost of tent pitch? From £8.00 per night
Electricity at the pitch? Yes
Showers? Yes
Onsite Entertainment? No
Opening times? April - October

Honeypot Camp & Caravan Park

Address: Honeypot Farm, Long Green, Wortham, Diss, Norfolk IP22 1PW
Telephone: 01379 783312
Website: www.honeypotcamping.co.uk

Extra charge for dogs? Yes
Any breed restrictions? No
Dog bins? No
Area for walking dogs? Yes
Static caravans? No
Cost of static?
Mobile caravans? Yes
Cost of mobile? From £15.00 per night with electric for 2 people
Tents? Yes
Cost of tent pitch? From £15.00 per night with electric for 2 people
Electricity at the pitch? Yes
Showers? Yes
Onsite Entertainment? No
Opening times? 1st May - End September
Comments: Dogs must be kept on a lead.

Hopton Holiday Village

Address: Hopton-on-Sea, Nr Great Yarmouth, Norfolk NR31 9BW
Telephone: 01502 730214
Website: www.haven.com
Extra charge for dogs? Yes
Any breed restrictions? Yes
Dog bins? Yes
Area for walking dogs? Yes
Static caravans? Yes
Cost of static? Prices vary as discounts may apply
Mobile caravans? No
Cost of mobile?
Tents? No
Cost of tent pitch?
Electricity at the pitch? No
Showers? No
Onsite Entertainment? Yes
Opening times? March - Early November
Comments: Dogs must be kept on a lead.

Hunters Hall

Address: Swanton Morley, Dereham, Norfolk NR20 4JU
Telephone: 01362 637457
Website: www.huntershall.com
Extra charge for dogs? No
Any breed restrictions? No
Dog bins? No
Area for walking dogs? Off Site
Static caravans? No
Cost of static?
Mobile caravans? Yes
Cost of mobile? From £10.00 per night with electric
Tents? Yes
Cost of tent pitch? From £7.00 per night
Electricity at the pitch? Yes
Showers? Yes
Onsite Entertainment? No
Opening times? All Year
Comments: Dogs must be kept on a lead.

Ivy Farm Holiday Park

Address: 1, High Street, Overstand, Cromer, Norfolk NR27 0AB
Telephone: 01263 579239
Website: www.ivy-farm.co.uk
Extra charge for dogs? Yes
Any breed restrictions? No
Dog bins? Yes
Area for walking dogs? Yes
Static caravans? Yes
Cost of static? From £99.00 per week
Mobile caravans? Yes
Cost of mobile? From £14.50 per night
Tents? Yes

Cost of tent pitch? From £5.00 per pitch + £3.00 per adult £2.00 per child
Electricity at the pitch? Yes
Showers? Yes
Onsite Entertainment? No
Opening times? March - October
Comments: There is a swimming pool on site.

Keelers Meadow

Address: Staithe Road, Norfolk NR12 9QR
Telephone: 01692 580424
Website: www.caravanandcamping sites.co.uk
Extra charge for dogs? No
Any breed restrictions? No
Dog bins? ?
Area for walking dogs? Off Site
Static caravans? No
Cost of static?
Mobile caravans? Yes
Cost of mobile? From £5.00 per night
Tents? No
Cost of tent pitch?
Electricity at the pitch? Yes
Showers? No
Onsite Entertainment? No
Opening times? All Year (Weather Permitting)
Comments: There is a pub across the road.

Kelling Heath Holiday Park

Address: Sandy Hill Lane, Weybourne, Holt, Norfolk NR25 7HW
Telephone: 01263 588181
Website: www.kellingheath.co.uk
Extra charge for dogs? Yes
Any breed restrictions? Yes
Dog bins? ?
Area for walking dogs? Yes
Static caravans? No
Cost of static?
Mobile caravans? Yes
Cost of mobile? From £16.50 per night
Tents? Yes
Cost of tent pitch? From £16.50 per night
Electricity at the pitch? Yes
Showers? Yes
Onsite Entertainment? Yes
Opening times? Mid February - Mid December
Comments: No Dangerous Breeds.

Kiln Cliffs Caravan Park

Address: 126, Cromer Rd, Mundesley, Norwich, Norfolk NR11 8DF
Telephone: 01263 720449
Website:
Extra charge for dogs? Yes
Any breed restrictions? No
Dog bins? Yes
Area for walking dogs? Off Site
Static caravans? Yes
Cost of static? From £175.00 per week
Mobile caravans? No
Cost of mobile?
Tents? No
Cost of tent pitch?
Electricity at the pitch? No
Showers? No
Onsite Entertainment? No
Opening times? 17th March - 1st November

Kings Lynn Caravan & Camping Park

Address: Parkside House, New Rd, North Runcton, King's Lynn, Norfolk PE33 0QR

Telephone: 01553 840004
Website: www.kl-cc.co.uk
Extra charge for dogs? Yes
Any breed restrictions? No
Dog bins? No
Area for walking dogs? Yes
Static caravans? No
Cost of static?
Mobile caravans? Yes
Cost of mobile? From £5.00 per night
Tents? Yes
Cost of tent pitch? From £5.00 per night
Electricity at the pitch? Yes
Showers? Yes
Onsite Entertainment? No
Opening times? All Year

Laburnum Caravan Park

Address: Water Lane, West Runton, Cromer, Norfolk NR27 9QP
Telephone: 01263 837473
Website: www.laburnumcaravanpark.co.uk
Extra charge for dogs? No
Any breed restrictions? No
Dog bins? No
Area for walking dogs? Yes
Static caravans? No
Cost of static?
Mobile caravans? Yes
Cost of mobile? From £15.50 per night
Tents? No
Cost of tent pitch?
Electricity at the pitch? Yes
Showers? Yes
Onsite Entertainment? No
Opening times? Easter - October

Lakeside Caravan Park & Fisheries

Address: Sluice Road, Denver, Downham Market, Norfolk PE38 0DZ
Telephone: 01366 387074
Website: www.west-hall-farm.co.uk
Extra charge for dogs? No
Any breed restrictions? No
Dog bins? Yes
Area for walking dogs? Yes
Static caravans? Yes
Cost of static? From £200.00 per week
Mobile caravans? Yes
Cost of mobile? From £12.00 per night
Tents? Yes
Cost of tent pitch? From £12.00 per night
Electricity at the pitch? Yes
Showers? Yes
Onsite Entertainment? No
Opening times? All Year

Leakes Caravan Park

Address: Cromer Rd, East Runton, Cromer, Norfolk NR27 9NH
Telephone: 01945 880400/524
Website:
Extra charge for dogs? Yes
Any breed restrictions? No
Dog bins? No
Area for walking dogs? No
Static caravans? Yes
Cost of static? From £175.00 per week
Mobile caravans? No
Cost of mobile?
Tents? No
Cost of tent pitch?
Electricity at the pitch? No
Showers? No
Onsite Entertainment? No
Opening times? March - October

Links Caravan Site

Address: Heath Lane, Mundesley, Norwich, Norfolk NR11 8ER
Telephone: 01263 720665
Website:
Extra charge for dogs? No
Any breed restrictions? No
Dog bins? Yes
Area for walking dogs? Yes
Static caravans? No
Cost of static?
Mobile caravans? Yes
Cost of mobile? From £12.00 per night
Tents? Yes
Cost of tent pitch? From £5.00 per night
Electricity at the pitch? Yes
Showers? Yes
Onsite Entertainment? No
Opening times? End March - End October
Comments: Dogs must be kept on a lead.

Little Haven Caravan Park

Address: The St, Erpingham, Norwich, Norfolk NR11 7QB
Telephone: 01263 768959
Website:
Extra charge for dogs? No
Any breed restrictions? No
Dog bins? No
Area for walking dogs? Off Site
Static caravans? No
Cost of static?
Mobile caravans? Yes
Cost of mobile? From £11.00 per night with electric
Tents? Yes
Cost of tent pitch? From £11.00 per night with electric
Electricity at the pitch? Yes
Showers? Yes
Onsite Entertainment? No
Opening times? 1st March - End October
Comments: Dogs must be kept on a lead. Adults only.

Little Lakeland Caravan Park

Address: Wortwell, Harleston, Norfolk IP20 0EL
Telephone: 01986 788646
Website: www.littlelakeland.co.uk
Extra charge for dogs? No
Any breed restrictions? No
Dog bins? No
Area for walking dogs? Off Site
Static caravans? Yes
Cost of static? From £260.00 - £380.00 per week
Mobile caravans? Yes
Cost of mobile? From £10.80 per night
Tents? Yes
Cost of tent pitch? From £10.80 per night
Electricity at the pitch? Yes
Showers? Yes
Onsite Entertainment? No
Opening times? 15th March - End October

Long Beach Caravan Park

Address: 2, Long Beach Estate, Hemsby, Great Yarmouth, Norfolk NR29 4JD
Telephone: 01493 730023
Website: www.lone-beach.co.uk
Extra charge for dogs? Yes
Any breed restrictions? No
Dog bins? Yes
Area for walking dogs? Yes
Static caravans? No
Cost of static?
Mobile caravans? Yes
Cost of mobile? From £9.50 per night

Tents? Yes

Cost of tent pitch? From £9.50 per night

Electricity at the pitch? Yes

Showers? Yes

Onsite Entertainment? Yes

Opening times? March - Beg November

Comments: Dogs must be kept on a lead.

Lowe Caravan Park

Address: Ashdale, Hills Rd, Saham Hills, Thetford, Norfolk IP25 7EZ

Telephone: 01953 881051

Website: www.lowecaravanpark.co.uk

Extra charge for dogs? No

Any breed restrictions? No

Dog bins? No

Area for walking dogs? Yes

Static caravans? No

Cost of static?

Mobile caravans? Yes

Cost of mobile? From £12.00 per night

Tents? No

Cost of tent pitch?

Electricity at the pitch? Yes

Showers? Yes

Onsite Entertainment? No

Opening times? All Year

Manor Caravan Park

Address: Happisburgh, Norwich, Norfolk NR12 0PW

Telephone: 01692 652228

Website:

Extra charge for dogs? No

Any breed restrictions? Yes

Dog bins? No

Area for walking dogs? Off Site

Static caravans? Yes

Cost of static? ?

Mobile caravans? Yes

Cost of mobile? From £12.00 per night

Tents? Yes

Cost of tent pitch? From £10.00 per night for 2 adults & 2 children

Electricity at the pitch? Yes

Showers? Yes

Onsite Entertainment? No

Opening times? April - October

Comments: No Big Dogs.

Manor Farm Caravan Site

Address: Manor Farm, East Runton, Cromer, Norfolk NR27 9PR

Telephone: 01263 512858

Website: www.manorfarmcaravansite.co.uk

Extra charge for dogs? Yes

Any breed restrictions? Yes

Dog bins? No

Area for walking dogs? Yes

Static caravans? No

Cost of static?

Mobile caravans? Yes

Cost of mobile? From £12.00 per night for 2 people

Tents? Yes

Cost of tent pitch? From £12.00 per night for 2 people

Electricity at the pitch? Yes

Showers? Yes

Onsite Entertainment? No

Opening times? Easter - End September

Comments: No Dangerous Breeds. Dogs must be kept on a lead.

Manor Park Holiday Village

Address: Manor Rd, Hunstanton, Norfolk PE36 5AZ

Telephone: 01485 532300

Website: www.manor-park.co.uk
Extra charge for dogs? Yes
Any breed restrictions? Yes
Dog bins? Yes
Area for walking dogs? Off Site
Static caravans? Yes
Cost of static? From £200.00 per week
Mobile caravans? Yes
Cost of mobile? From £20.00 per night
Tents? No
Cost of tent pitch?
Electricity at the pitch? Yes
Showers? Yes
Onsite Entertainment? Yes
Opening times? March - Beg November
Comments: No Dangerous Breeds.

Mill Farm

Address: Gt Ellingham, Attleborough, Norfolk NR17 1LE
Telephone: 01953 452769
Website:
Extra charge for dogs? No
Any breed restrictions? Yes
Dog bins? No
Area for walking dogs? Yes
Static caravans? No
Cost of static?
Mobile caravans? Yes
Cost of mobile? From £10.00 - £12.00 per night with electric
Tents? No
Cost of tent pitch?
Electricity at the pitch? Yes
Showers? Yes
Onsite Entertainment? No
Opening times? All Year

Mill Farm Fishery Lakes & Camping

Address: Mill Farm, Aylsham Rd, Felmingham, North Walsham, Norfolk NR28 0LA
Telephone: 01263 735106
Website:
Extra charge for dogs? No
Any breed restrictions? Yes
Dog bins? No
Area for walking dogs? Yes
Static caravans? No
Cost of static?
Mobile caravans? Yes
Cost of mobile? From £10.00 per night
Tents? Yes
Cost of tent pitch? From £10.00 per night
Electricity at the pitch? Yes
Showers? Yes
Onsite Entertainment? No
Opening times? March - End September
Comments: No Big Dogs.

Moat Farm

Address: Low Rd, Breckles, Attleborough, Norfolk NR17 1EP
Telephone: 01953 498510
Website:
Extra charge for dogs?
Any breed restrictions?
Dog bins?
Area for walking dogs?
Static caravans?
Cost of static?
Mobile caravans?
Cost of mobile?
Tents?
Cost of tent pitch?
Electricity at the pitch?

Showers?
Onsite Entertainment?
Opening times?

Moorland Park

Address: Holt Rd, Aylmerton, Norwich, Norfolk NR11 8QA
Telephone: 01263 837508
Website: www.moatfarm-cp.co.uk
Extra charge for dogs? Yes
Any breed restrictions? No
Dog bins? No
Area for walking dogs? No
Static caravans? No
Cost of static?
Mobile caravans? Yes
Cost of mobile? From £7.50 per pitch per night for 2 people
Tents? Yes
Cost of tent pitch? From £7.50 per pitch per night for 2 people
Electricity at the pitch? Yes
Showers? Yes
Onsite Entertainment? No
Opening times? All Year

Oak Tree Caravan Park

Address: 66, Norwich Rd, Attleborough, Norfolk NR17 2JX
Telephone: 01953 455565
Website: www.oaktreepark.co.uk
Extra charge for dogs? No
Any breed restrictions? Yes
Dog bins? Yes
Area for walking dogs? Off Site
Static caravans? No
Cost of static?
Mobile caravans? Yes
Cost of mobile? From £11.00 per night
Tents? No
Cost of tent pitch?
Electricity at the pitch? Yes
Showers? Yes
Onsite Entertainment? No
Opening times? March - December
Comments: No Dangerous Breeds. Dogs must be kept on a lead at all times.

Old Brick Kilns Camping Park

Address: Little Barney Lane, Barney, Fakenham, Norfolk NR21 0NL
Telephone: 01328 878305
Website: www.old-brick-kilns.co.uk
Extra charge for dogs? Yes
Any breed restrictions? No
Dog bins? Yes
Area for walking dogs? Yes
Static caravans? No
Cost of static?
Mobile caravans? Yes
Cost of mobile? From £14.50 - £26.00 per night
Tents? Yes
Cost of tent pitch? From £12.50 - £18.50 per night
Electricity at the pitch? Yes
Showers? Yes
Onsite Entertainment? Yes
Opening times? 1st March - 4th January
Comments: Maximum 2 dogs. No tents over 6 metres. There is a restaurant on site.

Orchard Caravan Norfolk Ltd

Address: Great Eastern Way, Wells-Next-The-Sea, Norfolk NR23 1LT
Telephone: 01328 710394
Website: www.orchardcaravansnorfolk .ltd.uk
Extra charge for dogs? Yes

Any breed restrictions? No
Dog bins? Yes
Area for walking dogs? Yes
Static caravans? Yes
Cost of static? From £275.00 per week
Mobile caravans? No
Cost of mobile?
Tents? No
Cost of tent pitch?
Electricity at the pitch? No
Showers? No
Onsite Entertainment? No
Opening times? March - 1st November

Ostend Place Chalets

Address: Ostend Place, Walcott, Norfolk NR12 0NJ
Telephone: 01692 650462
Website:
Extra charge for dogs? No
Any breed restrictions? No
Dog bins? No
Area for walking dogs? Off Site
Static caravans? No
Cost of static?
Mobile caravans? Yes
Cost of mobile? From £4.50 per night
Tents? No
Cost of tent pitch?
Electricity at the pitch? Yes
Showers? No
Onsite Entertainment? No
Opening times? All Year

Pampas Lodge Caravan Site

Address: The Street, Haddiscoe, Norwich, Norfolk NR14 6AA
Telephone: 01502 677265
Website:
Extra charge for dogs? Yes
Any breed restrictions? No
Dog bins? No
Area for walking dogs? Off Site
Static caravans? Yes
Cost of static? From £150.00 per week
Mobile caravans? Yes
Cost of mobile? From £12.00 per night
Tents? No
Cost of tent pitch?
Electricity at the pitch? Yes
Showers? Yes
Onsite Entertainment? No
Opening times? March - End October

Parkdean Cherry Tree

Address: Mill Rd, Burgh Castle, Great Yarmouth, Norfolk NR31 9QR
Telephone: 01493 780229
Website: www.parkdeanholidays.co.uk
Extra charge for dogs? Yes
Any breed restrictions? Yes
Dog bins? Yes
Area for walking dogs? No
Static caravans? Yes
Cost of static? From £170.00 per week
Mobile caravans? No
Cost of mobile?
Tents? No
Cost of tent pitch?
Electricity at the pitch? No
Showers? No
Onsite Entertainment? Yes
Opening times? March - End October
Comments: Dogs are not allowed in the main complex. No Dangerous Breeds.

Peewit Farm

Address: Workhouse Lane, Briston, Holt, Norfolk NR24 2BE
Telephone: 01263 587878

Website: www.thecampingandcaravanningclub.co.uk
Extra charge for dogs? No
Any breed restrictions? Yes
Dog bins? No
Area for walking dogs? No
Static caravans? No
Cost of static?
Mobile caravans? Yes
Cost of mobile? From £5.00 per night
Tents? Yes
Cost of tent pitch? From £5.00 per night
Electricity at the pitch? No
Showers? No
Onsite Entertainment? No
Opening times? March - October
Comments: No Dangerous Breeds. Dogs must be kept on a lead. Must be members of The Camping and Caravanning Club.

Pentney Park Caravan & Camping Site

Address: Main Road, Pentney, Kings Lynn, Norfolk PE32 1HU
Telephone: 01760 337479
Website: www.pentneypark.co.uk
Extra charge for dogs? Yes
Any breed restrictions? Yes
Dog bins? Yes
Area for walking dogs? Yes
Static caravans? No
Cost of static?
Mobile caravans? Yes
Cost of mobile? From £8.00 per night
Tents? Yes
Cost of tent pitch? From £8.00 per night
Electricity at the pitch? Yes
Showers? Yes
Onsite Entertainment? No
Opening times? All Year
Comments: No Dangerous Breeds. Dogs must be kept on a lead at all times.

Pond Farm

Address: Sidestrand, Cromer, Norfolk NR27 0LW
Telephone: 01263 579326
Website:
Extra charge for dogs? Yes
Any breed restrictions? No
Dog bins? No
Area for walking dogs? Yes
Static caravans? No
Cost of static?
Mobile caravans? Yes
Cost of mobile? From £7.00 per adult per night £2.00 per child per night
Tents? Yes
Cost of tent pitch? From £7.00 per adult per night £2.00 per child per night
Electricity at the pitch? No
Showers? Yes
Onsite Entertainment? No
Opening times? All Year
Comments: Dogs must be kept on a lead. Only quiet dogs allowed.

Poppyland Touring Park

Address: The Green, Thorpe Market, Norfolk NR11 8AJ
Telephone: 01263 833219
Website: www.poppyland.com
Extra charge for dogs? No
Any breed restrictions? No
Dog bins? No
Area for walking dogs? Off Site
Static caravans? No
Cost of static?
Mobile caravans? Yes
Cost of mobile? From £12.00 per night
Tents? Yes

Cost of tent pitch? From £8.00 per night
Electricity at the pitch? Yes
Showers? Yes
Onsite Entertainment? No
Opening times? 20th March - End October

Rectory Farm Campsite Site

Address: Watton Road, Hingham, Norfolk NR9 4NN
Telephone: 01953 850596
Website:
Extra charge for dogs? No
Any breed restrictions? No
Dog bins? No
Area for walking dogs? Yes
Static caravans? No
Cost of static?
Mobile caravans? Yes
Cost of mobile? From £8.50 per night with electric
Tents? Yes
Cost of tent pitch? From £5.00 per night
Electricity at the pitch? Yes
Showers? Yes
Onsite Entertainment? Yes
Opening times? All Year
Comments: There are 2 Fishing Lakes on site. Dogs must be kept on a lead.

Red House Farm

Address: Thurne, Norfolk NR29 3AP
Telephone: 01692 670551
Website:
Extra charge for dogs? No
Any breed restrictions? No
Dog bins? No
Area for walking dogs? Off Site
Static caravans? No
Cost of static?
Mobile caravans? Yes
Cost of mobile? From £6.50 per night
Tents? No
Cost of tent pitch?
Electricity at the pitch? Yes
Showers? No
Onsite Entertainment? No
Opening times? March - October

Rickels Caravan Site

Address: Bircham Road, Stanhoe, Kings Lynn, Norfolk PE31 8PU
Telephone: 01485 518671
Website:
Extra charge for dogs? Yes
Any breed restrictions? No
Dog bins? No
Area for walking dogs? Yes
Static caravans? No
Cost of static?
Mobile caravans? Yes
Cost of mobile? From £11.00 per night
Tents? Yes
Cost of tent pitch? From £11.00 per night
Electricity at the pitch? Yes
Showers? Yes
Onsite Entertainment? No
Opening times? April - October
Comments: Maximum 2 dogs.

Rose Farm Touring Park

Address: Stepshort, Belton, Great Yarmouth, Norfolk NR31 9JS
Telephone: 01493 780896
Website: www.rosefarmtouringpark.co.uk
Extra charge for dogs? No
Any breed restrictions? Yes

Dog bins? Yes
Area for walking dogs? Yes
Static caravans? No
Cost of static?
Mobile caravans? Yes
Cost of mobile? From £11.00 per night
Tents? Yes
Cost of tent pitch? From £11.00 per night
Electricity at the pitch? Yes
Showers? Yes
Onsite Entertainment? No
Opening times? All Year
Comments: No Dangerous Breeds.

Sandy Gulls Caravan Park Ltd

Address: Cromer Rd, Mundesley, Norwich, Norfolk NR11 8DF
Telephone: 01263 720513
Website:
Extra charge for dogs? No
Any breed restrictions? No
Dog bins? No
Area for walking dogs? Yes
Static caravans? No
Cost of static?
Mobile caravans? Yes
Cost of mobile? From £10.00 per night
Tents? No
Cost of tent pitch?
Electricity at the pitch? Yes
Showers? Yes
Onsite Entertainment? No
Opening times? March - November

Scatby Hall Caravan Park Ltd

Address: Thoroughfare Lane, Scratby, Great Yarmouth, Norfolk NR29 3PL
Telephone: 01493 730283
Website:
Extra charge for dogs? No
Any breed restrictions? Yes
Dog bins? Yes
Area for walking dogs? Yes
Static caravans? No
Cost of static?
Mobile caravans? Yes
Cost of mobile? From £7.00 per night
Tents? Yes
Cost of tent pitch? From £7.00 per night
Electricity at the pitch? Yes
Showers? Yes
Onsite Entertainment? No
Opening times? Easter - End September
Comments: Maximum 2 dogs. No Dangerous Breeds.

Searles Leisure Resort

Address: South Beach Road, Hunstanton, Norfolk PE36 5BB
Telephone: 01485 534211
Website: www.searles.co.uk
Extra charge for dogs? Yes
Any breed restrictions? Yes
Dog bins? No
Area for walking dogs? No
Static caravans? No
Cost of static?
Mobile caravans? Yes
Cost of mobile? From £13.00 per night
Tents? Yes
Cost of tent pitch? From £12.00 per night
Electricity at the pitch? Yes
Showers? Yes
Onsite Entertainment? Yes
Opening times? All Year
Comments: Dogs must be kept on a lead. Rottweilers, Dobermans, Alsatians, German Shepherds, Pitbulls, Staffordshire Bull Terriers and any crosses of these breeds are not allowed.

Seashore Holiday Park

Address: Rottenstone Lane, Great Yarmouth, Norfolk NR29 3QU

Telephone: 01493 851131

Website: www.havenholidays.co.uk

Extra charge for dogs? Yes

Any breed restrictions? Yes

Dog bins? Yes

Area for walking dogs? No

Static caravans? Yes

Cost of static? From £199.00 per week

Mobile caravans? No

Cost of mobile?

Tents? No

Cost of tent pitch?

Electricity at the pitch? No

Showers? No

Onsite Entertainment? Yes

Opening times? March - November

Comments: No Dangerous Breeds.

Shrublands Farm

Address: Northrepps, Cromer, Norfolk NR27 0AA

Telephone: 01263 579297

Website: www.shrublandsfarm.com

Extra charge for dogs? No

Any breed restrictions? No

Dog bins? No

Area for walking dogs? Yes

Static caravans? No

Cost of static?

Mobile caravans? Yes

Cost of mobile? From £12.00 per night

Tents? Yes

Cost of tent pitch? From £10.00 per night

Electricity at the pitch? Yes

Showers? Yes

Onsite Entertainment? No

Opening times? March - End October

Comments: Dogs must be kept on a lead.

Springview

Address: Druidslane, Litcham, Fakenham, Norfolk PE32 2YA

Telephone: 01328 701388

Website:

Extra charge for dogs? No

Any breed restrictions? No

Dog bins? No

Area for walking dogs? Yes

Static caravans? No

Cost of static?

Mobile caravans? Yes

Cost of mobile? From £6.50 per night with electric

Tents? No

Cost of tent pitch?

Electricity at the pitch? Yes

Showers? No

Onsite Entertainment? No

Opening times? All Year

Stoney Brook Caravan Site Adults Only

Address: North Walsham Road, Edingthorpe, North Walsham, Norfolk NR28 9SL

Telephone: 01692 402337

Website: www.stoney-brook.co.uk

Extra charge for dogs? No

Any breed restrictions? No

Dog bins? No

Area for walking dogs? Yes

Static caravans? No

Cost of static?

Mobile caravans? Yes

Cost of mobile? From £10.00 per night

Tents? No

Cost of tent pitch?
Electricity at the pitch? Yes
Showers? Yes
Onsite Entertainment? No
Opening times? March - End October

Sunnydene Farm Caravan Club

Address: The Common, Fakenham Road, South Creake, Norfolk NR21 9JB
Telephone: 01328 823301
Website: www.sunnydenefarm.com
Extra charge for dogs? No
Any breed restrictions? Yes
Dog bins? No
Area for walking dogs? Off Site
Static caravans? No
Cost of static?
Mobile caravans? Yes
Cost of mobile? From £10.00 per night
Tents? No
Cost of tent pitch?
Electricity at the pitch? Yes
Showers? Yes
Onsite Entertainment? No
Opening times? All Year

Swans Harbour

Address: Style House, Style Loke, Barford, Norwich, Norfolk NR9 4BE
Telephone: 01603 759658
Website: www.swanharbour.co.uk
Extra charge for dogs? No
Any breed restrictions? No
Dog bins? No
Area for walking dogs? Yes
Static caravans? No
Cost of static?
Mobile caravans? Yes
Cost of mobile? From £7.50 per pitch with electric + £2.00 per person per night
Tents? Yes
Cost of tent pitch? From £5.50 per night
Electricity at the pitch? Yes
Showers? Yes
Onsite Entertainment? No
Opening times? All Year

The Black Swan

Address: Church Lane, Harleston, Norfolk IP20 0ET
Telephone: 01986 788204
Website:
Extra charge for dogs? No
Any breed restrictions? No
Dog bins? No
Area for walking dogs? Yes
Static caravans? No
Cost of static?
Mobile caravans? Yes
Cost of mobile? From £8.00 per night
Tents? Yes
Cost of tent pitch? From £8.00 per night
Electricity at the pitch? Yes
Showers? No
Onsite Entertainment? No
Opening times? All Year

The Camping & Caravanning Club

Address: Martineau Lane, Lakenham, Norwich, Norfolk NR1 2HX
Telephone: 01603 620060
Website: www.thecampingand caravanningclub.co.uk
Extra charge for dogs? No
Any breed restrictions? No
Dog bins? Yes
Area for walking dogs? Yes
Static caravans? No
Cost of static?

Mobile caravans? Yes

Cost of mobile? From £5.15 per person per night for members £6.00 extra for non members

Tents? Yes

Cost of tent pitch? From £5.15 per person per night for members £6.00 extra for non members

Electricity at the pitch? Yes

Showers? Yes

Onsite Entertainment? No

Opening times? March - End October

Comments: Dogs must be kept on a lead.

The Camping & Caravanning Club

Address: The Sandringham Estate, Double Lodges, Sandringham, Norfolk PE35 6EA

Telephone: 01485 542555

Website: www.thecampingand caravanningclub.co.uk

Extra charge for dogs? No

Any breed restrictions? No

Dog bins? Yes

Area for walking dogs? Yes

Static caravans? No

Cost of static?

Mobile caravans? Yes

Cost of mobile? From £6.60 - £8.60 per adult per night

Tents? Yes

Cost of tent pitch? From £6.60 - £8.60 per adult per night

Electricity at the pitch? Yes

Showers? Yes

Onsite Entertainment? No

Opening times? February - End November

Comments: Dogs must be kept on a lead.

The Caravan Club Ltd

Address: Broadlands, Johnsons St, Ludham, Great Yarmouth, Norfolk NR29 5NY

Telephone: 01692 630357

Website: www.thecaravanclub.co.uk

Extra charge for dogs? No

Any breed restrictions? No

Dog bins? Yes

Area for walking dogs? Yes

Static caravans? No

Cost of static?

Mobile caravans? Yes

Cost of mobile? From £14.90 per night

Tents? No

Cost of tent pitch?

Electricity at the pitch? Yes

Showers? Yes

Onsite Entertainment? No

Opening times? March - November

The Caravan Club Ltd

Address: Ingleborough Fields, West Runton, Cromer, Norfolk NR27 9QH

Telephone: 01263 837419

Website: www.thecaravanclub.co.uk

Extra charge for dogs? No

Any breed restrictions? No

Dog bins? Yes

Area for walking dogs? Off Site

Static caravans? No

Cost of static?

Mobile caravans? Yes

Cost of mobile? From £13.10 for members per night for 2 people

Tents? No

Cost of tent pitch?

Electricity at the pitch? Yes

Showers? Yes

Onsite Entertainment? No

Opening times? Mid March - Mid

November

Comments: Dogs must be kept on a lead at all times. Members of the Caravan Club only.

The Caravan Club Ltd

Address: Royal Norfolk Showground, Long Lane, Bawburgh, Norwich, Norfolk NR9 3LX

Telephone: 01603 742708

Website: www.thecaravanclub.co.uk

Extra charge for dogs? No

Any breed restrictions? Yes

Dog bins? Yes

Area for walking dogs? Yes

Static caravans? No

Cost of static?

Mobile caravans? Yes

Cost of mobile? From £12.10 per night for 2 adults for members

Tents? No

Cost of tent pitch?

Electricity at the pitch? Yes

Showers? Yes

Onsite Entertainment? No

Opening times? March - November

Comments: Dogs must be kept on a lead at all times. No Dangerous Breeds.

The Caravan Club Ltd

Address: The Covert, High Ash, Hilborough, Thetford, Norfolk IP26 5BZ

Telephone: 01842 878356

Website: www.thecaravanclub.co.uk

Extra charge for dogs? No

Any breed restrictions? No

Dog bins? No

Area for walking dogs? Yes

Static caravans? No

Cost of static?

Mobile caravans? Yes

Cost of mobile? From £7.60 - £11.80 per night for 2 people + electric

Tents? No

Cost of tent pitch?

Electricity at the pitch? Yes

Showers? No

Onsite Entertainment? No

Opening times? March - November

Comments: Dogs must be kept on a lead at all times.

The Caravan Club Ltd

Address: The Racecourse, Jellicoe Rd, Great Yarmouth, Norfolk NR30 4AU

Telephone: 01493 855223

Website: www.thecaravanclub.co.uk

Extra charge for dogs? No

Any breed restrictions? No

Dog bins? Yes

Area for walking dogs? No

Static caravans? No

Cost of static?

Mobile caravans? Yes

Cost of mobile? From £13.10 for members per night for 2 people

Tents? No

Cost of tent pitch?

Electricity at the pitch? Yes

Showers? Yes

Onsite Entertainment? No

Opening times? March - November

Comments: Dogs must be kept on a lead at all times.

The Dower House

Address: Caravan & Camping Park, West Harling, Norwich, Norfolk NR16 2SE

Telephone: 01953 717314

Website: www.dowerhouse.co.uk

Extra charge for dogs? No
Any breed restrictions? Yes
Dog bins? No
Area for walking dogs? Yes
Static caravans? No
Cost of static?
Mobile caravans? Yes
Cost of mobile? From £11.50 per night
Tents? Yes
Cost of tent pitch? From £11.50 per night
Electricity at the pitch? Yes
Showers? Yes
Onsite Entertainment? Yes
Opening times? March - End September
Comments: Dogs must kept on a lead. Dogs are allowed in the bar. There is a swimming pool on site.

The Duke of Edinburgh

Address: Coast Road, Bacton, Norfolk NR12 0EU
Telephone: 01692 650280
Website: www.thedukeatbacton.co.uk
Extra charge for dogs? No
Any breed restrictions? No
Dog bins? Yes
Area for walking dogs? Yes
Static caravans? No
Cost of static?
Mobile caravans? Yes
Cost of mobile? From £7.00 per night
Tents? Yes
Cost of tent pitch? From £5.00 per night
Electricity at the pitch? Yes
Showers? Yes
Onsite Entertainment? Yes
Opening times? March - End September

The Fox Public House

Address: Cromer Road, Hevingham, Norwich, Norfolk NR10 5LY
Telephone: 01603 755362
Website:
Extra charge for dogs? No
Any breed restrictions? No
Dog bins? No
Area for walking dogs? Yes
Static caravans? No
Cost of static?
Mobile caravans? Yes
Cost of mobile? From £8.50 per night
Tents? Yes
Cost of tent pitch? From £6.00 per night
Electricity at the pitch? Yes
Showers? Yes
Onsite Entertainment? Yes
Opening times? All Year

The Grange

Address: Long Row, Tibenham, Norfolk, NR16 1PF
Telephone: 01953 860330
Website: www.thegrangecl.co.uk
Extra charge for dogs? No
Any breed restrictions? No
Dog bins? No
Area for walking dogs? Yes
Static caravans? No
Cost of static?
Mobile caravans? Yes
Cost of mobile? From £7.50 per night
Tents? No
Cost of tent pitch?
Electricity at the pitch? Yes
Showers? Yes
Onsite Entertainment? No
Opening times? All Year

Comments: Dogs must be kept on a lead.

The Leas Beach Park

Address: Mill Lane, Bacton, Norwich, Norfolk NR12 0HS
Telephone: 01692 652115
Website: www.theleasbeachpark.co.uk
Extra charge for dogs? No
Any breed restrictions? No
Dog bins? No
Area for walking dogs? No
Static caravans? Yes
Cost of static? From £125.00 - £373.00 per week
Mobile caravans? No
Cost of mobile?
Tents? No
Cost of tent pitch?
Electricity at the pitch? No
Showers? No
Onsite Entertainment? No
Opening times? 1st March - End October

The Old Rectory

Address: The Old Rectory, Southrepps Road, Antingham, Norfolk, NR28 0NW
Telephone: 01263 833375
Website: www.caravanandcampingsites.co.uk
Extra charge for dogs? No
Any breed restrictions? No
Dog bins? Yes
Area for walking dogs? Off Site
Static caravans? No
Cost of static?
Mobile caravans? Yes
Cost of mobile? From £7.00 per night
Tents? No
Cost of tent pitch?
Electricity at the pitch? Yes
Showers? No
Onsite Entertainment? No
Opening times? Easter - October

The Red Hart Inn Caravan Club

Address: The Street, Bodham, Holt, Norfolk NR25 6AD
Telephone: 01263 588270
Website: www.theredhart.co.uk
Extra charge for dogs? No
Any breed restrictions? No
Dog bins? No
Area for walking dogs? Off Site
Static caravans? No
Cost of static?
Mobile caravans? Yes
Cost of mobile? From £9.00 per night
Tents? No
Cost of tent pitch?
Electricity at the pitch? Yes
Showers? No
Onsite Entertainment? No
Opening times? All Year
Comments: There is a pub next door.

The Shieling

Address: Holt Road, Cley-next-the-sea, Holt, Norfolk NR257TX
Telephone: 01263 740628
Website:
Extra charge for dogs? No
Any breed restrictions? No
Dog bins? No
Area for walking dogs? Yes
Static caravans? No
Cost of static?
Mobile caravans? Yes
Cost of mobile? From £10.00 per night Caravan Club members only

Tents? No
Cost of tent pitch?
Electricity at the pitch? Yes
Showers? Yes
Onsite Entertainment? No
Opening times? All Year
Comments: Dogs must be kept on a lead.

The Water Meadow Site

Address: Water End, Great Cressingham, Norfolk IP25 6NN
Telephone: 01760 756232
Website: www.oldewindmillinn.co.uk
Extra charge for dogs? No
Any breed restrictions? No
Dog bins? No
Area for walking dogs? Off Site
Static caravans? No
Cost of static?
Mobile caravans? Yes
Cost of mobile? From £7.25 per night
Tents? Yes
Cost of tent pitch? No charge just contribution to a charity
Electricity at the pitch? Yes
Showers? Yes
Onsite Entertainment? Yes
Opening times? All Year
Comments: Shower is being built will be ready at beginning of August. There is entertainment once a week.

Thetford Forest Camping & Caravanning Club Site

Address: Puddledock Farm, Wretham Rd, Great Hockham, Thetford, Norfolk IP24 1PA
Telephone: 01953 498455
Website: www.thetfordatthefriendly club.co.uk
Extra charge for dogs? No
Any breed restrictions? No
Dog bins? Yes
Area for walking dogs? Yes
Static caravans? No
Cost of static?
Mobile caravans? Yes
Cost of mobile? From £6.60 per person per night
Tents? Yes
Cost of tent pitch? From £6.60 per person per night
Electricity at the pitch? Yes
Showers? Yes
Onsite Entertainment? No
Opening times? All Year
Comments: Dogs must be kept on a lead.

Top Farm Camping & Caravan Site

Address: Top Farm, Kittles Lane, Marsham, Norwich, Norfolk NR10 5QF
Telephone: 01263 733962
Website: www.top-farm.info
Extra charge for dogs? No
Any breed restrictions? No
Dog bins? No
Area for walking dogs? Yes
Static caravans? No
Cost of static?
Mobile caravans? Yes
Cost of mobile? From £12.00 per night
Tents? Yes
Cost of tent pitch? From £5.00 for 1st person £3.00 for 2nd person per night
Electricity at the pitch? Yes
Showers? Yes
Onsite Entertainment? No
Opening times? Easter - October

Trimingham Caravan Park

Address: Trimingham House, Beacon Rd, Trimingham, Norwich, Norfolk NR11 8DX

Telephone: 01263 720421

Website:

Extra charge for dogs? No

Any breed restrictions? No

Dog bins? No

Area for walking dogs? Yes

Static caravans? No

Cost of static? From £260.00 per week

Mobile caravans? No

Cost of mobile?

Tents? No

Cost of tent pitch?

Electricity at the pitch? No

Showers? No

Onsite Entertainment? Yes

Opening times? 1st March - 15th January

Two Mills Touring Park

Address: Yarmouth Rd, North Walsham, Norfolk NR28 9NA

Telephone: 01692 405829

Website: www.twomills.co.uk

Extra charge for dogs? Yes

Any breed restrictions? No

Dog bins? Yes

Area for walking dogs? Yes

Static caravans? No

Cost of static?

Mobile caravans? Yes

Cost of mobile? From £11.50 per night

Tents? Yes

Cost of tent pitch? From £11.50 per night

Electricity at the pitch? Yes

Showers? Yes

Onsite Entertainment? No

Opening times? 1st March - 3rd January

Virginia Lake Caravan Park

Address: Sneath Road, Marshland, St John's Fen End, Norfolk PE14 8JF

Telephone: 01945 430332

Website: www.virginialake.co.uk

Extra charge for dogs? No

Any breed restrictions? Yes

Dog bins? Yes

Area for walking dogs? Yes

Static caravans? No

Cost of static?

Mobile caravans? Yes

Cost of mobile? From £20.00 per night

Tents? Yes

Cost of tent pitch? From £10.00 for 1 man tent per night

Electricity at the pitch? Yes

Showers? Yes

Onsite Entertainment? Yes

Opening times? All Year

Comments: No Dangerous Breeds, No Rottweilers, Dobermans, Staffordshire Bull Terriers or Bull Mastifs. Dogs must be kept on a lead at all times. There is a Clubhouse on site.

Waveney River Centre

Address: Staithe Road, Burgh Saint Peter, Beccles, Norfolk NR34 0BT

Telephone: 01502 677343

Website: www.waveneyrivercentre.co.uk

Extra charge for dogs? Yes

Any breed restrictions? No

Dog bins? No

Area for walking dogs? No

Static caravans? No

Cost of static?

Mobile caravans? Yes

Cost of mobile? From £10.00 - £24.00 per night

Tents? Yes

Cost of tent pitch? From £10.00 - £24.00 per night
Electricity at the pitch? Yes
Showers? Yes
Onsite Entertainment? Yes
Opening times? All Year
Comments: There is a pub, shop and swimming pool on site. The shop and swimming pool are closed from End November - March.

Waveney Valley Holiday Park

Address: Airstation Lane, Rushall, Diss, Norfolk IP21 4QF
Telephone: 01379 741690
Website: www.caravanparksnorfolk.co.uk
Extra charge for dogs? Yes
Any breed restrictions? No
Dog bins? No
Area for walking dogs? No
Static caravans? Yes
Cost of static? From £209.00 per week
Mobile caravans? Yes
Cost of mobile? From £14.00 per night
Tents? Yes
Cost of tent pitch? From £14.00 per night
Electricity at the pitch? Yes
Showers? Yes
Onsite Entertainment? No
Opening times? March - October

Waxham Sands Holiday Parks

Address: Warren Farm, Horsey, Great Yarmouth, Norfolk NR29 4EJ
Telephone: 01692 598325
Website:
Extra charge for dogs? Yes
Any breed restrictions? No
Dog bins? Yes
Area for walking dogs? Yes
Static caravans? No
Cost of static?
Mobile caravans? Yes
Cost of mobile? From £11.00 per night
Tents? Yes
Cost of tent pitch? From £11.00 per night
Electricity at the pitch? Yes
Showers? Yes
Onsite Entertainment? No
Opening times? May - September
Comments: Dogs must be kept on a lead.

Whitehall Farm

Address: Burnham, Thorpe, Norfolk PE31 8HN
Telephone: 01328 738416
Website: www.whitehallfarm-accomodation.com
Extra charge for dogs? No
Any breed restrictions? No
Dog bins? Yes
Area for walking dogs? Off Site
Static caravans? No
Cost of static?
Mobile caravans? Yes
Cost of mobile? From £12.00 per night
Tents? Yes
Cost of tent pitch? From £10.00 per night
Electricity at the pitch? Yes
Showers? Yes
Onsite Entertainment? No
Opening times? All Year

White House Farm

Address: Thornage Road, Holt, Norfolk NR25 6SQ
Telephone: 01263 713106
Website:

Extra charge for dogs? No
Any breed restrictions? No
Dog bins? No
Area for walking dogs? Yes
Static caravans? No
Cost of static?
Mobile caravans? Yes
Cost of mobile? From £8.00 per night with electric
Tents? No
Cost of tent pitch?
Electricity at the pitch? Yes
Showers? No
Onsite Entertainment? No
Opening times?

Willoways Caravan Site

Address: Willoways Touring Club, Mill Rd, Burgh Castle, Great Yarmouth, Norfolk NR31 9QS
Telephone: 01493 780065
Website:
Extra charge for dogs? No
Any breed restrictions? No
Dog bins? No
Area for walking dogs? Yes
Static caravans? No
Cost of static?
Mobile caravans? Yes
Cost of mobile? From £8.00 per night
Tents? No
Cost of tent pitch?
Electricity at the pitch? Yes
Showers? No
Onsite Entertainment? Yes
Opening times? All Year
Comments: Dogs must be kept on a lead. There is fishing on site.

Willows Camping & Caravanning Park

Address: Diss Road, Scole, Norfolk IP21 4DH
Telephone: 01379 740271
Website:
Extra charge for dogs? No
Any breed restrictions? No
Dog bins? No
Area for walking dogs? Yes
Static caravans? No
Cost of static?
Mobile caravans? Yes
Cost of mobile? From £13.00 per night with electric for 2 people
Tents? Yes
Cost of tent pitch? From £10.00 per night for 2 people
Electricity at the pitch? Yes
Showers? Yes
Onsite Entertainment? No
Opening times? Easter - End October

Woodhill Park

Address: Cromer Rd, East Runton, Cromer, Norfolk NR27 9PX
Telephone: 01263 512242
Website: www.woodhill-park.com
Extra charge for dogs? Yes
Any breed restrictions? No
Dog bins? Yes
Area for walking dogs? Yes
Static caravans? No
Cost of static?
Mobile caravans? Yes
Cost of mobile? From £9.80 - £12.20 per pitch + £2.50 per adult £1.00 per child per night with electric
Tents? Yes
Cost of tent pitch? From £6.40 - £9.00 per pitch + £2.50 per adult £1.00 per

child per night
Electricity at the pitch? Yes
Showers? Yes
Onsite Entertainment? No
Opening times? 19th March - End October
Comments: Dogs must be kept on a lead.

Woodlands Caravan Park

Address: Holt Road, Upper Sheringham, Sheringham, Norfolk NR26 8TU
Telephone: 01263 823802
Website: www.woodlandscaravanpark.co.uk
Extra charge for dogs? No
Any breed restrictions? No
Dog bins? Yes
Area for walking dogs? Yes
Static caravans? No
Cost of static?
Mobile caravans? Yes
Cost of mobile? From £14.00 per night
Tents? No
Cost of tent pitch?
Electricity at the pitch? Yes
Showers? Yes
Onsite Entertainment? Yes
Opening times? March - October

Woodlands Leisure Park

Address: Hall Farm, Church Street, Trimingham, Norwich, Norfolk NR11 8AL
Telephone: 01263 579208
Website: www.woodland-park.co.uk
Extra charge for dogs? Yes
Any breed restrictions? No
Dog bins? ?
Area for walking dogs? Yes
Static caravans? Yes
Cost of static? From £220.00 per week
Mobile caravans? Yes
Cost of mobile? From £18.00 per night
Tents? Yes
Cost of tent pitch? From £18.00 per night up to a 4 man tent
Electricity at the pitch? Yes
Showers? Yes
Onsite Entertainment? Yes
Opening times? February - December
Comments: Dogs must be kept on a lead. Maximum of 2 dogs per party.

Causeway Cottage Caravan Park

Address: Bridge Rd, Potter Heigham, Great Yarmouth, Norfolk NR29 5JB
Telephone: 01692 670238
Website:
Extra charge for dogs? Yes
Any breed restrictions? No
Dog bins? No
Area for walking dogs? Yes
Static caravans? Yes
Cost of static? From £165.00 - £260.00 per week
Mobile caravans? Yes
Cost of mobile? From £10.00 - £12.00 per night
Tents? Yes
Cost of tent pitch? From £10.00 - £12.00 per night
Electricity at the pitch? Yes
Showers? Yes
Onsite Entertainment? No
Opening times? March - October

Heath Farm

Address: Sutton Road, Hickling, Norfolk NR12 0AS
Telephone: 01692 598534
Website:

Extra charge for dogs? No
Any breed restrictions? No
Dog bins? No
Area for walking dogs? Yes
Static caravans? No
Cost of static?
Mobile caravans? Yes
Cost of mobile? From £6.00 per night
Tents? No
Cost of tent pitch? From £6.00 per night
Electricity at the pitch? Yes
Showers? No
Onsite Entertainment? No
Opening times? All Year

Jane Scarrott

Address: Warren House, Brandon Rd, Methwold, Thetford, Norfolk IP26 4RL
Telephone: 01366 728238
Website:
Extra charge for dogs? No
Any breed restrictions? No
Dog bins? No
Area for walking dogs? Yes
Static caravans? No
Cost of static?
Mobile caravans? Yes
Cost of mobile? From £6.00 per night
Tents? Yes
Cost of tent pitch? From £6.00 per night
Electricity at the pitch? No
Showers? Yes
Onsite Entertainment? No
Opening times? March - October

Norfolk Broads Caravan Park

Address: Bridge Rd, Potter Heigham, Great Yarmouth, Norfolk NR29 5JB
Telephone: 0870 1188162
Website: www.norfolkbroadsparkand leisurehomes.com
Extra charge for dogs? No
Any breed restrictions? Yes
Dog bins? Yes
Area for walking dogs? Yes
Static caravans? Yes
Cost of static? From £295.00 per week
Mobile caravans? No
Cost of mobile?
Tents? No
Cost of tent pitch?
Electricity at the pitch? Yes
Showers? Yes
Onsite Entertainment? No
Opening times? March - October then December
Comments: Only small dogs.

The Camping & Caravanning Club

Address: Holgate Lane, West Runton, Cromer, Norfolk NR27 9NW
Telephone: 01263 837544
Website: www.thecampingand caravanningclub.co.uk
Extra charge for dogs? No
Any breed restrictions? No
Dog bins? Yes
Area for walking dogs? Off Site
Static caravans? No
Cost of static?
Mobile caravans? Yes
Cost of mobile? From £6.60 per adult for non members
Tents? Yes
Cost of tent pitch? From £6.60 per adult per night for non members
Electricity at the pitch? Yes
Showers? Yes
Onsite Entertainment? Yes
Opening times? March - Beg November
Comments: Dogs must be kept on a 2m lead at all times.

Thorpewood

Address: Nursery Farm, Cromer Road, Thorpe Market, Norfolk NR11 8TU

Telephone: 01263 834493

Website: www.thorpewoodcottages.co.uk

Extra charge for dogs? No

Any breed restrictions? No

Dog bins? No

Area for walking dogs? Yes

Static caravans? No

Cost of static?

Mobile caravans? Yes

Cost of mobile? From £8.00 per night

Tents? No

Cost of tent pitch?

Electricity at the pitch? Yes

Showers? Yes

Onsite Entertainment? No

Opening times? All Year

Woodside Farm

Address: Common Lane Thurne, Great Yarmouth, Norfolk NR29 3BX

Telephone: 01692 670367

Website:

Extra charge for dogs? No

Any breed restrictions? No

Dog bins? No

Area for walking dogs? Off Site

Static caravans? No

Cost of static?

Mobile caravans? Yes

Cost of mobile? From £17.00 per night

Tents? Yes

Cost of tent pitch? From £17.00 per night

Electricity at the pitch? Yes

Showers? Yes

Onsite Entertainment? No

Opening times? All Year

Comments: Dogs must be kept on a lead at all times.

Woodstock Farm

Address: Boughton Road, Wereham, Kings Lynn, Norfolk PE33 9BE

Telephone: 01366 500559

Website: www.woodstockfarm.co.uk

Extra charge for dogs? No

Any breed restrictions? No

Dog bins? No

Area for walking dogs? Off Site

Static caravans? No

Cost of static?

Mobile caravans? Yes

Cost of mobile? From £10.00 per pitch per night

Tents? Yes

Cost of tent pitch? From £10.00 per pitch per night

Electricity at the pitch? Yes

Showers? Yes

Onsite Entertainment? No

Opening times? All Year

Comments: Dogs must be kept on a lead at all times.

Northamptonshire

Braunston Marina Caravan Club

Address: The Wharf, Braunston, Daventry, Northamptonshire NN11 7JH

Telephone: 01788 891761

Website: www.braunstonmarina.co.uk

Extra charge for dogs? No

Any breed restrictions? No

Dog bins? No

Area for walking dogs? Off Site

Static caravans? No

Cost of static?

Mobile caravans? Yes

Cost of mobile? From £9.95 per night

Tents? No

Cost of tent pitch?

Electricity at the pitch? Yes

Showers? Yes

Onsite Entertainment? No

Opening times? All Year

Gayton Wood Farm

Address: Gayton, Northampton, Northamptonshire NN7 3HG

Telephone: 01604 858210

Website:

Extra charge for dogs? No

Any breed restrictions? No

Dog bins? No

Area for walking dogs? Off Site

Static caravans? No

Cost of static?

Mobile caravans? Yes

Cost of mobile? From £6.00 per night

Tents? Yes

Cost of tent pitch? From £6.00 per night

Electricity at the pitch? No

Showers? No

Onsite Entertainment? No

Opening times? All Year

Comments: Dogs must be kept on a lead.

Glebe Farm CL Site

Address: 32 Overstone Road, Sywell, Northamptonshire NN6 0AW

Telephone: 01604 790523

Website: www.5van.co.uk

Extra charge for dogs? No

Any breed restrictions? No

Dog bins? No

Area for walking dogs? Off Site

Static caravans? No

Cost of static?

Mobile caravans? Yes

Cost of mobile? From £9.00 per night with electric

Tents? No

Cost of tent pitch?

Electricity at the pitch? Yes

Showers? No

Onsite Entertainment? No

Opening times? All Year

Comments: Dogs must be kept on a lead at all times. There is free WiFi internet access.

Grendon Lakes

Address: Main Road, Grendon, Northamptonshire NN7 1JW

Telephone: 01933 665303
Website: www.grendonlakes.co.uk
Extra charge for dogs? No
Any breed restrictions? No
Dog bins? No
Area for walking dogs? No
Static caravans? No
Cost of static?
Mobile caravans? Yes
Cost of mobile? From £12.00 per night
Tents? Yes
Cost of tent pitch? From £8.00 per night up to a 4 man tent
Electricity at the pitch? Yes
Showers? Yes
Onsite Entertainment? Yes
Opening times? March/April (Depending on Weather) - End September
Comments: Dogs must be kept on a lead. There is a bar/restaurant on site.

Rectory Farm

Address: Sywell, Northamptonshire NN6 0AW
Telephone: 01604 643321
Website: www.5van.co.uk
Extra charge for dogs? No
Any breed restrictions? No
Dog bins? No
Area for walking dogs? No
Static caravans? No
Cost of static?
Mobile caravans? Yes
Cost of mobile? From £9.00 per night with electric
Tents? No
Cost of tent pitch?
Electricity at the pitch? Yes
Showers? No
Onsite Entertainment? No
Opening times? All Year
Comments: Dogs must be kept on a lead. Must be members of the Caravan Club.

The Whitehouse Caravan Park

Address: WhiteHouse, Sywell Rd, Holcot, Northampton, Northamptonshire NN6 9SN
Telephone: 01604 495102
Website:
Extra charge for dogs? No
Any breed restrictions? No
Dog bins? No
Area for walking dogs? Yes
Static caravans? No
Cost of static?
Mobile caravans? Yes
Cost of mobile? From £8.00 per night
Tents? Yes
Cost of tent pitch? From £8.00 per night
Electricity at the pitch? Yes
Showers? No
Onsite Entertainment? No
Opening times? Easter - October
Comments: There is a small area at the end of the field where dogs can be exercised.

Top Lodge Caravan Club Site

Address: Fineshade, Corby, Northamptonshire NN17 3BB
Telephone: 01780 444617
Website:
Extra charge for dogs? No
Any breed restrictions? No
Dog bins? No
Area for walking dogs? Yes
Static caravans? No
Cost of static?
Mobile caravans? Yes
Cost of mobile? ?

Tents? No
Cost of tent pitch?
Electricity at the pitch? Yes
Showers? No
Onsite Entertainment? No
Opening times? March - November
Comments: Dogs must be kept on a lead.

Wicksteed Park

Address: Barton Road, Kettering, Northamptonshire NN15 6NJ
Telephone: 08700 621191
Website: www.wicksteedpark.co.uk
Extra charge for dogs? No
Any breed restrictions? No
Dog bins? ?
Area for walking dogs? Yes
Static caravans? No
Cost of static?
Mobile caravans? Yes
Cost of mobile? From £10.00 per pitch per night
Tents? Yes
Cost of tent pitch? From £10.00 per pitch per night
Electricity at the pitch? No
Showers? Yes
Onsite Entertainment? Yes
Opening times? ?
Comments: Dogs must be kept on a lead and are not allowed in the Playground.

Nottinghamshire

New Hall Farm

Address: Newhall Lane, Edingley, Nr Southwell, Nottinghamshire NG22 8BS

Telephone: 01623 883041

Website: www.newhallfarm.co.uk

Extra charge for dogs? No

Any breed restrictions? No

Dog bins? Yes

Area for walking dogs? Yes

Static caravans? No

Cost of static?

Mobile caravans? Yes

Cost of mobile? From £8.00 per nights

Tents? Yes

Cost of tent pitch? From £8.00 per night

Electricity at the pitch? Yes

Showers? Yes

Onsite Entertainment? No

Opening times? March - October

Top House Farm

Address: Lamins Lane, Mansfield Road, Arnold, Nottinghamshire NG5 8PH

Telephone: 01159 670089

Website: www.thecaravanclub.co.uk

Extra charge for dogs? No

Any breed restrictions? No

Dog bins? No

Area for walking dogs? Yes

Static caravans? No

Cost of static?

Mobile caravans? Yes

Cost of mobile? From £8.00 per night

Tents? No

Cost of tent pitch?

Electricity at the pitch? Yes

Showers? No

Onsite Entertainment? No

Opening times? All Year

Bridleways Holiday Homes & Guest House

Address: Newlands Road, Mansfield, Nottinghamshire NG19 0HU

Telephone: 01623 635725

Website: www.stayatbridleways.co.uk

Extra charge for dogs? Yes

Any breed restrictions? No

Dog bins? No

Area for walking dogs? Yes

Static caravans? Yes

Cost of static? From £265.00 per week

Mobile caravans? No

Cost of mobile?

Tents? No

Cost of tent pitch?

Electricity at the pitch? No

Showers? No

Onsite Entertainment? No

Opening times? All Year

Carlton Manor Caravan Park

Address: Ossington Road, Carlton on Trent, Newark, Nottinghamshire NG23 6NU

Telephone: 01530 835662

Website:

Extra charge for dogs? Yes

Any breed restrictions? No

Dog bins? No

Area for walking dogs? Off Site

Static caravans? No
Cost of static?
Mobile caravans? Yes
Cost of mobile? From £10.00 per night
Tents? Yes
Cost of tent pitch? From £10.00 per night
Electricity at the pitch? Yes
Showers? Yes
Onsite Entertainment? No
Opening times? March - November
Comments: Dogs must be kept on a lead. There is a hotel opposite that has entertainment.

Clumber Park Caravan Club Site

Address: Limetree Avenue, Clumber Park, Worksop, Nottinghamshire S80 3AE
Telephone: 01909 484758
Website: www.thecaravanclub.co.uk
Extra charge for dogs? No
Any breed restrictions? No
Dog bins? Yes
Area for walking dogs? Off Site
Static caravans? No
Cost of static?
Mobile caravans? Yes
Cost of mobile? From £14.90 for 2 people per night for members
Tents? No
Cost of tent pitch?
Electricity at the pitch? Yes
Showers? Yes
Onsite Entertainment? No
Opening times? All Year
Comments: Dogs must be kept on a lead at all times.

Greenacres

Address: Lincoln Rd, Tuxford, Newark, Nottinghamshire NG22 0JN
Telephone: 01777 870264
Website: www.greenacres-tuxford.co.uk
Extra charge for dogs? Yes
Any breed restrictions? Yes
Dog bins? No
Area for walking dogs? Off Site
Static caravans? No
Cost of static?
Mobile caravans? Yes
Cost of mobile? From £15.00 per night for 2 people with electric
Tents? Yes
Cost of tent pitch? From £15.00 per night for 2 people with electric
Electricity at the pitch? Yes
Showers? Yes
Onsite Entertainment? No
Opening times? Mid March - End October
Comments: No Dangerous Breeds.

Hallcroft Fishery & Caravan Park

Address: Hallcroft Road, East Retford, Nottinghamshire DN22 7RA
Telephone: 01777 710448
Website: www.hallcroftfishery.co.uk
Extra charge for dogs? Yes
Any breed restrictions? No
Dog bins? No
Area for walking dogs? Yes
Static caravans? Yes
Cost of static? From £180.00 per week for 2 people including Fishing
Mobile caravans? Yes
Cost of mobile? From £8.00 per night
Tents? Yes
Cost of tent pitch? From £6.00 per night for 1 man tent
Electricity at the pitch? Yes
Showers? Yes
Onsite Entertainment? Yes
Opening times? All Year

Comments: Dogs must be kept on a lead. There is Fishing, Tackle Shop and Café on site.

Heronbrook

Address: Peashill Lane, Cotgrave, Nottinghamshire NG12 3HD

Telephone: 0115 989 9285

Website: www.thecaravanclub.co.uk

Extra charge for dogs? No

Any breed restrictions? No

Dog bins? No

Area for walking dogs? Yes

Static caravans? No

Cost of static?

Mobile caravans? Yes

Cost of mobile? From £8.00 per night

Tents? No

Cost of tent pitch?

Electricity at the pitch? Yes

Showers? No

Onsite Entertainment? No

Opening times? All Year

Holme Pierrepoint Camping & Caravan Park

Address: Nottingham, Nottingham NG12 2LU

Telephone: 0115 9824721

Website: www.nationalwatersportsevents.co.uk

Extra charge for dogs? No

Any breed restrictions? No

Dog bins? No

Area for walking dogs? Yes

Static caravans? No

Cost of static?

Mobile caravans? Yes

Cost of mobile? From £12.00 per night

Tents? Yes

Cost of tent pitch? From £9.00 per night

Electricity at the pitch? Yes

Showers? Yes

Onsite Entertainment? No

Opening times? Easter - January

Comments: Dogs must be kept on a lead. There is a restaurant and bar 5 minute walk away at main centre.

Lakeside Touring Caravan

Address: The Chestnuts, Thorney, Newark, Nottinghamshire NG23 7DL

Telephone: 01522 703412

Website:

Extra charge for dogs? No

Any breed restrictions? No

Dog bins? Yes

Area for walking dogs? Yes

Static caravans? No

Cost of static?

Mobile caravans? Yes

Cost of mobile? From £18.00 per night including Fishing

Tents? Yes

Cost of tent pitch? From £18.00 per night including Fishing

Electricity at the pitch? Yes

Showers? Yes

Onsite Entertainment? Yes

Opening times? March - October

Comments: There is fishing on site.

Little Acres

Address: Mill Lane, Claypole, Newark, Nottinghamshire NG23 5AH

Telephone: 01636 626337

Website: www.little-acres.co.uk

Extra charge for dogs? No

Any breed restrictions? No

Dog bins? No

Area for walking dogs? Yes
Static caravans? No
Cost of static?
Mobile caravans? Yes
Cost of mobile? From £9.00 per night
Tents? No
Cost of tent pitch?
Electricity at the pitch? Yes
Showers? No
Onsite Entertainment? No
Opening times? All Year

Manor Farm Caravan Site

Address: Thrumpton, Nottinghamshire NG11 0AX

Telephone: 0115 9830341

Website:

Extra charge for dogs? No
Any breed restrictions? No
Dog bins? No
Area for walking dogs? Yes
Static caravans? No
Cost of static?
Mobile caravans? Yes
Cost of mobile? From £8.00 per night
Tents? No
Cost of tent pitch?
Electricity at the pitch? Yes
Showers? Yes
Onsite Entertainment? No
Opening times? All Year

Comments: Dogs must be kept on a lead.

Manor House Caravan Site

Address: Laneham, Nottinghamshire DN22 0NJ

Telephone: 01777 228428

Website: www.tingdeneliftestyle.co.uk

Extra charge for dogs? No
Any breed restrictions? No
Dog bins? No
Area for walking dogs? Yes
Static caravans? No
Cost of static?
Mobile caravans? Yes
Cost of mobile? From £14.00 per night
Tents? Yes
Cost of tent pitch? From £14.00 per night
Electricity at the pitch? Yes
Showers? Yes
Onsite Entertainment? No
Opening times? March - October

Milestone Caravan Park

Address: Milestone House, North Rd, Cromwell, Newark, Nottinghamshire NG23 6JE

Telephone: 01636 821244

Website: www.milestonecaravanpark.co.uk

Extra charge for dogs? No
Any breed restrictions? No
Dog bins? Yes
Area for walking dogs? Yes
Static caravans? No
Cost of static?
Mobile caravans? Yes
Cost of mobile? From £14.90 for 2 adults per night
Tents? No
Cost of tent pitch?
Electricity at the pitch? Yes
Showers? Yes
Onsite Entertainment? No
Opening times? All Year

Comments: Maximum of 4 dogs per pitch.

Orchard Park

Address: Marnham Rd, Tuxford, Newark, Nottinghamshire NG22 0PY
Telephone: 01777 870228
Website: www.orchardcaravanpark.co.uk
Extra charge for dogs? Yes
Any breed restrictions? Yes
Dog bins? Yes
Area for walking dogs? Yes
Static caravans? No
Cost of static?
Mobile caravans? Yes
Cost of mobile? From £15.00 per night for 2 people
Tents? Yes
Cost of tent pitch? From £8.00 per night for single man tent
Electricity at the pitch? Yes
Showers? Yes
Onsite Entertainment? No
Opening times? March - November
Comments: No Dangerous or Large Breeds. Dogs must be kept on a lead at all times.

Redbrick House Caravan & Camping

Address: Edwinstowe, Nottinghamshire NG20 0EW
Telephone: 01623 846499
Website: www.redbrickhouse.co.uk
Extra charge for dogs? No
Any breed restrictions? Yes
Dog bins? Yes
Area for walking dogs? Yes
Static caravans? No
Cost of static?
Mobile caravans? Yes
Cost of mobile? From £7.50 per person per night minimum of £15.00
Tents? Yes
Cost of tent pitch? From £7.00 per person per night minimum of £14.00
Electricity at the pitch? Yes
Showers? Yes
Onsite Entertainment? No
Opening times? April - End September
Comments: No Dangerous Breeds. There is bar and restaurant within easy walking distance.

Redhill Marina

Address: Ratcliffe On Soar, Nottingham, Nottinghamshire NG11 0EB
Telephone: 01509 672770
Website: www.redhill-marina.co.uk
Extra charge for dogs? No
Any breed restrictions? No
Dog bins? No
Area for walking dogs? Off Site
Static caravans? No
Cost of static?
Mobile caravans? Yes
Cost of mobile? From £10.00 per night
Tents? Yes
Cost of tent pitch? From £8.00 per night
Electricity at the pitch? Yes
Showers? No
Onsite Entertainment? No
Opening times? All Year

Riverside Caravan Park

Address: Central Avenue, Worksop, Nottinghamshire S80 1ER
Telephone: 01909 474118
Website: www.riversideworksop.co.uk
Extra charge for dogs? No
Any breed restrictions? No
Dog bins? No
Area for walking dogs? Off Site
Static caravans? No
Cost of static?

Mobile caravans? Yes
Cost of mobile? From £16.00 per night for 2 people
Tents? Yes
Cost of tent pitch? From £16.00 per night for 2 people
Electricity at the pitch? Yes
Showers? Yes
Onsite Entertainment? No
Opening times? All Year

Sawley Marina Caravan Park

Address: Long Eaton, Nottinghamshire NG10 3AE
Telephone: 0115 9734278
Website: www.bwml.co.uk
Extra charge for dogs? No
Any breed restrictions? No
Dog bins? Yes
Area for walking dogs? Yes
Static caravans? No
Cost of static?
Mobile caravans? Yes
Cost of mobile? From £14.00 per night
Tents? No
Cost of tent pitch?
Electricity at the pitch? Yes
Showers? Yes
Onsite Entertainment? No
Opening times? Easter - October

Shelford Nurseries Caravan Park

Address: The Hill, Shelford, Nottingham, Nottinghamshire NG12 1ED
Telephone: 0115 933 3433
Website: www.shelfordnurseries caravanpark.co.uk
Extra charge for dogs? No
Any breed restrictions? No
Dog bins? No
Area for walking dogs? Off Site
Static caravans? No
Cost of static?
Mobile caravans? Yes
Cost of mobile? From £10.00 per night for 2 people
Tents? Yes
Cost of tent pitch? From £10.00 per night for 2 people
Electricity at the pitch? Yes
Showers? Yes
Onsite Entertainment? No
Opening times? Easter - October

Sherwood Forest Holiday Park

Address: Edwinstowe, Mansfield, Nottinghamshire NG21 9HW
Telephone: 01623 823132
Website: www.sherwoodforestholiday park.co.uk
Extra charge for dogs? Yes
Any breed restrictions? No
Dog bins? Yes
Area for walking dogs? Yes
Static caravans? No
Cost of static?
Mobile caravans? Yes
Cost of mobile? From £11.00 per night mid week
Tents? Yes
Cost of tent pitch? From £11.00 per night mid week
Electricity at the pitch? Yes
Showers? Yes
Onsite Entertainment? No
Opening times? All Year
Comments: Dogs must be kept on a lead.

Smeaton's Lakes

Address: Great North Rd, South Muskham, Newark, Nottinghamshire NG23 6ED

Telephone: 01636 605088

Website: www.smeatonslakes.co.uk

Extra charge for dogs? No

Any breed restrictions? No

Dog bins? Yes

Area for walking dogs? Yes

Static caravans? No

Cost of static?

Mobile caravans? Yes

Cost of mobile? From £13.00 - £18.00 per night

Tents? Yes

Cost of tent pitch? From £13.00 - £18.00 per night

Electricity at the pitch? Yes

Showers? Yes

Onsite Entertainment? No

Opening times? All Year

The Anchor Inn

Address: 80 Main Street, Gunthorpe, Nottingham, Nottinghamshire NG14 7EU

Telephone: 0115 966 3291

Website:

Extra charge for dogs? No

Any breed restrictions? No

Dog bins? ?

Area for walking dogs? Yes

Static caravans? No

Cost of static?

Mobile caravans? Yes

Cost of mobile? From £6.00 per night

Tents? No

Cost of tent pitch?

Electricity at the pitch? Yes

Showers? No

Onsite Entertainment? Yes

Opening times? All Year

Comments: There is a pub on site.

The Camping & Caravanning Club Site

Address: Silverhill Lane, Teversal, Sutton-In-Ashfield, Nottinghamshire NG17 3JJ

Telephone: 01623 551838

Website: www.thecampingand caravanningclub.co.uk

Extra charge for dogs? No

Any breed restrictions? No

Dog bins? Yes

Area for walking dogs? Off Site

Static caravans? Yes

Cost of static? From £250.00 per week

Mobile caravans? Yes

Cost of mobile? From £15.00 per night for 2 people

Tents? Yes

Cost of tent pitch? From £15.00 per night for 2 people

Electricity at the pitch? Yes

Showers? Yes

Onsite Entertainment? No

Opening times? All Year

Thornton's Holt

Address: Stragglethorpe, Radcliffe-on-Trent, Nottingham, Nottinghamshire NG12 2JZ

Telephone: 0115 933 2125

Website: www.thorntons-holt.co.uk

Extra charge for dogs? No

Any breed restrictions? No

Dog bins? No

Area for walking dogs? Yes

Static caravans? No

Cost of static?

Mobile caravans? Yes
Cost of mobile? From £10.50 per night
Tents? Yes
Cost of tent pitch? From £10.50 per night
Electricity at the pitch? Yes
Showers? Yes
Onsite Entertainment? No
Opening times? All Year

Trentfield Farm

Address: Retford, Nottinghamshire DN22 0NJ
Telephone: 01777 228651
Website: www.trentfield.co.uk
Extra charge for dogs? Yes
Any breed restrictions? No
Dog bins? Yes
Area for walking dogs? Off Site
Static caravans? No
Cost of static?
Mobile caravans? Yes
Cost of mobile? From £12.00 per night
Tents? Yes
Cost of tent pitch? From £12.00 per night
Electricity at the pitch? Yes
Showers? Yes
Onsite Entertainment? No
Opening times? April - October

Tall Trees Park

Address: Old Mill Lane, Forest Town, Mansfield, Nottinghamshire NG19 0JP
Telephone: 01623 626503
Website: www.jamesparkhomes.com
Extra charge for dogs? Yes
Any breed restrictions? No
Dog bins? No
Area for walking dogs? Yes
Static caravans? No
Cost of static?
Mobile caravans? Yes
Cost of mobile? From £7.50 per night
Tents? No
Cost of tent pitch?
Electricity at the pitch? Yes
Showers? Yes
Onsite Entertainment? No
Opening times? All Year

Wildwood Touring Park

Address: Newark, Nottinghamshire NG23 7BQ
Telephone: 01522 778806
Website:
Extra charge for dogs? No
Any breed restrictions? No
Dog bins? Yes
Area for walking dogs? Yes
Static caravans? No
Cost of static?
Mobile caravans? Yes
Cost of mobile? From £7.50 per night
Tents? No
Cost of tent pitch?
Electricity at the pitch? Yes
Showers? Yes
Onsite Entertainment? No
Opening times? All Year

Oxfordshire

Anita's Holiday Cottages

Address: The Yews, Mollington, Banbury, Oxfordshire OX17 1AZ
Telephone: 01295 750731
Website:
Extra charge for dogs? Yes
Any breed restrictions? No
Dog bins? Yes
Area for walking dogs? Yes
Static caravans? No
Cost of static?
Mobile caravans? Yes
Cost of mobile? From £12.50 - £13.50 per night
Tents? Yes
Cost of tent pitch? From £6.00 - £10.00 + £1.00 per person per night
Electricity at the pitch? Yes
Showers? Yes
Onsite Entertainment? No
Opening times? All Year

Barnstones Caravan & Camping Site

Address: Main St, Great Bourton, Banbury, Oxfordshire OX17 1QU
Telephone: 01295 750289
Website:
Extra charge for dogs? No
Any breed restrictions? No
Dog bins? Yes
Area for walking dogs? Yes
Static caravans? No
Cost of static?
Mobile caravans? Yes
Cost of mobile? From £10.00 per night for 2 people
Tents? Yes
Cost of tent pitch? From £10.00 per night for 2 people
Electricity at the pitch? Yes
Showers? Yes
Onsite Entertainment? Yes
Opening times? All Year
Comments: Dogs must be kept on a lead. There is a childrens playground on site.

Benson Waterfront Holiday Park

Address: Oxford, Oxfordshire OX10 6SJ
Telephone: 01491 838304
Website: www.bensonwaterfront.com
Extra charge for dogs? No
Any breed restrictions? No
Dog bins? No
Area for walking dogs? Off Site
Static caravans? No
Cost of static?
Mobile caravans? Yes
Cost of mobile? From £16.00 per night
Tents? Yes
Cost of tent pitch? From £12.00 per night
Electricity at the pitch? Yes
Showers? Yes
Onsite Entertainment? No
Opening times? Easter - September
Comments: Dogs must be kept on a lead.

Bladon Chains Caravan Club Site

Address: Bladon Road, Woodstock, Oxfordshire OX20 1QD

Telephone: 01993 812390
Website: www.thecaravanclub.co.uk
Extra charge for dogs? No
Any breed restrictions? No
Dog bins? Yes
Area for walking dogs? Yes
Static caravans? No
Cost of static?
Mobile caravans? Yes
Cost of mobile? From £4.30 per pitch + £3.95 per adult per night
Tents? No
Cost of tent pitch?
Electricity at the pitch? Yes
Showers? Yes
Onsite Entertainment? No
Opening times? March - October

Blewbury Centre and Cs

Address: Bessels Way, Blewbury, Didcot, Oxfordshire OX11 9NH
Telephone: 01235 851016
Website: www.blewburycentre.co.uk
Extra charge for dogs? No
Any breed restrictions? No
Dog bins? No
Area for walking dogs? Yes
Static caravans? Yes
Cost of static? From £40.00 per week
Mobile caravans? Yes
Cost of mobile? From £4.00 per night
Tents? Yes
Cost of tent pitch? From £4.00 per night
Electricity at the pitch? Yes
Showers? No
Onsite Entertainment? No
Opening times? All Year

Bo Peep Caravan Park

Address: Aynho Rd, Adderbury, Banbury, Oxfordshire OX17 3NP
Telephone: 01295 810605
Website: www.bo-peep.co.uk
Extra charge for dogs? Yes
Any breed restrictions? No
Dog bins? Yes
Area for walking dogs? Yes
Static caravans? No
Cost of static?
Mobile caravans? Yes
Cost of mobile? From £13.50 - £18.00 for 2 people per night with electric
Tents? Yes
Cost of tent pitch? From £13.00 - £15.00 per night without electric
Electricity at the pitch? Yes
Showers? Yes
Onsite Entertainment? No
Opening times? March - End October

Bridge House Caravan Park

Address: Bridge House, Clifton Hampden, Abingdon, Oxfordshire OX14 3EH
Telephone: 01865 407725
Website:
Extra charge for dogs? No
Any breed restrictions? No
Dog bins? No
Area for walking dogs? Yes
Static caravans? Yes
Cost of static? From £195.00 per week
Mobile caravans? Yes
Cost of mobile? From £16.00 per night with electric
Tents? Yes
Cost of tent pitch? From £12.00 per night
Electricity at the pitch? Yes
Showers? Yes
Onsite Entertainment? No
Opening times? April - October
Comments: Dogs must be kept on a lead. There is a pub next door to site.

Bridge Villa Camping & Caravan Park

Address: Wallingford, Oxfordshire OX10 8HB

Telephone: 01491 836860

Website: www.tiscover.co.uk

Extra charge for dogs? No
Any breed restrictions? No
Dog bins? No
Area for walking dogs? Off Site
Static caravans? No
Cost of static?
Mobile caravans? Yes
Cost of mobile? From £14.00 - £17.00 per night
Tents? Yes
Cost of tent pitch? From £14.00 - £17.00 per night
Electricity at the pitch? Yes
Showers? Yes
Onsite Entertainment? No
Opening times? February - December

Britchcombe Countryside Holidays Oxfordshire

Address: Britchcombe Farm, Uffington, Faringdon, Oxfordshire SN7 7QJ

Telephone: 01367 820667

Website:

Extra charge for dogs? No
Any breed restrictions? Yes
Dog bins? No
Area for walking dogs? Yes
Static caravans? Yes
Cost of static? From £150.00 per week
Mobile caravans? Yes
Cost of mobile? From £6.00 per person per night
Tents? Yes
Cost of tent pitch?
Electricity at the pitch? Yes
Showers? Yes
Onsite Entertainment? No
Opening times? All Year

Comments: No Dangerous Breeds.

Burgess Farm Caravan Site

Address: Middleton Cheney, Banbury, Oxfordshire OX17 2NE

Telephone: 01295 711288

Website:

Extra charge for dogs? No
Any breed restrictions? No
Dog bins? No
Area for walking dogs? Yes
Static caravans? No
Cost of static?
Mobile caravans? Yes
Cost of mobile? From £8.50 per night
Tents? Yes
Cost of tent pitch? From £8.50 per night
Electricity at the pitch? Yes
Showers? Yes
Onsite Entertainment? No
Opening times? March - October

Cheney Manor House

Address: Cheney Manor, Barford, St Michael, Oxfordshire OX15 0RJ

Telephone: 01869 338207

Website:

Extra charge for dogs? No
Any breed restrictions? No
Dog bins? No
Area for walking dogs? Yes
Static caravans? No
Cost of static?
Mobile caravans? Yes
Cost of mobile? From £6.00 per night
Tents? Yes
Cost of tent pitch? From £6.00 per night

Electricity at the pitch? Yes
Showers? Yes
Onsite Entertainment? No
Opening times? All Year

Cotswold View Touring Park

Address: Enstone Rd, Charlbury, Chipping Norton, Oxfordshire OX7 3JH
Telephone: 01608 810314
Website: www.cotswoldview.co.uk
Extra charge for dogs? No
Any breed restrictions? No
Dog bins? No
Area for walking dogs? Yes
Static caravans? No
Cost of static?
Mobile caravans? Yes
Cost of mobile? From £15.00 per night
Tents? Yes
Cost of tent pitch? From £15.00 per night
Electricity at the pitch? Yes
Showers? Yes
Onsite Entertainment? No
Opening times? April - October

Diamond Farm Caravan & Camping Park

Address: Diamond Farm, Islip Rd, Heathfield, Bletchingdon, Kidlington, Oxfordshire OX5 3DR
Telephone: 01869 350909
Website: www.diamondpark.co.uk
Extra charge for dogs? No
Any breed restrictions? No
Dog bins? No
Area for walking dogs? Off Site
Static caravans? No
Cost of static?
Mobile caravans? Yes
Cost of mobile? From £15.00 per night
Tents? Yes
Cost of tent pitch? From £12.00 per night
Electricity at the pitch? Yes
Showers? Yes
Onsite Entertainment? Yes
Opening times? All Year
Comments: There is a bar and a swimming pool on site.

Bridge Villa Camping & Caravan Park

Address: Bridge Villa, The Street, Crowmarsh Gifford, Wallingford, Oxfordshire OX10 8HB
Telephone: 01491 836860
Website:
Extra charge for dogs? No
Any breed restrictions? No
Dog bins? No
Area for walking dogs? Off Site
Static caravans? No
Cost of static?
Mobile caravans? Yes
Cost of mobile? From £14.00 per night
Tents? Yes
Cost of tent pitch? From £8.00 per tent no vehicle per night
Electricity at the pitch? Yes
Showers? Yes
Onsite Entertainment? No
Opening times? 1st February - 31st December

Fir Tree Farm Caravan Site

Address: Warmington, Banbury, Oxfordshire OX17 1JL
Telephone: 01295 690522

Website:
Extra charge for dogs? No
Any breed restrictions? No
Dog bins? No
Area for walking dogs? No
Static caravans? No
Cost of static?
Mobile caravans? Yes
Cost of mobile? From £10.00 per night
Tents? Yes
Cost of tent pitch? From £10.00 per night
Electricity at the pitch? Yes
Showers? No
Onsite Entertainment? No
Opening times? All Year

Four Oaks Caravan Club Site

Address: Marlow Road, Henley On Thames, Oxfordshire RG9 2HY
Telephone: 01491 572312
Website: www.thecaravanclub.co.uk
Extra charge for dogs? No
Any breed restrictions? No
Dog bins? Yes
Area for walking dogs? Yes
Static caravans? No
Cost of static?
Mobile caravans? Yes
Cost of mobile? From £12.20 per night for 2 people
Tents? No
Cost of tent pitch?
Electricity at the pitch? Yes
Showers? Yes
Onsite Entertainment? No
Opening times? March - Mid November
Comments: This is a members only site.

Greenhill Leisure Park

Address: Greenhill Farm, Bletchingdon, Oxfordshire OX5 3BQ
Telephone: 01869 351600
Website: www.greenhill-leisure-park.co.uk
Extra charge for dogs? Yes
Any breed restrictions? No
Dog bins? Yes
Area for walking dogs? Yes
Static caravans? No
Cost of static?
Mobile caravans? Yes
Cost of mobile? From £10.00 per night
Tents? Yes
Cost of tent pitch? From £10.00 per night
Electricity at the pitch? Yes
Showers? Yes
Onsite Entertainment? Yes
Opening times? All Year (Dogs only allowed March - October)
Comments: Maxiumum of 2 dogs. There is a games room and play area on site.

Gubbins Farm Adventures

Address: Marsh Gibbon, Bicester, Oxfordshire OX26 0AN
Telephone: 01296 770259
Website: www.thecaravanclub.co.uk
Extra charge for dogs? No
Any breed restrictions? No
Dog bins? No
Area for walking dogs? Yes
Static caravans? No
Cost of static?
Mobile caravans? Yes
Cost of mobile? From £6.00 per night
Tents? No
Cost of tent pitch?

Electricity at the pitch? Yes
Showers? No
Onsite Entertainment? No
Opening times? All Year

Hardwick Parks

Address: Standlake, Oxfordshire OX8 7PZ
Telephone: 01865 300501
Website: www.hardwickparks.co.uk
Extra charge for dogs? No
Any breed restrictions? No
Dog bins? Yes
Area for walking dogs? Yes
Static caravans? No
Cost of static?
Mobile caravans? Yes
Cost of mobile? From £13.00 per night
Tents? Yes
Cost of tent pitch? From £13.00 per night
Electricity at the pitch? Yes
Showers? Yes
Onsite Entertainment? Yes
Opening times? Easter - End October
Comments: There is a bar and restaurant.

Heyford Leys Camping Park

Address: Camp Road, Upper Heyford, Bicester, Oxfordshire OX25 5LX
Telephone: 01869 232048
Website: www.heyfordleyspark.co.uk
Extra charge for dogs? Yes
Any breed restrictions? No
Dog bins? Yes
Area for walking dogs? Yes
Static caravans? No
Cost of static?
Mobile caravans? Yes
Cost of mobile? From £12.00 per night
Tents? Yes
Cost of tent pitch? From £10.00 per night
Electricity at the pitch? Yes
Showers? Yes
Onsite Entertainment? No
Opening times? All Year

Leys Farm

Address: Waterperry Common, Waterperry, Oxford, Oxfordshire OX33 1LQ
Telephone: 01865 351266
Website: www.commonleysfarm.com
Extra charge for dogs? Yes
Any breed restrictions? No
Dog bins? No
Area for walking dogs? Off Site
Static caravans? No
Cost of static?
Mobile caravans? Yes
Cost of mobile? From £10.00 per night
Tents? Yes
Cost of tent pitch? From £10.00 per night
Electricity at the pitch? Yes
Showers? No
Onsite Entertainment? Yes
Opening times? All Year
Comments: There is a restaurant on site. Shower Block is currently being built, but there are washing facilities in the farmhouse. There is a massage and spa facility available.

Lincoln Farm Park Oxfordshire

Address: High St, Standlake, Witney, Oxfordshire OX29 7RH
Telephone: 01865 300239
Website: www.lincolnfarmpark.co.uk
Extra charge for dogs? Yes
Any breed restrictions? No

Dog bins? Yes
Area for walking dogs? Yes
Static caravans? No
Cost of static?
Mobile caravans? Yes
Cost of mobile? From £14.95 per night
Tents? Yes
Cost of tent pitch? From £13.95 per night
Electricity at the pitch? Yes
Showers? Yes
Onsite Entertainment? Yes
Opening times? 1st February - November

Comments: Dogs must be kept on a lead. There are 2 swimming pools on site.

Manor Farm

Address: Northampton Road, Weston on the green, Bicester, Oxfordshire OX25 3QL

Telephone: 01869 351647

Website:

Extra charge for dogs? No
Any breed restrictions? No
Dog bins? No
Area for walking dogs? Yes
Static caravans? No
Cost of static?
Mobile caravans? Yes
Cost of mobile? From £12.50 per night
Tents? Yes
Cost of tent pitch? From £10.00 per night
Electricity at the pitch? Yes
Showers? Yes
Onsite Entertainment? Yes
Opening times? March - October

Comments: There is an ice cream parlor on site.

The Burford Caravan Club Site

Address: Bradwell Grove, Burford, Oxfordshire OX18 4JJ

Telephone: 01993 823080

Website: www.thecaravanclub.co.uk

Extra charge for dogs? No
Any breed restrictions? No
Dog bins? Yes
Area for walking dogs? Yes
Static caravans? No
Cost of static?
Mobile caravans? Yes
Cost of mobile? From £4.70 per pitch + £4.20 per adult + £1.30 per child per night
Tents? No
Cost of tent pitch?
Electricity at the pitch? Yes
Showers? Yes
Onsite Entertainment? No
Opening times? March - November

Comments: Dangerous Dogs must be muzzled.

The Camping & Caravanning Club

Address: 426, Abingdon Rd, Oxford, Oxfordshire OX1 4XG

Telephone: 01865 244088

Website: www.thecampingandcaravanningclub.co.uk

Extra charge for dogs? No
Any breed restrictions? No
Dog bins? Yes
Area for walking dogs? No
Static caravans? No
Cost of static?
Mobile caravans? Yes
Cost of mobile? From £6.65 - £9.25 per person per night
Tents? Yes

Cost of tent pitch? From £6.65 - £9.25 per person per night
Electricity at the pitch? Yes
Showers? Yes
Onsite Entertainment? No
Opening times? All Year
Comments: Dog must be kept on a 6ft lead at all times. Tents can only stay a maximum of 2 nights.

The Camping & Caravanning Club

Address: Chipping Norton Rd, Chadlington, Chipping Norton, Oxfordshire OX7 3PE
Telephone: 01608 641993
Website: www.thecampingandcaravanningclub.co.uk
Extra charge for dogs? No
Any breed restrictions? No
Dog bins? Yes
Area for walking dogs? Yes
Static caravans? No
Cost of static?
Mobile caravans? Yes
Cost of mobile? From £5.15 per person per night
Tents? Yes
Cost of tent pitch? From £5.15 per person per night
Electricity at the pitch? Yes
Showers? Yes
Onsite Entertainment? No
Opening times? March - End October

Twilite Leisure Park

Address: Twyford Wharf, Banbury, Oxfordshire OX17 3JN
Telephone: 01295 810214
Website:
Extra charge for dogs? No
Any breed restrictions? No
Dog bins? No
Area for walking dogs? Yes
Static caravans? No
Cost of static?
Mobile caravans? Yes
Cost of mobile? From £10.00 per night
Tents? No
Cost of tent pitch?
Electricity at the pitch? Yes
Showers? No
Onsite Entertainment? No
Opening times? All Year
Comments: Dog must be kept on a lead at all times on the site.

Wysdom Touring Park

Address: The Bungalow, Burford School, Burford, Oxfordshire OX18 4JG
Telephone: 01993 823207
Website:
Extra charge for dogs? No
Any breed restrictions? No
Dog bins? No
Area for walking dogs? Off Site
Static caravans? No
Cost of static?
Mobile caravans? Yes
Cost of mobile? From £12.00 per night
Tents? Yes
Cost of tent pitch? From £12.00 per night
Electricity at the pitch? Yes
Showers? Yes
Onsite Entertainment? No
Opening times? End January - Mid December

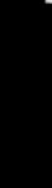

Notes

Notes

Notes